Statistical Sources and Techniques

Statistical Sources and Techniques

F. J. Rendall, BSc, MA
D. M. Wolf, BA, MSc
Both of Leicester Polytechnic

McGRAW-HILL Book Company (UK) Limited

London · New York · St Louis · San Francisco · Auckland · Bogotá · Guatemala
Hamburg · Johannesburg · Lisbon · Madrid · Mexico · Montreal · New Delhi
Panama · Paris · San Juan · São Paulo · Singapore · Sydney · Tokyo · Toronto

Published by
McGRAW-HILL Book Company (UK) Limited
MAIDENHEAD · BERKSHIRE · ENGLAND

British Library Cataloguing in Publication Data

Rendall, F. J.
    Statistical sources and techniques
     1. Great Britain—Statistical services
    I. Title   II. Wolf, D. M.
    314.2   HA37.G7

ISBN 0–07–084658–8

Library of Congress Cataloging in Publication Data

Rendall, F. J.
    Includes index.
     1. Commercial statistics.   2. Economics—Statistical
methods. 3. Statistics. 4. Statistical services.
I. Wolf, D. M.   II. Title.
HF1017.R44   1982   519.5'024658   82–17257
ISBN 0–07–084658–8

12345 WC 843

To
Linda, Charlotte, and Ashley,
and
Katharine and Ben

Contents

Preface

It has always seemed rather strange to us that in the area of economic, business, or commercial statistics, practically all the major texts concentrate on statistical techniques and by and large ignore the whole debate on statistical sources. Even where 'applied' is part of the title, the application invariably turns out to be nothing more than a few worked examples using dubious and mainly inappropriate data. On the other hand, the few books available on sources tend to be only partially useful because statistical techniques and measures are excluded.

We are at a loss to explain this strange dichotomy, but strange it is, as a moment's reflection will suggest. It is rather obvious, for example, that even the most sophisticated and complicated statistical technique will be of little use if applied to data that are highly inaccurate and unreliable. The corollary, of course, is where very accurate and reliable data are available but are not fully utilized because of lack of knowledge of techniques.

Clearly, what we are suggesting here is that the only appropriate approach to this subject, if dealt with in an 'applied' way, is an integrated one—one that emphasizes knowledge of sources and knowledge of techniques, and through applying both elements, produces a meaningful result.

This is the *raison d'être* for the book, which is based on the realization that there are four interrelated elements to any quantitative analysis. These are:

1. *Knowledge of sources.* What is meant here is not simply knowing the whereabouts of published data (useful though this may be) but understanding the strengths and weaknesses of published data. By and large this will be determined by such things as administrative difficulties in the collection, processing, and publication of data, and definitions used and problems associated with the classification of economic and business units.

   Of course, although official published data are likely to form a part of the decision-making framework of individual firms, they are certain to make decisions on the basis of more specific, internally generated data. Examples of these and how they are handled by companies will be included.

2. *Organizing the raw data for statistical application.* It is quite likely that published data are not in a 'manageable' form for statistical investigation and, therefore, have to be restructured or represented in a different way. Thus data may be converted into frequency distributions, or in index form, or simply given approximate values through 'rounding' because of the large number of digits that would otherwise have to be handled.

3. *The application of appropriate statistical techniques.* Having made the data manageable, the next step is obviously to apply the statistical techniques. Knowledge of the weaknesses and strengths of different measures and techniques is clearly vital to ensure both a reasonable choice and correct usage and interpretation. Indeed, a common mistake among researchers is to claim rather too much for their results, for example, incorrectly interpreting correlation coefficients as evidence of causation.

   'You can prove anything by statistics' is certainly not the case. What is the case is that statistical evidence can be misinterpreted or misleadingly presented. It is not hard to find examples in, for instance, the newspapers or the speeches of politicians.

4. *Interpreting the results.* The final stage is, quite clearly, a report or document or summary,

detailing and interpreting one's results. On the face of it, this would seem to be the easiest of the four stages, but in many respects, and for many students, it turns out to be the most difficult. 'Correct' interpretation would include a summary of one's findings, together with an analysis of what those findings tell us about the characteristic(s) of the variable or variables examined. In addition, these results might have to be qualified because of certain weaknesses in the basic data used and/or the statistical techniques applied. Thus, our interpretation stage is really an integrating exercise pulling together the other three elements of our quantitative analysis.

We have decided that in order to emphasize the integrated approach taken here, consideration of statistical techniques will be interspersed with consideration of sources. The sources will be dealt with under major macroeconomic indicators such as prices, production, employment/unemployment, wages and earnings, etc. A detailed description of available data under these headings will illustrate the problems and difficulties associated with collecting and providing such data. The question of reliability and usefulness of data will clearly depend on the uses to which such data may be put and therefore a discussion of potential uses and users will be included in each section. In most cases the main users identified will be the central government, who is likely to use data for framing macro/microeconomic and social policies; business units in making output, employment, wages and prices decisions; organized labour who are likely to be interested in a similar range of subjects under the heading of collective bargaining, as well as growing concern shown for 'social' type legislation (e.g., equal opportunities, minimum wage legislation, social welfare provisions, etc.); and finally researchers in the social sciences field attempting to understand the nature of their disciplines more fully.

Statistical techniques will be introduced where they would seem most appropriate. In many cases this presents little difficulty. For example, the theory and practice of index numbers will be dealt with next to the section on production data and the index of industrial production; 'Lorenz' curves will be covered in the section on income and wealth distribution; moving average and seasonal adjustment techniques will be introduced alongside unemployment and vacancy statistics. However, the majority of techniques are of more general application (measures of central tendency and dispersion, correlation and regression analysis, etc.) and it therefore must be admitted that it was rather arbitrarily determined where these were to be initially included in the text as they are utilized in other sections. On the other hand, we have been careful to introduce techniques in a systematic way, generally based on gradually increasing the degree of difficulty involved. Thus we commence with statistical representation and descriptive measures, introduce regression techniques and time series analysis, and probability, and conclude with elements of sampling theory.

The statistical techniques will be illustrated by examples using economic and business data and in a final chapter some more extended examples will be presented which bring together many of the ideas presented in previous chapters. We shall also, at appropriate points in the text, include some consideration of the statistics generated by the typical business organization.

We feel that this is not only the most suitable approach to the subject but reflects the change in emphasis in business education towards a more relevant, practical, and integrated approach. Therefore, we feel that the treatment and subject matter makes it particularly suitable for introductory statistics courses under the new Business Education Council provisions for higher awards and for first year degree courses which include an applied quantitative input.

Finally, it should be said that the best way to learn statistics is by doing it. To this end, many examples and practical assignments are included and the reader is strongly urged to work through some of these. As with the rest of the book, much 'real' data are used so that the results may be meaningful in themselves rather than just classroom exercises.

Acknowledgements

Our thanks are due to many colleagues at Leicester Polytechnic for their advice and constructive comments during the writing of this book. In particular, we are indebted to Mr Graham Adams for his help, guidance, and encouragement.

We are also grateful to the Controller of Her Majesty's Stationery Office for the kind permission to reproduce the many tables and parts of tables from official publications.

Part One

Every organization generates data and the range of published data is enormous. A mass of figures—what the statistician calls 'raw data'—sounds as indigestible as it is. Chapter 1 looks at the presentation of data in the form of tables and diagrams. This is the simplest way of describing data, and will be encountered frequently throughout the book. The first step in analysing data is the calculation of summary measures, of which the most obvious example is an average. This topic is covered in Chapter 2. Again, summary measures will be encountered throughout the book, so it is important to be clear about what they mean and how they are calculated. Both of these chapters use examples typical of the type of data generated by an organization and also use some published data relating to the economy as a whole. This practice will be continued throughout the book.

Chapter 3 is the first of the chapters to deal specifically with published sources of data. It looks at the national income accounts. These provide an overall picture of the economy against which the more specific data of later chapters can be judged. This is not an easy area to understand and involves a number of concepts from macroeconomic theory. It is important, however, since it provides the context within which all economic activity takes place.

Part One therefore provides a context and some of the most basic statistical techniques for the rest of the book. It concludes with some straightforward questions which can be used to assess understanding—answers will be found at the end of the book. There are also some more open-ended questions which can be used as assignments on this part of the book. These are more demanding and require written reports as answers. This will be the pattern for the rest of the book, with the assignment questions involving some extension or application of the ideas presented.

1. Representing data

1.1 Tabulation

The starting point for statistical description or analysis is a table of data. Of course national economic data are already in this form, but the data generated by an individual business enterprise may not be. We start, then, with a brief consideration of tabulating data.

The first important point which must be considered is the purpose of the table. Tables may be used to record data as they arise. This is the case with many government statistical publications, and in the same way companies keep their own records of, for instance, financial and sales data. The object here is to be as accurate as possible and to record in as much detail as is available.

Very often, however, tables are used as descriptions. Data are extracted from published or internal company records to form a table which illustrates something. This may just be for a descriptive report or to provide a simple check on 'how things are going'. The first step is to start with some meaningful categorization. Thus we may decide on broad categories of expenditure for the gross national product (GNP), months of the year for retail sales, etc. We may use the numbers themselves to form the categories. For instance, personal income statistics (see Chapter 13) are divided into the categories 'under £735', '£735 to £1000', and so on.

A table may consist of a two-way categorization; thus categories of expenditure for GNP are cross-referenced by year. More complex schemes with three or more types of classification are also possible, but too much complexity is likely to detract from the descriptive value of the table. A good rule of thumb is to keep the table as simple as possible; it is not necessary to try and show everything in one table.

The next important point to consider is the number of digits to display for each number. The numbers should be presented in a form which is as accurate as is required for the purpose of the table and no more, certainly no more than is warranted by the reliability of the data. It would obviously be absurd, for instance, to report GNP correct to the nearest pound! The resulting eight-digit figure would give a totally spurious impression of the accuracy of that figure. As an example, suppose we wanted to give an impression of the changing amount of the gross domestic product (GDP) accounted for by public expenditure and the manufacturing sector. An examination of Table 1.11 of *The National Income and Expenditure Survey*[1] (The Blue Book) for 1976 gives the data needed, but it is difficult to see the pattern from the mass of detail presented in that table. Table 1.1 below gives a clearer picture. Another rule of thumb, then, is to use as few digits as possible.

Finally, there is the actual layout of the table. As a guide, separate rows and columns by lines or spaces and try to order things so that numbers to be compared are close together. There is obviously a considerable art to producing good tables and only a brief discussion is possible here.

To conclude this section, mention should be made of a particular sort of table much used by the statistician. It was mentioned above that we may categorize data using the values of the numbers themselves, as in the published personal income statistics. A table may then be

Table 1.1   Gross domestic product at factor cost, before providing for depreciation

Selected categories of GDP	GDP (£'000 millions)		
	1965	1970	1975
Public Expenditure (Public Administration, defence, health, and education)	3	5	14
Manufacturing	11	14	27
Other	18	26	55
Total GDP	32	45	96

formed by recording the frequency with which measurements fall into each numerical category. This is called a *frequency table*. For example, suppose the number of industrial accidents occurring per week were recorded for a large company. Over a period of 50 weeks, the frequency table might look like Table 1.2. Thus, for instance, in 12 of the 50 weeks, two accidents occurred. Percentage frequency is often recorded instead of actual frequency.

Table 1.2

Number of accidents per week	Frequency
0	6
1	17
2	12
3	8
4	5
5	1
6	1

When there are more than a small number of possible values, they are usually grouped, as for instance in Table 1.3, which shows a typical pattern of order sizes for a company manufacturing drums of chemicals. Here the table is based on the sizes of 50 orders.

Table 1.3

Size of order range	Frequency
1–10	1
11–20	2
21–30	4
31–40	12
41–50	13
51–60	8
61–70	8
71–80	1
81–90	1

It is important to avoid ambiguity when classifying the different ranges. Thus if the ranges were described as 0–10, 10–20, 20–30, etc., it would not be clear which range an order of 10 or

20 should come in. The problem is removed if we specify 'greater than 0 but less than or equal to 10', and so on.

1.2   Graphical representation

A table of data is essential for detailed discussion or further analysis, but if we want to show just some main features of a set of data, a graphical representation may be useful. There are many ways of doing this and numerous examples can be found in newspapers and magazines for instance. Some government publications include many good examples. We next illustrate the use of a few widely used methods.

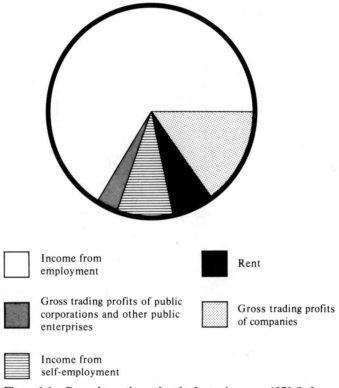

☐ Income from employment

■ Rent

▨ Gross trading profits of public corporations and other public enterprises

▦ Gross trading profits of companies

▤ Income from self-employment

Figure 1.1   Gross domestic product by factor incomes, 1979 (before providing for depreciation and stock appreciation)

The pie chart

This is a common way of showing how a total is split into its component parts. Figure 1.1 shows a pie chart for the 1979 GDP by factor incomes (for data, see Table 3.1 in Chapter 3).

The areas indicated are proportional to the percentage of GDP accounted for by each category of income. The chart is drawn by dividing up the 360° of the circle in proportion to these percentages. For instance, income from self-employment (£15 274m) is approximately 8.8 per cent of the total GDP (£173 624m) and is thus represented by a segment accounting for 32°.

5

The bar chart

A bar chart represents different categories of data by areas of vertical or horizontal bars. There are many forms of bar chart. In some of them the bars are divided into different sections to show sub-categories; these are referred to as component bar charts. Actual figures or percentages can be used. When used for one set of data, bar charts perform the same function as pie charts and there is not much to choose between them. However, when several sets of data are to be compared, bar charts are usually preferable. Two examples are illustrated in Figs 1.2 and 1.3, both of which show the GDP for 1965, 1970, and 1975 and two of its components: manufacturing and public expenditure. Figure 1.2 shows absolute values and how both components and the total have increased. Figure 1.3 shows relative changes by charting the percentage of GDP accounted for by both components. This shows clearly that public services have taken an increasing proportion of GDP, whereas manufacturing has,

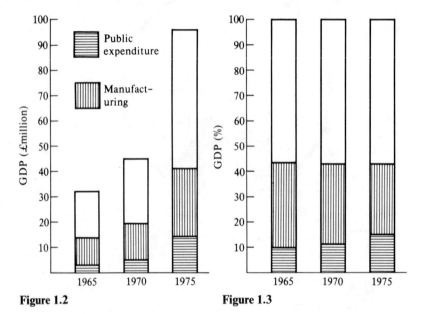

Figure 1.2   **Figure 1.3**

relatively, declined. It is difficult to show both absolute and relative change successfully in the same chart but it is necessary to be clear about which change a graph is designed to show.

Line charts, histograms, and frequency polygons

These are all methods used to illustrate frequency distributions. Where a small number of discrete values are involved a line chart (or possibly a bar chart) can be used. This is the case with the industrial accidents data given in Table 1.2; Fig. 1.4 shows a line chart for these data.

The vertical lines are proportional to the frequencies. Percentage frequency may be used instead of the absolute values.

For grouped frequency data, a similar idea is employed in the histogram. This is like a bar chart, except that the bars (with areas proportional to frequency) are all joined together. Figure 1.5 shows two histograms for the order size data given in Table 1.3.

Figure 1.5 (a) shows the data as given in Table 1.3. Figure 1.5 (b) shows the same data with

6

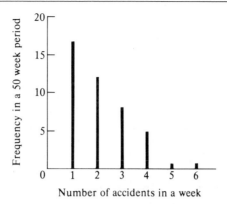

Figure 1.4

the first two and the last two ranges combined. This illustrates the point that the area of a bar is proportional to frequency. The first bar represents a frequency of 3, but it is drawn with half this height, as measured on the vertical scale, because its width has doubled. Similarly for the last bar, which represents a frequency of 2 and is thus drawn with a height of 1.

The frequency polygon is constructed by plotting the height of the histogram bars at the mid points of their related ranges. These points are then joined up. The frequency polygon for the order size data shown in Fig. 1.5 (a) is illustrated in Fig. 1.6.

Conventionally the line joins the horizontal axis at what would be the mid points of the ranges next to the first and last ranges. This diagram is not nearly so informative as a histogram. Its main interest lies in demonstrating how the 'shape' of a distribution can be approximated by a theoretical frequency curve. That is a smooth curve derived from a mathematical formula. In fact, the order size data can be approximated by the most widely used of such curves—that of the normal distribution. We will be seeing the properties and uses of this curve later.

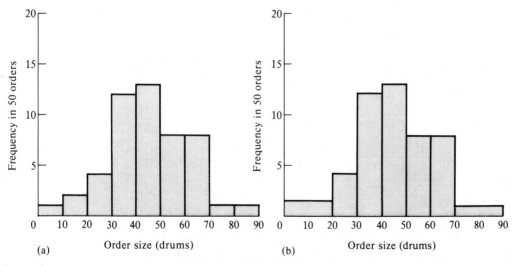

Figure 1.5

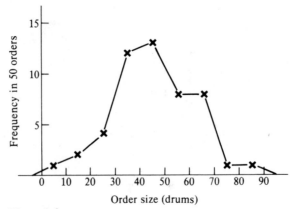

Figure 1.6

Ogives

It is sometimes useful to consider cumulative frequency; Table 1.4 gives cumulative frequencies for the data of Table 1.3. In this case, it is the cumulative frequency less than or equal to the upper end of the related range. Thus there are 32 orders of 50 or less. The cumulative frequency for the highest range will be the same as the total frequency. It is also possible to use 'greater than' cumulative frequencies, which are the total frequencies greater than or equal to the lower ends of each range. In this example we would have 50 for the first range, 49 for the second, 47 for the third, and so on.

The ogive gives a graphical representation of the cumulative frequencies, which are plotted against the upper ends of their related ranges (for less than cumulative frequencies) as shown in Fig. 1.7.

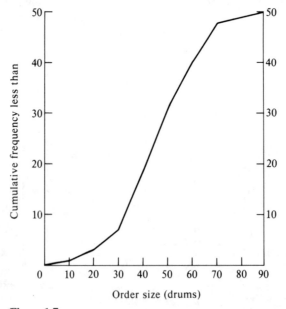

Figure 1.7

8

Table 1.4

Size of order range	Frequency	Cumulative frequency
1–10	1	1
11–20	2	3
21–30	4	7
31–40	12	19
41–50	13	32
51–60	8	40
61–70	8	48
71–80	1	49
81–90	1	50

This concludes a brief coverage of some ways of representing data. Many elementary statistics texts give a more detailed treatment, but perhaps the best guide is to look at the many published examples available.

2. Measures of average and variation

We have seen how data can be described in tabular and graphical form. It is often useful and convenient to describe data in terms of one or more characteristic values or summary measurements. This is analogous to the way we often describe other things. For instance, we can form some impression of a particular model of motor car without drawing a complete picture or describing every component. In this case our summary measurements might be engine size, number of doors, price, petrol consumption, etc.

Suppose, for example, that we wanted to describe the distribution of incomes in the United Kingdom. The most obvious summary measurement to use would be average income. Another useful summary measurement would be a measure which indicated the spread or variation of individual incomes. Both of these summary measurements would differ widely from country to country with, roughly speaking, the average increasing and the variation decreasing as we went from less developed to more developed countries. These are the two types of summary measurements most widely used in describing data and most of this chapter will be concerned with the different ways of measuring averages and variation.

2.1 Measures of the average

There are several ways of measuring the average of a set of data, depending on what sort of data they are, how they are recorded and the use we want to put the measure to. We next consider the main types of measure in statistical use, their main advantages and disadvantages, and some of the areas in which it is appropriate to apply each measure.

The arithmetic mean

This is usually called simply 'the mean' and is what, in everyday language, we would think of as the average of a set of data. Suppose, for instance, we recorded the numbers of orders received for a particular item on each of five days, as follows:

$$1,2,0,3,2$$

The mean daily demand would be

$$\frac{1+2+0+3+2}{5}=\frac{8}{5}=1.6$$

To express this rule mathematically, we introduce some notation widely used in statistics. The thing we are measuring or recording is called a *variable, x* say (any letter would do). Suppose we have n values of x:

$$x_1, x_2, \ldots x_n$$

We define the sum of these values as $\sum x$; so

$$\sum x = x_1 + x_2 + \cdots + x_n$$

The mean value of x, referred to as $\bar{x}$ ('x bar') is therefore

$$\bar{x} = \frac{1}{n}\sum x \qquad (2.1)$$

Where data are arranged in the form of a frequency table, we find the sum of the values by multiplying each *different* value by its frequency of occurrence and adding the results. Adding the frequencies will give the total number of observations. Thus, the mean number of industrial accidents per week, from the data given Table 1.2, is found to be

$$\frac{6(0) + 17(1) + 12(2) + \cdots}{6 + 17 + 12 + \cdots} = \frac{96}{50} = 1.92$$

Formula (2.1) is simply modified to include this case. If we let the n *different* values x takes be

$$x_1, x_2, \ldots, x_n$$

with frequencies

$$f_1, f_2, \ldots, f_n$$

then the mean value of x, $\bar{x}$, is

$$\bar{x} = \frac{1}{N}\sum fx \qquad (2.2)$$

where $N = \sum f$.

Finally, we must consider the case where the data are only available in the form of a grouped frequency table, such as the distribution of drum order sizes given in Table 1.3. Here we only know that, for instance, 12 orders were for somewhere between 31 and 40 drums. It is only possible, therefore, to *estimate* the mean in such a case. To do so we treat all the values in each category or class as if they were the same. We normally pick the mid point of the range of values that define the class as this representative value (this is usually called the *class mark*). Thus in the above example we treat all 12 orders as if they were for 35.5 drums. We then estimate the mean using formula (2.2) just as before, using the class marks as our x values. The calculations for estimating the mean order size for drums can be set out as shown in Table 2.1.

Table 2.1

Order size range	Class mark, x	Frequency, f	fx
1–10	5.5	1	5.5
11–20	15.5	2	31
21–30	25.5	4	102
31–40	35.5	12	426
41–50	45.5	13	591.5
51–60	55.5	8	444
61–70	65.5	8	524
71–80	75.5	1	75.5
81–90	85.5	1	85.5
		$N = \sum f = 50$	$\sum fx = 2285.0$

$$\text{Mean order size} = \frac{2285}{50} = 45.7$$

We have assumed, of course, that the actual values are spread evenly over each range, which is not likely to be the case in practice. In fact, we would expect the average for a class below the mean to be slightly higher than the mid point of its range and lower for a class above the mean. This is on the assumption that values are more likely to be close to the mean than further away. However, where the distribution is fairly symmetrical about the mean, i.e. approximately the same number of values at equal distances above and below the mean, these errors should nearly cancel out and our estimate will be quite good. It is possible to modify this approach for asymmetrical distributions, but this will rarely give an appreciable increase in accuracy. If greater accuracy is required it is necessary to use the data in the original ungrouped form.

It sometimes happens that grouped frequency tables contain open classes. For instance, personal income statistics are published in a table (see Chapter 13) which includes the classes 'under £735' and '£100 000 and over'. In such cases we can usually make an intelligent guess at an appropriate class mark. If we are totally ignorant of the likely spread of values in an open class a reasonable and simple assumption would be that it has the same width as the nearest closed class. It is an instructive exercise to estimate the mean income from the table referred to using the method outlined above. It will be found to give a remarkably accurate result (the actual mean can be calculated exactly using the total income also given in the table). This is despite the fact that the distribution is far from symmetrical and even true if a crude estimate of the class marks for the two open classes is used. Incidentally, if a class mark estimate is dubious it is worth recalculating the estimate making an alternative assumption. If the estimate is insensitive to the assumption we can have more confidence in it, a procedure which is in general most valuable in any kind of mathematical analysis.

A final point will be made about notation. In the examples used above of accidents recorded and order sizes, we were dealing with only a sample of the possible data. The personal income data, however, include every income recorded in the given year. Such data are said to relate to a *population* rather than a sample. The population is all possible observations rather than a selection of them as in a sample. A population mean is usually referred to using the symbol μ. A sample mean, $\bar{x}$, may be used as an estimate of the mean of the population from which the sample is taken. This point is elaborated in Chapter 11.

The median

When we are mainly concerned with simply describing a set of data, by giving an average or 'typical' value, it is sometimes preferable to find the median rather than the mean. The median is defined as a value such that exactly half the observations exceed it and half are below it. If the data are arranged in increasing order of magnitude, it will thus be the central value. For example:

$$\underbrace{0 \quad 0 \quad 1 \quad 1 \quad 1 \quad 2}_{\text{six values}} \quad \underset{\underset{\text{median}=2}{\uparrow}}{2} \quad \underbrace{2 \quad 3 \quad 4 \quad 6 \quad 8 \quad 9}_{\text{six values}}$$

Had we had an even number of values, the median would lie between two of them. Their mid point would, conventionally, be taken as the median. Thus, the median of the first 10 values given above is 1.5.

As another example, consider the data on accident frequencies (Table 1.2). There are 50 observations and by cumulating the frequencies we see that there are 6 zeros, 23 less than or equal to 1 and 35 less than or equal to 2. Therefore, the median is clearly 2.

With grouped frequency data we have to estimate the median, as for the mean. For example, consider again the order size data of Table 1.3 (repeated above). Cumulating the frequencies we find:

19 orders are less than or equal to 40

32 orders are less than or equal to 50

The median order size is thus between 40 and 50. If we assume the 13 values in this class are evenly spread, the median, being the twenty-fifth observation in order of magnitude will be $\frac{6}{13}$ into this class. Thus:

$$\text{Median order size} = 40 + \frac{25-19}{32-19}(50-40)$$

$$= 40 + \frac{6}{13} \times 10 = 44.6 \quad \text{(approximately)}$$

Technically, the median lies between the twenty-fifth and the twenty-sixth largest orders, but this nicety is not worth worrying about where there are a large number of observations, especially when we are estimating as in this case.

Consider again the first example of this section. The mean value is easily found to be 3, whereas the median was found to be 2. In a sense the median is the more representative of the data, since only four of the values are greater than 3 with nine at 3 or less. This is because a few high and untypical values have pulled up the value of the mean. A more extreme example would occur if we wanted to indicate the average turnover of chemical companies from a sample which included ICI. The mean in this case would be almost meaningless (no pun intended!). In these cases the median would be better as a description of the average. We return to this point later when we compare measures of the average.

The median of a grouped frequency table can also be estimated graphically using the ogive (cumulative frequencies plotted against the end points of the data ranges). The ogive for the drum order size data has already been plotted (Fig. 1.7). If a horizontal line is drawn from the point representing half the total frequency on the vertical axis, it will cross the ogive immediately above the median. In this example the line is drawn from 25 on the frequency scale, and it can be seen to cross the ogive approximately above the median order size of 44.6, as calculated above.

The mode

The mode of a set of data is the value which occurs most frequently. Thus the mode for the industrial accidents data (Table 1.2) is 1 accident per week. If you asked a shirt salesman for the average collar size of the shirts he sold, he might answer 'size 15', meaning the size most frequently demanded, i.e., the mode of the distribution of his shirt sales by their collar size.

When data are given in the form of a grouped frequency table, it is difficult to estimate with any accuracy where the mode lies. We can readily identify the modal class, but the mode may not necessarily lie within this range of values. If we approximate the frequency polygon by a smooth curve, its peak will give a rough estimate of the mode. There are formulae for estimating the mode, but fairly heroic assumptions are necessary about precisely how the values are spread across the class ranges, and this approach is rarely used in practice.

13

An extension of the idea of the mode is to consider also the second, third, etc., most frequently occurring value. If the shirt salesman did this he would almost certainly find that nearly all of his demand was for a small number of shirt sizes. This type of analysis may be useful in, for instance, establishing stock control procedures.

Other measures of the average

The arithmetic mean is a special case of the general *weighted mean*. This is found by multiplying each value by some appropriate weighting factor and dividing the result by the sum of the weights. Where the data consist of single observations or measurements, the frequency with which each value occurs is obviously the appropriate weight to use and we find the arithmetic mean as before. Suppose, however, that our data consist of values which are themselves the means derived from some other sets of data. In this case, we might use as the weights the number of observations used to derive each mean value. For example, suppose we found:

$$\text{Mean daily sales for January} = £550 \quad (22 \text{ working days})$$
$$\text{Mean daily sales for February} = £580 \quad (20 \text{ working days})$$

Then the mean daily sales for the two month period would be

$$\text{Mean sales} = \frac{22 \times 550 + 20 \times 580}{22 + 20} = \frac{23\,700}{42} = 564 \quad \text{(approximately)}$$

The idea of a weighted mean is also important in the calculation of index numbers, as we shall see in Chapter 5. As a final example we may use weights based on an estimate of the importance or reliability of our values, as in averaging measurements of the same thing by different people or forecasts for the same period of time derived in different ways.

Finally, we mention two rarely used measures. The *geometric mean* is found by calculating the mean of the logarithms of each value and taking the antilogarithm of the result. The *harmonic mean* is found by inverting the mean of the reciprocals of the numbers.

A comparison of measures of the average

The mean is the most widely used measure of the average in statistics. Most of its advantages stem from the fact that it is calculated using all of the data, and so in a sense it gives the most possible information about the data. It is also straightforward to calculate and intuitively understood. As we have seen, it is possible to combine means together as a further step in analysing data. It is by far the most widely used measure of the average in the statistical analysis of sample data, because it varies less from sample to sample of the same population than any other measure. This means that, for instance, a sample mean is likely to be closer to its corresponding population mean than would be the case for any other measure.

The main disadvantage of the mean occurs when we simply want to give a purely descriptive average of a distribution of values that are not spread symmetrically about the mean. As we have seen, when consideraing the calculation of the median, the mean may give a distorted impression because of the influence of a relatively small number of exceptional values. These types of data, called *skewed* distributions, are best described using the median. A minor problem with the mean is the sometimes laborious arithmetic which may be required to calculate it. Much attention used to be given to ways of simplifying this arithmetic. Nowadays, however, with the wide availability and cheapness of calculators and even computers, this is not a very significant problem.

The median is also widely used as a measure of the average. It is easy to understand and even easier to find than the mean, requiring little or no calculation. Since it is only concerned with the middle range of values, open-ended classes present no problem as they will occur at the extreme ranges of the data. Its main importance as a descriptive measure is for skewed distributions of data. It is used for indicating average incomes, wages, and wealth, for instance, all of which have highly skewed distributions. It can also be used where we have a set of ranks, rather than numerical measures. Thus if items are placed in order, according to some criterion, we can identify the one with the median rank, whereas the mean would be inapplicable.

The main disadvantages of the median stem from the fact that it only takes account of a single value, or possibly the middle range of values. Medians cannot be combined and are not very useful for any further analysis of the data. Although for symmetrically distributed data the mean and the median should nearly coincide, if as is often the case we have only a sample of values, the median will be the less reliable measure. As already mentioned, this is because it will vary more from sample to sample than the mean.

The mode is mainly used where we really mean by average, 'most typical'. Thus we might use it to describe the average family size, for instance. It is the only way of giving an average for data arranged into qualitative categories. Its disadvantages are that it is often difficult to estimate, it may not be unique if two values occur with equal frequency, and it will vary more widely from sample to sample than even the median. It is not useful for any further analysis.

2.2 Measures of variation

As already mentioned, it is often valuable to have a measure of the spread or variation of a set of data, as well as its average. This is useful for purely descriptive purposes and is of vital importance in the anlaysis of sample data. For instance, if we want to estimate some characteristic of a population from a sample, we need to know how variable the sample characteristic may be in order to judge what confidence can be placed in the estimate. This is necessary in assessing the results of market research, opinion polling, and the many surveys carried out by the Government Statistical Service, for instance.

Measures of position

We first consider a number of measures that identify particular points in the spread of the data. The other measures, considered later, are concerned with the average variation of all the data values about some central point (usually the mean).

The *range* is the simplest possible measure of variation and is the difference between the largest and the smallest of the data values. Thus the range of weekly accidents given in Table 1.2 is

$$\text{Range} = 6 - 0 = 6$$

If the data are arranged in order from the smallest to the largest value, we can give more information about the spread by finding the values that lie at various intermediate points. The values that divide the observations into four equal-sized groups are often chosen and are called the *quartiles*. For the accidents data, there are 50 observations, so the quartiles will lie at positions $12\frac{1}{2}$, 25, and $37\frac{1}{2}$. For fractional positions, we take a point between the values which lie in the positions on either side. Thus we have

First quartile $= Q_1 = 1$ (twelfth and thirteenth value $= 1$)
Second quartile $=$ median $= 2$
Third quartile $= Q_3 = 3$ (thirty-seventh and thirty-eighth value $= 3$)

Notice that the second quartile is the same as the median (already found for these data). If, for instance, the twelfth and thirteenth value had been different, we would have taken the point halfway between them, and similarly for any other fractional position.

The first and third quartiles enclose the middle 50 per cent of the values. Their difference, the *interquartile range*, is sometimes quoted and in this case we have

Interquartile range $= Q_3 - Q_1 = 3 - 1 = 2$

Other measures of position that are occasionally used are the *deciles*, which divide the data into 10 equal groups, and the *percentiles*, which divide the data into 100 equal groups. Of course, all 100 percentiles would never be used, but extreme ones, such as the fifth, tenth, ninetieth, and ninety-fifth, are sometimes of particular interest. For instance, the company might require a special report if in any week the number of accidents exceeded the ninetieth percentile point (four accidents).

For grouped frequency data, these measures of position must be estimated. The same approaches apply as were used for finding the median. They can either be found arithmetically or by using the ogive. As an example, the quartiles for the drum order size data (Table 1.4) are found as follows:

$$Q_1 = 30 + \frac{12\frac{1}{2} - 7}{19 - 7}(40 - 30) = 34.6$$

$$Q_3 = 50 + \frac{37\frac{1}{2} - 32}{40 - 32}(60 - 50) = 56.9$$

This makes the same assumption as before—that the data are evenly spread within each range. For this reason, these measures should not be quoted too exactly; the impression of accuracy will be quite spurious. Horizontal lines drawn from the $12\frac{1}{2}$ and $37\frac{1}{2}$ points on the frequency scale of Fig. 1.7 can be seen to cut the ogive approximately above the values calculated above.

The mean absolute deviation

The other approach to measuring variation in data is to consider the average variation of all the values about some central point. The mean is almost always chosen as this central point, but there are several ways of measuring the variation about it.

The most intuitively obvious approach is to simply difference each value from the mean. However, it is not difficult to see from the definition of the mean that these differences must always sum to zero. A simple way of avoiding this problem is to ignore the sign of the differences and just sum their magnitudes or *absolute* values, as they are termed in mathematics. The mean of these absolute differences is the *mean absolute deviation* (MAD).

16

For example, using the orders received data whose mean we have already found to be 1.6 we obtain the result shown in Table 2.2.

Table 2.2

Numbers of orders	Deviations from mean	Absolute deviations
1	−0.6	0.6
2	0.4	0.4
0	−1.6	1.6
3	1.4	1.4
2	0.4	0.4
	0	4.4

$$\text{MAD} = \frac{4.4}{5} = 0.88$$

The MAD is an easy to calculate and easy to understand measure of the variability of data, although some problems arise when it is used for grouped frequency data. It provides a simple means of comparing two sets of data. Perhaps its major application is in the monitoring of forecasting errors, where for instance regular monthly forecasts of sales, say, are produced. The cumulative sum of the errors (including signs) provide a check on whether the forecasts are biased, since this should not be too far from zero unless we are consistently over- or underestimating. The MAD is an estimate of the average magnitude of the errors, since we are in effect measuring their deviations from zero.

Unfortunately the MAD is not a convenient measure to deal with mathematically, so it is not much used in statistical analysis. The measures which are described next are almost universally used in statistical theory as measures of variability.

The variance and the standard deviation

An alternative way of removing the signs of the deviations from the mean is to square them all. The *variance* is defined as the mean of the squared deviations. Thus, for the previous example we have

$$\text{Variance} = \frac{(-0.6)^2 + (0.4)^2 + (-1.6)^2 + (1.4)^2 + (0.4)^2}{5} = \frac{5.2}{5} = 1.04$$

To express this in a mathematical formula, if we have the n values of a variable x,

$$x_1, x_2, \ldots, x_n$$

with mean $\bar{x}$, then the variance is

$$\frac{(x_1 - \bar{x})^2 + (x_2 - \bar{x})^2 + \cdots + (x_n - \bar{x})^2}{n} \tag{2.3}$$

This can be put more succinctly using the summation notation as:

$$\text{Variance} = \frac{1}{n}\sum(x - \bar{x})^2 \tag{2.4}$$

17

It is possible to rearrange this formula in a way which makes the calculation of the variance much easier in general. If the squared terms in (2.3) are expanded a little manipulation yields the result:

$$\text{Variance} = \frac{1}{n}\sum x^2 - \bar{x}^2 \qquad (2.5)$$

Using this formula, the variance for the data used above is calculated as follows:

$$\text{Variance} = \tfrac{1}{5}(1^2 + 2^2 + 0^2 + 3^2 + 2^2) - 1.6^2$$
$$= \tfrac{18}{5} - 2.56$$
$$= 1.04$$

The result is, of course, the same as the one we derived before. The disadvantage of the variance is that it is measured in units that are the square of the units of the original data. This difficulty is overcome by deriving from it a measure called the *standard deviation*, which is defined as

$$\text{Standard deviation} = \sqrt{(\text{variance})} \qquad (2.6)$$

Thus, for the above example, we have

$$\text{Standard deviation} = \sqrt{(1.04)}$$
$$= 1.02 \quad \text{(approximately)}$$

Formulas (2.4) and (2.5) need to be modified if the calculations are to be made for frequency data. The x values will then be the n *different* values in the data, and any operation on them will need to be multiplied by the frequency with which each value occurs. Formula (2.5) is nearly always the best to use, and its modified form for frequency data is

$$\text{Variance} = \frac{1}{N}\sum fx^2 - \bar{x}^2 \qquad (2.7)$$

where $\quad N = \sum f$

Here f is used for the frequency of each data value, as in the formula for the mean. Notice again the difference between n (the number of different values) and N (the sum of the frequencies). To test understanding of this formula, calculate the variance for the industrial accidents data of Table 1.2. It should be found to be 1.87 (approximately). The standard deviation can be found, as before, by taking the square root, and is approximately 1.37. It is interesting to note that in this case the variance is quite close in value to the mean, which we previously found to be 1.92. When phenomena (such as the accidents in this example) occur independently and at random over time, their frequencies of occurrence should approximate to a theoretical frequency distribution called the *Poisson distribution* (see Chapter 10). One of the properties of this distribution is that the mean and the variance are equal. As another example, it will often apply to the number of customers arriving, per unit of time, at the end of a queue.

With grouped frequency data, we can only estimate the variance and the standard deviation. The same approach as for the mean can be used, with the x values now standing for the mid points of each class. The calculations for the order size data of Table 1.3 are shown in Table 2.3.

The calculations for the mean have been repeated for convenience. Once again we have made the assumption that the data are evenly spread over the class ranges. This tends to

Table 2.3

Order size range	Class mark, x	Frequency, f	fx	fx^2
1–10	5.5	1	5.5	30.25
11–20	15.5	2	31	480.5
21–30	25.5	4	102	2 601
31–40	35.5	12	426	15 123
41–50	45.5	13	591.5	26 913.25
51–60	55.5	8	444	24 642
61–70	65.5	8	524	34 322
71–80	75.5	1	75.5	5 700.25
81–90	85.5	1	85.5	7 310.25
		$N = \sum f = 50$	$\sum fx = 2285.0$	$\sum fx^2 = 117\,122.5$

$$\text{Mean} = \frac{2285}{50} = 45.7$$

$$\text{Variance} = \frac{117\,122.5}{50} - 45.7^2 = 253.96$$

$$\text{Standard deviation} = \sqrt{(253.96)} = 15.9 \quad \text{(approximately)}$$

introduce slightly more error into the estimation of the variance than it did for the mean, and in some cases it is possible to make some correction. This is not usually worth while, and for most purposes the estimate will be good enough. If greater accuracy is required, the original ungrouped data should be used.

The variance and the standard deviation do not have the intuitive appeal of the MAD for measuring variability in data. They serve equally well, however, in comparing different sets of data. Clearly the higher the MAD, the higher the variance and the standard deviation. Sometimes sets of data measured in different units are compared, and to remove this effect the *coefficient of variation* can be used, where

$$\text{Coefficient of variation} = \frac{\text{standard deviation}}{\text{mean}} \qquad (2.8)$$

This is often multiplied by 100 and expressed as a percentage.

We have already mentioned the mathematical advantages of the variance and the standard deviation. For descriptive purposes, they are most useful in describing data whose frequency distributions approximate to the theoretical *normal distribution*. That is, the values are symmetrically distributed about the mean, and the frequency polygon approximates to the type of smooth curve shown in Fig. 2.1.

The properties of this curve will be described later (Chapter 10), but it is completely described by measures of the mean and standard deviation. From these two values, we can determine the frequency of occurrence of values in any range. For instance, 95 per cent of the frequency will occur in the range:

Mean ± 2 standard deviations

For the drum order size data this range is

$45.7 \pm 2 \times 15.9$ or 13.9 to 77.5

It can be seen, for instance from the ogive, that this is approximately true.

This use of the standard deviation is particularly important when analysing sample data, as

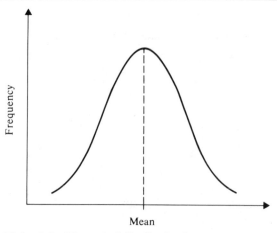

Figure 2.1 The normal distribution frequency curve

we shall see, since the means of samples drawn from the same population will always be approximately normally distributed, no matter what distribution of the data they are derived from.

Finally, a word about notation. The variance of a population is referred to as σ^2 and its standard deviation as σ. For sample data the symbols used are s^2 and s respectively. The *sample variance*, s^2, is usually calculated in such a way as to estimate the population variance. When so used, the formulas given above are not, technically, correct. This is because they can be shown to give a consistent underestimation. To correct for this, the variance as calculated by formulas (2.4) or (2.5) is multiplied by the factor $n/(n-1)$. Since this will only be significant for small samples there is little point in modifying the formulas for frequency data. The subjects of sampling and estimation are more thoroughly treated in Chapter 11.

A comparison of measures of variation

Measures of position are easy to find and are easily understood. They are useful for descriptive purposes, especially for data with skewed frequency distributions. They are not very suitable for any further statistical analysis. Derived measures such as the range and the interquartile range are not often used. The range suffers from the particular disadvantage that it is very susceptible to exceptional values occurring in the data, which can make it very misleading. Its big advantage is the great simplicity with which it can be found in small samples of data. For this reason, it is sometimes used in quality control checks on the output of a production process. Here a measure of variability may be frequently required and exceptional values are highly unlikely unless something has gone wrong. In most other circumstances where samples are taken, the range will vary too much from sample to sample to be of much use.

As a measure of the average variability of all the data, the MAD has an intuitive appeal. Of such measures it is the easiest to calculate, and is useful for providing a quick check, for instance, when comparing two sets of data. Its main disadvantage is the mathematical difficulties it creates when further analysis is required. Also, it will vary more from sample to sample than the variance or the standard deviation, so is of less use in estimating the variability of a population from a sample. It is, however, sometimes used, for instance, in monitoring forecasting errors.

By far the most important measures of variability in statistical theory are the variance and the standard deviation. They are, however, difficult to interpret in a descriptive sense, except to say that the larger they are, the more variable are the data. When the data approximately follow a normal distribution, they do provide a most powerful descriptive tool, as alluded to above. As mentioned, this makes them very useful in analysing sample data. It is interesting to note that for a normal distribution, the following relationship holds:

$$\text{Standard deviation} = 1.25 \times \text{MAD} \qquad (2.9)$$

The variance does require more arithmetic than the other measures to calculate, but with a little practice and a calculator this is not too much of a problem. Where large numbers are involved, it may be necessary to code the data to avoid calculator overflow. If a constant value is subtracted from each of the data values or class marks, the variance is unaffected. If they are all divided by a constant, as is usually necessary in this case, the variance found for the coded data must be multiplied by the square of that constant in order to apply to the original data. There is also the problem of open classes, and our estimate of their class marks will be more crucial than it was for the mean. These extreme ranges will be the furthest from the mean, and since deviations from the mean are squared to calculate the variance, they can have a substantial effect.

2.3 Other descriptive measures

We have already had cause to remark on the skewness or otherwise of data; after the average and the variation, this is the next most important characteristic of a set of data. Figure 2.2 illustrates the concept.

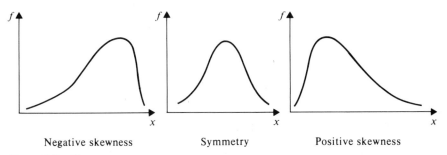

Figure 2.2 **Skewness**

The normal distribution is the most commonly occurring symmetrical frequency distribution. Positive skewness is also quite common; it is, for instance, the shape of the distribution of personal incomes. Another example is the distribution of the time intervals between randomly occurring events, such as the arrival of customers at the end of a queue. Negative skewness is less common, but occurs, for instance, in the distribution of times to failure of certain types of equipment.

Several measures of skewness have been proposed, but are rarely used in practice. The simplest way of describing skewness is to quote the mean, the median, and, where possible, the mode. For symmetrical distributions, these three measures will approximately coincide. For positively skewed distributions, the mode will be less than the median, which will in turn be less than the mean. This is very noticeable for the distribution of personal incomes. For negatively skewed distributions, these three measures will be in the reverse order. The differences between the measures give some indication of the extent of the skewness.

A characteristic of distributions which is occasionally used when describing them is their *kurtosis*. This simply means their 'peakedness', and we can distinguish between distributions where there is a sharp fall-off of frequencies on either side of the mode, and hence a sharp peaked shape, and those distributions where the fall-off is more gradual and a smoother shape results. Again, the measures that have been proposed for this are rarely used.

Finally, in statistical theory, use is sometimes made of a general set of measures called the *moments* of a distribution. The variance is the second moment about the mean; higher moments are obtained by averaging higher powers of the differences from the mean. These are mainly of use in fitting theoretical frequency distributions to data, and need not concern us here.

This concludes our coverage of descriptive measures, save for an important class of measures called *index numbers* that are treated on their own in Chapter 5. We have inevitably strayed into some more general treatment of frequency distributions, and this is taken up in Chapter 10. We have also introduced some ideas about the analysis of sample data, which are treated more thoroughly in Chapter 11.

3. National income accounts

The national income accounts are compiled by the Central Statistical Office (CSO) and published annually by HM Stationery Office (HMSO) under the title *The National Income and Expenditure Survey*[1] (The Blue Book). The publication is often referred to by commentators as the 'Blue Book', not because it contains salacious stories and pin-ups but because of the colour of its soft cover.

The accounts themselves are intended to represent the monetary value of the total output of goods and services produced in the economy in a discrete time period. It should be realized immediately, however, that since the real world is dynamic and not static, and since the Blue Book is attempting to represent the real world with real values, then the 'flow' (i.e., dynamic) concept is adopted rather than the 'stock' (i.e., static) concept. Thus the accounts attempt to represent the flow of goods and services produced in the economy within a calendar year in monetary terms.

Students of economics will be familiar with the notion of a flow of economic activity from the basic theory of macroeconomics known as the circular flow of income. Indeed, this theory demonstrates that the value of the flow of goods and services can be represented in three different ways: first, the income generated from the production of goods and services; second, the output or production created; third, the value of expenditure on those goods and services. All this can be shown as in Fig. 3.1.

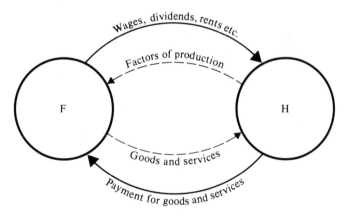

Figure 3.1   The basic circular flow of income

If we assume that 'households' (H) own all the factors of production (land, labour, and capital) and supply these factors to 'firms' (F), then they would clearly expect compensation in return. This is shown in the diagram with the upper flow representing monetary payments to the owners of resources and would include such things as wages and salaries (for labour), rates of interest, dividends, and profits (for capital), and rent (for land). With the factors employed, 'firms' would be able to produce goods and services which in turn would be purchased by households with the income received for supplying their factors to the firms in the first place. Thus a counter-flow of income will go from 'households' to 'firms' to pay for goods and services and is shown as the lower payment flow in the diagram.

Clearly, if we are careful about how we define, and what we include, as income and take care to allow for stock changes when measuring production and expenditure, then the total value of incomes will be identical to the total value of expenditure. In terms of Fig. 3.1 it is easily demonstrated that if we assume no stocks are held by firms, nor any incomes retained either by firms or households, then it follows that the value of the upper flow (i.e., incomes) will be identical to the lower flow (i.e., expenditure) which must, therefore, be identical to the value of goods and services produced (represented by the flow of commodities from firms to households). The argument that these relationships only hold because of the restrictive assumptions made is not valid. All that is required is for stock changes and all forms of income to be accounted for in the recording process and equality will be achieved.

It should be apparent by now that national income could be presented in three ways; in fact, all three approaches are used by the CSO in the Blue Book. Let us look at these three approaches in detail.

3.1 The income approach

Here, the value of the flow of goods and services produced in the economy is measured in terms of the various types of income created in the process of that production, and is illustrated by an extract from the summary tables in the Blue Book (see Table 3.1).

Table 3.1

	£ million for 1979
Income from employment	113927
Income from self-employment	15274
Gross trading profits of companies	25978
Gross trading surplus of public corporations	5585
Gross trading surplus of general government enterprises	131
Rent	11078
Imputed charge for consumption of non-trading capital	1651
Total domestic income	173624
Less stock appreciation	−8542
Gross domestic product (income based)	165082
Residual error	−1435
Gross domestic product (expenditure based)	163647
Net property income from abroad	289
Gross national product	163936

Reproduced from *The National Income and Expenditure Survey*, 1980, Table 1.2, with the permission of the Controller of Her Majesty's Stationery Office.

As can be seen, income is disaggregated into employed and self-employed income, profits of private and public concerns (referred to euphemistically as a 'surplus'), and rent. The term 'general government enterprises' covers both central and local authorities in their provision of passenger transport, harbours, docks, etc., and 'public corporations' refer to the nationalized industries and public boards (coal, electricity, gas, etc.). Before total domestic income is

24

shown an item is included described as 'imputed charge for consumption of non-trading capital'. This is an estimate of the effective income resulting from being an owner-occupier of property. It is effective income since the users of the property, if they were not owner-occupiers, would find their incomes lowered by having to pay rent. Although no flow of income is seen, nevertheless a real income benefit is derived for being an owner-occupier, which is why the term 'imputed' is used. This imputed income relates only to general government and private non-profit-making concerns who are owner-occupiers of non-trading property.

These various forms of income then have to be adjusted to compensate for different price valuations of quantities of stocks. During an inflationary period when prices are rising, the value of stocks will be greater at the end of the period than at the beginning, even if the physical stock quantities are identical. Therefore a value would have to be deducted from the figures to allow for such 'over-recording' and is called 'less stock appreciation'. With the inclusion of this item a sub-total, 'gross domestic product (income base)', is shown, which is then converted into 'gross domestic product (expenditure based)' with a value for the 'residual error' (which will be discussed later). The expenditure-based measure of the GDP is the total value of goods and services produced at factor cost and is identical to that shown in the expenditure account.

To convert this valuation from a *domestic* to a *national* one we would have to introduce a foreign trade element. Clearly, the part of foreign trade relevant to the income approach would be those foreign income flows not already included, and therefore the final item in this part of the accounts is called 'net property income from abroad'. The major aggregate resulting from the inclusion of this item then becomes the gross national product (GNP).

3.2 Production (or output) approach

It can be seen from Table 3.2 that this approach actually measures the value of the total flow of goods and services during a calendar year and breaks the information down into a large number of industrial classifications. To avoid double-counting, the value of output represents that which is added at each stage of production. Thus, for example, if the motor vehicle industry purchases £1 million of steel during a year and, with this steel, produces vehicles over the same time period valued at £5 million, then it would be recorded in the accounts as £1 million output of steel and £4 million output of vehicles since this would be the 'value added' by the vehicle industry. The total output would, therefore, be a sum of all the values added for all enterprises at each stage of production. It follows, of course, that imports of materials and sub-parts will be excluded from the calculations.

It should be noted that service sector categories are included as well as primary and manufacturing sectors. The derived sub-total is followed by an item called 'adjustment for financial services' which represents the net interest receipts of the insurance, banking, finance, and business services sector. The logic behind this treatment is that net interest receipts correspond to the financial services provided to many of the listed industries and therefore relates to intermediate demand. Since this element is included in the financial sector it should correspondingly be deducted from the individual totals of the user industries. In practice, however, it is difficult to assign these values individually and therefore an aggregate estimation is made. With the inclusion, once again, of the residual error, we arrive at the GDP at factor cost.

Table 3.2

	£ million for 1979
Agriculture, forestry, and fishing	3 792
Petroleum and natural gas	5 111
Other mining and quarrying	2 696
Manufacturing	45 582
Construction	10 237
Gas, electricity, and water	4 752
Transport	9 491
Communication	4 307
Distributive trades	17 146
Insurance, banking, finance, and business services	14 891
Ownership of dwellings	9 837
Public administration and defence	11 752
Public health and educational services	11 030
Other services	22 267
Total	172 891
Adjustment for financial services	−7 809
Residual error	−1 435
Gross domestic product at factor cost	163 647

Reproduced from *The National Income and Expenditure Survey*, 1980, Table 1.9, with the permission of the Controller of Her Majesty's Stationery Office.

3.3 Expenditure approach

The expenditure approach simply breaks down the national income into the major spending units in the economy and is once again illustrated from the Blue Book (see Table 3.3).

Table 3.3

		£ million for 1979
Consumers expenditure		114 805
General government final consumption		38 316
Gross domestic fixed capital formation		33 646
Value of physical increase in stocks and work in progress		2 760
Total domestic expenditure		189 527
Exports of goods and services		54 676
Total final expenditure		244 203
Less imports of goods and services		−54 501
Gross domestic product at market prices		189 702
Less taxes on expenditure	−30 361	
Subsidies	4 306	
	−26 055	−26 055
Gross domestic product at factor cost		163 647
Net property income from abroad		289
Gross national product at factor cost		163 936

Reproduced from *The National Income and Expenditure Survey*, 1980, Table 1.1, with the permission of the Controller of Her Majesty's Stationery Officer.

Thus the major spending units include consumers (the equivalent of our 'householders' in the simplified macro theory utilized earlier), spending on durable and non-durable commodities, general govenment final consumption (current expenditure of central and local authorities), spending by private and public concerns on capital equipment (which would be referred to as 'investment' by economists, but is given the rather clumsy title of 'gross domestic fixed capital formation'), and an item taking into account physical stock and work-in-progress changes.

The sum of these items is total domestic expenditure, but unlike the two earlier approaches this is being measured at market prices, since these are the prices that consumers, etc., are having to pay when purchasing.

The inclusion of values for exports and imports results in the gross domestic product at the market price being calculated. The difference between market price and factor cost measurements would be the amount of indirect taxation and expenditure subsidies included in the price of commodities. Thus indirect taxes (value added tax, excise duties, etc.) are deducted and subsidies added to convert the data to the gross domestic product at factor cost. Once again net property income from abroad will adjust the data from a domestic to a national basis, resulting in the gross national product at factor cost being measured.

The tables are included not simply to indicate the component parts but to establish that the major aggregates have identical values regardless of the approach taken. Thus, the gross domestic product at factor cost has the same value in all three tables, while the gross national product is the same in the income and expenditure tables.

Of course, the observant reader would have realized that these aggregates are identical only because of the inclusion of an item called the residual error. We will say a lot more about the residual error later; suffice it for the moment simply to point out that this is a balancing item, made necessary because of the existence of errors and omissions in the compilation of the accounts. It is to these practical problems that we now turn.

3.4   Difficulties in compiling the national income accounts

Given the very wide range of data presented in the Blue Book the obvious first question is: where does the data originate? The answer is also the first problem, namely, a very wide range of sources is utilized. However, a large amount of information originates from only three sources:

1. *Tax assessment statistics.* These are compiled by the Inland Revenue and provide a great deal of information for the national income accounts, being particularly relevant for the income approach. Income from employment and self-employment, company profits, and payment and receipts of interest and dividends are all, clearly, important items which the Inland Revenue can provide. In addition, tax assessment statistics could provide some estimate of capital depreciation (since some of this can be written off against tax).
2. *Census of production.* This census can provide useful data on such things as wages and salaries, capital expenditure (i.e., 'fixed capital formation' in the terminology of the Blue Book), and stock changes. All these elements are broken down into certain industrial categories.
3. *Central government accounts.* A whole host of information can be obtained from these accounts, although the most important would be the payment of government employees, including the armed forces, the profits of government trading bodies, government capital

27

expenditure and stock changes, and transfer payments in the form of social security benefits.

Other data come from as wide a variety of sources as retail sales statistics, customs statistics, local authority accounts, motor vehicle registration, accounts of public corporations, and many more. The problems created by such a diversified range of sources would include the probability of a wide range of accuracy in the basic data and the necessity to modify or process the raw data. Furthermore, solutions to these problems tend to introduce yet more difficulties which will be considered later.

The question of accuracy in the basic sources is a difficult one to answer. Presumably this would depend on such things as the administrative process and efficiency of the various departments. However, one range of statistics whose validity may be questioned to some extent would be the data provided by the Inland Revenue, for these are based on tax returns where avoidance and evasion is always possible. Just how significant tax avoidance and evasion is, is difficult to estimate, but some inaccuracies are bound to be present.

The problem involving the necessity to 'process' the raw data is a more pervasive and more difficult one that the CSO has to face. It stems from the fact that any set of data would have been collected by a department for its own particular purpose and not collected ostensibly for passing on to the CSO for inclusion in the national income accounts. Thus, definitions and classifications adopted by a department may be eminently suitable for that department but not quite so suitable when the data are required for national income accounting purposes. A good example of this is the tax assessment statistics. Here, the Inland Revenue collects tax data primarily to ensure that correct taxes are paid and also to provide a tax profile of the economy to the Chancellor, particularly when budgetary policy is being framed. Clearly this income and profit data would be invaluable to the CSO, but by themselves are incomplete since the Inland Revenue would define incomes as being 'taxable' incomes, whereas the CSO would have to define incomes much more widely, given the nature of the statistics they have to produce.

The essential point is that the CSO has the task of presenting a set of figures that represents the value of the flow of goods and services in the economy, whereas each department, in collecting its own data, has a much more parochial view. The result is that the raw data received by the CSO have to be modified, adjusted, or, in other words, 'processed', in order to achieve consistency among such varied sources and in accordance with the main objective of presenting the national income accounts.

Of course, in order to process the basic data, certain conventions and principles have to be adopted. In practice, each single item in the accounts would be affected, but the following are given as examples of the difficulties faced and solutions adopted by the CSO:

1. Some estimate is made of the amount and value of foodstuff produced and consumed (and therefore not marketed) by farmers and agricultural workers themselves. It is felt desirable to make this estimate because the CSO is attempting to measure true economic values and not just monetary transactions, and presumably because such 'imputed' income is felt to be substantial. On the other hand, no attempt is made to estimate the imputed income and output of crops grown and consumed by householders in their own gardens and allotments. The reason for this inconsistent approach is the purely practical one of extreme difficulty involved in making a sufficiently reliable estimate for inclusion in the accounts.

2. On the same lines as the above, whereas the income and output of services provided by

domestic servants are included, similar work carried out by housewives is not included—for the same reasons as above, namely, the difficulty of arriving at a reliable estimate.

3. The fact that the ownership of dwellings is included in the production approach to the accounts shows that dwellings themselves provide a real service to the user but raises the problem of how this service can be measured. For rentable property it would be rational to assume that the value of the service provided would be equal to the rent payable. For owner-occupiers, however, there is no direct measure of this imputed income afforded by the dwelling and therefore a proxy has to be used, and is, in fact, the rateable valuation of the property, adjusted for changes since the last valuation in the general level of rents as shown by the retail prices index.

4. For some items in the accounts, detailed information is only available when a census or survey takes place. If these are held infrequently then in the intercensal years (the years when censuses are not held) the CSO has to use the previous census as a benchmark and attempt to estimate changes since that period. Clearly, where the time period between surveys is lengthy then the estimates must be particularly hazardous and doubtful.

5. The figures for profits, in the income section of the accounts, also create measurement difficulties for the CSO. This is because the prime source of data—the Inland Revenue—works on a financial year basis, whereas the national income accounts are presented for each calendar year. Consequently, the figures emanating from the Inland Revenue have to be adjusted by the CSO, with, of course, all the attendant risks of errors being introduced.

6. Much of the data in the Blue Book, including the summary tables, is presented in terms of current prices. However, since this records a combination of rising monetary values for expenditure, output and incomes resulting from the inflationary process, and any 'real' increases in the quantity of goods and services, it is impossible to distinguish between the two. Given the importance of attempting to measure 'real' as opposed to monetary valuations the Blue Book also includes national income data on the basis of constant prices, i.e., a base year is established and the annual data thereafter are recalculated in terms of prices ruling in the base year. Thus any changes since the base year should reflect real and not inflationary effects. However, discounting for price charges is, in practice, a difficult exercise, particularly when representing something as complex as the national income.

7. In the production approach, the enquiring student would have been wondering how production, or output, could be measured in the service sector part of the accounts—such industrial classifications as insurance, banking and finance, distributive trades, public administration, and defence, etc. The answer is that the total wages bill is taken as a proxy of the value of output on the grounds that the wage paid must be equal to the service provided. Whether one agrees with this convention or not, the important point is that such a convention is adopted and users of these data should be aware of the fact.

At this juncture it should, perhaps, be emphasized that the above seven estimating problems in no way make a definitive list, since every single item involves some practical difficulty in arriving at a figure. Instead, they serve to show a range of difficulties faced by the CSO, the response to those difficulties by the CSO, and problems of reliability and usefulness of the published data created by that response.

However, this is still not the end of the story, for despite the very wide range of primary sources used there are still some items for which no specific measurement is available. By and large, the solution adopted is to estimate the value of these missing items on a 'residual' basis. Two examples will demonstrate the approach.

29

1. *Personal savings.* The estimate of personal savings is derived from the difference between the estimate of total personal income and the sum of consumer expenditure, direct taxation, and national insurance contributions, and is clearly based on the realization that all income will either be spent or saved.* Thus the difference between income and expenditure must, by definition, be savings, and since we have estimates for these other items then it follows that savings can be derived as a residual amount.

   Though logically correct, it would be a mistake to place too much faith in the value thus estimated as personal savings. In fact, the value is really a balancing item to ensure that personal income and expenditure are equalized in the accounts. The CSO not only recognizes this, but admits to it as well, by using the word 'balance' alongside the word 'savings'. What this means is that the value for savings will be influenced by the errors and omissions included in every item used to derive savings (i.e., incomes, consumers' expenditure, taxation, etc.) and is, therefore, quite unlikely to represent the true value of personal savings in the economy.

2. *Income from 'other services'.* It is difficult to obtain income estimates for certain categories in the service sector such as entertainment, catering, and domestic services. Once again, the CSO adopts the 'residual' approach to get round this difficulty. Thus, these unknown items would simply be the difference between total incomes and recorded incomes in the known categories. All the unknown items are therefore swept together under one heading and are used as a sort of balancing element.

Summary of compilation difficulties

The significance of the three compilation problems just examined, reliability and accuracy of the basic data, the necessity to process the basic data, and the problem of missing items, serves to underline the fact that one should be wary of interpreting the data published in the Blue Book as being factually correct. Two key words used continuously in this section have been 'processed' and 'estimate'. The reader will be aware by now that all the published data have been processed and are therefore estimates with the clear implication that errors and omissions are likely to be present in the accounts. Whether these inaccuracies destroy the usefulness of the national income accounts will depend on the uses that the accounts could be put to, but this will be discussed in a later section. At the moment it would be appropriate to turn to the item called the 'residual error' since its existence reflects the reality of errors and omissions.

3.5 The residual error

Perusal of the tables given at the beginning of this chapter will show that this item, the residual error, is included in the income and production sections of the income accounts, but not the expenditure section. This, however, is a convention adopted by the CSO and should not be taken as an indication that the expenditure approach is any more accurate than the other two approaches. The value, as mentioned earlier, is a balancing item representing the difference between the income and expenditure methods of presentation of the accounts and

---

* In algebraic terms: $Y = C + T + S$
$$S = Y - (C + T)$$
where Y is income, C is consumption, T is taxation, and S is savings. Savings must therefore be equal to incomes less the sum of expenditure and taxation.

can therefore be either a negative or positive value. As such it might be assumed that the magnitude of this balancing item would indicate the degree of reliability of the accounts, and, if correct, would imply a high degree of accuracy, for the highest value in recent years (£1706 millions for 1976) is only 1.5 per cent of the GNP. However, for a number of reasons it would be a mistake to rigorously interpret the residual error in this way.

First, we clearly do not know the make-up of the residual error figure, and it is possible that a low value is achieved despite many, but compensating, errors and omissions, whereas a high value recorded may stem from large errors, but in only a few elements of the accounts. If we know this to be true, then it follows that the year for which a high value is recorded could nevertheless be considered generally more reliable and accurate than in the former case of a small residual error figure in which practically every single element is incorrect.

Second, the income and expenditure estimates are not calculated using completely separate sources. Consequently, with the possibility of similar errors and omissions being made, the ability of the residual error to infer the degree of reliability is somewhat reduced.

Third, the reader should realize that the residual error figure is being continuously adjusted for earlier years as errors and omissions are located.

Analysis of the residual error over time would seem to suggest that there is no discernible trend but a high degree of variability, ranging from large positive to large negative values. The random characteristics thus exhibited are not really surprising, given a proper understanding of the residual error and its place in the national income accounts.

3.6 Capital consumption

The final item in the summary tables of the Blue Book is called capital consumption. The value of this item is subtracted from the GNP figure resulting in the final major aggregate, referred to as national income.

The term 'capital consumption' refers to the fact that fixed assets are used up or 'consumed' during the process of production. This is an important element because if we failed to make allowance for capital stock used up during a year we would be continuously exaggerating the true level of fixed assets in the economy. Thus gross domestic fixed capital formation (investment) less capital consumption would indicate the net additions to our stock of fixed assets during the year. However, despite its importance, capital consumption (or depreciation as it is sometimes referred to) has to be estimated since it is not directly measurable—this is because the gradual consumption is not directly observable. Estimating conventions therefore have to be adopted.

Of course, owners of fixed assets are likely to incorporate depreciation provisions in their own accounts, but these estimates would be unsuitable for inclusion in the national income figures for two reasons. First, they would almost certainly be based on the original cost of the fixed asset and by ignoring changes in prices of these assets since purchase they would be inconsistent with all the other items in the national income accounts which are being measured at current prices. Second, there is unlikely to be consistency between firms in their depreciation procedures.

For estimates of depreciation to be included in the accounts two elements have to be considered:

1. An estimate of the expected life of assets has to be made.
2. An assumption regarding their patterns of utilization has to be made.

31

The expected life of assets would clearly differ from one fixed asset to another, and therefore they have to be classified into specific groups for which the average life is then estimated. For buildings this average life is taken as 80 years; for plant and machinery five separate groups are identified whose average lives are 16, 19, 25, 34, and 50 years; for dwellings an average life of 100 years is assumed; a similar 100 years is assumed for railway track, buildings, and works; while 40 years is used for mine working. For coal mining, gas, electricity, railways (where not included above), and the Post Office the lengths of life assumed are taken from their own depreciation estimates. Depreciation of roads are not included in the accounts since no value is imputed for the use of roads when estimating the national product.

The pattern of utilization of fixed assets over these time periods is assumed to be the so-called 'straight line basis'. This means that assets are assumed to depreciate in equal amounts in each year of their life. This simplifying assumption, of course, might be more valid for some assets than for others.

Given the approximations of both expected lives and patterns of depreciation it is clear that the derived estimates of capital consumption will involve some margin of error. Consequently, reliability gradings have been established for the various fixed asset classifications and are shown in Table 3.4.[2]

Table 3.4

Asset classification	Reliability grading*
Agricultural plant and machinery	B
Mining and quarrying	D
Manufacturing, excluding textiles	B
Construction	C
Gas	C
Electricity	C
Water	D
Railways	D
Road passenger transport	C
Shipping	B
Harbours, docks, and canals	D
Air transport	C
Postal, telephone, and radio communications	C
Distribution and other services	D
Private dwellings	D
Public dwellings	C
Roads	D
Other public and social services	C
Other industries	D
Total gross capital stock	C

* Where   A ± less than 3 per cent
              B ± 3 to 10 per cent
              C ± 10 to 20 per cent
              D ± more than 20 per cent

Reproduced from *National Accounts Statistics: Sources and Methods, Studies in Official Statistics*, No. 13, 1968, with the permission of the Controller of Her Majesty's Stationery Office.

It should be noted that in total the margin of error involved in capital consumption estimates is greater than 10 per cent (grading C), but even with this acknowledgement several problems are worth considering. First, capital consumption will be overstated in the accounts if fixed assets actually last longer than estimated, although this may very well be compensated for by some assets lasting for a shorter period than estimated and the fact that not all assets will be included in the calculations. A more important weakness lies in the fact that in estimating capital consumption no allowance is made for technological change. This arises from the fact that capital consumption is being measured at current replacement cost and the easiest way to estimate the latter is to assume that existing assets would be replaced by identical assets. In reality, of course, assets will not be identical; there will always be some technological improvements of similar assets incorporated over time—referred to as 'embodied technological change' by economists. (Motor vehicles would be a good example of embodied technical change where the teething problems of a new model are gradually solved in later productions.) A third source of difficulty stems from the fact that price indices have to be formulated for the various classes of asset in order to arrive at a figure for depreciation at current prices. The construction of any price index is a difficult exercise, but is particularly so for fixed assets with continuously changing characteristics.

3.7 Uses of the national income accounts

One of the purposes of this book is to help breed a certain healthy scepticism of available data—the student should continuously be asking where the data come from, what definitions are used, and how reliable it may be—although there is always the danger of overreaction and the conclusion that published data are meaningless.

In fact, the three methods of presenting the national accounts are particularly useful since they shed light on different sets of economic, social, and business problems and are, therefore, likely to play some part in the process of decision-making. Since the income approach separates the various types of income this could serve as a base for analysing income distribution problems. The production approach could highlight the changing structure of the economy by indicating the stagnant, declining, and growth sectors, while the expenditure approach could serve as a basis for demand management by the government since it represents national income in terms of different types of demand.

This is not to suggest that the national income data are the sole, or even the most important, source of information for decision-making. Mention has been made before of the fact that government, employers, and trade unions will certainly require and use much more specific (and perhaps unpublished) data than are found in the Blue Book. However, what the Blue Book can indicate is a general picture of the performance of the economy in the previous year and provide estimates of the major segments of the economy. It may, therefore, serve as a starting point for more detailed analysis. If viewed in this way (particularly by placing more importance on establishing trends rather than placing too much faith on the precise values published) it may help to mitigate some of the inadequacies of the accounts which have been much of the subject of this chapter.

3.8 National income, welfare, and international comparisons

Since the national income accounts measure the economic performance of a country, it is tempting, and frequently used, to make international comparisons. Thus league tables are constructed based on each country's estimate of its national income and inference is drawn about the relative economic performance of different countries. Indeed, commentators generally go further than this and measure something called 'per capita income'. This is quite simply national income divided by the total population to derive a measure of income per head of the population. Per capita income is then compared internationally, and in most cases is interpreted as implying relative living standards and welfare levels of countries. However, despite their wide use many problems are involved (most of them hardly admitted) in making international comparisons and drawing welfare implications.

First, the preceding sections of this chapter were concerned with establishing the problems involved and conventions adopted in arriving at national income estimates for Britain. It would be absurd and presumptuous to assume that all other countries adopt identical conventions and once this is realized it follows that even superficially similar elements are likely to be measured and therefore defined differently. Thus like is not being compared with like. Moreover, we are 'blessed' in Britain with a highly skilled and extensive civil service sector which we might assume increases the general level of reliability of published data, whereas for many Third World countries with political instability and fragile institutions, any published data (noticeably population estimates) must be particularly suspect.

Second, per capita income comparisons rarely take into account the distribution of national income, which quite clearly could be markedly different from one country to another. Indeed, one of the significant characteristics of developing countries is the dichotomy of income and wealth ownership, with the majority of the population living in poverty at almost subsistence level while a minority live in great luxury. Clearly, in these circumstances, an average value, given by the per capital income measure, is hardly likely to be representative and makes international comparisons almost meaningless unless accompanied by some indication of the spread of incomes. It might be felt that per capita income comparisons are likely to be more meaningful when made between industrial countries, and of course this is almost certainly true. However, it should still be realized that a single-figure comparison makes the implicit assumption that the distribution of national income is identical in all countries being compared, and even among industrialized countries this will not be true.

Finally, we turn to a common misconception, namely, that of interpreting national income data in 'welfare' or 'living standard' terms. The reader will be aware by now that the national income accounts simply measure the flow of goods and services produced in the economy, and thus welfare and living standards must be held to be identical with such a measure. It would be legitimate to argue, for example, that living standards would have been raised if the *quality* of goods and services available for consumption had improved even if the quantity remained unchanged. But the national income accounts will fail to indicate the real improvement in living standards since all that is measured is the amount of goods and services available and not their quality. However, a more serious error lies in the realization that living standards and welfare should include far more than just the provision of goods and services. Something that we might call the 'quality of life' would, logically, include environmental factors, including the many types of pollution (air, river, noise, etc.) and a scarred and despoiled landscape. Indeed, there may very well be an inverse relationship between the growth of goods and services and the decline in environmental quality. The latter point is significant for these environmental factors are difficult to quantify and are not included in the national income accounts. It follows that there is a very real danger of interpreting the national accounts as evidence of improvements in living standards when in reality real living standards and welfare may have fallen because of a marked deterioration in the environment.

It is argued here, then, that the national income accounts can only give a partial view of living standards and welfare—a view compounded by the realization that significant changes in environmental quality (possibly improvements as well as deterioration) are likely to occur over time within any one country and are likely to be substantially different between countries.

Self-assessment questions—Part One

1. Using Table 1.11 of the Blue Book for the years 1965, 1970, and 1975, draw up a table showing the amounts of GDP accounted for by the manufacturing sector and the insurance, banking, finance, and business services sector. Show, using an appropriate graphical representation, how both have changed as a proportion of GDP.

2. A firm has 50 employees and records the number of hours of overtime each works. For the last month the figures are:

8	2	16	7	5
8	2	4	0	12
9	2	8	4	0
4	7	8	2	11
2	9	10	6	0
36	3	9	11	24
38	16	0	7	7
62	3	5	0	28
18	14	8	6	7
8	5	8	91	44

(a) Draw up a frequency table for the data of about five classes. You will find it best to use unequal class widths. Represent your table graphically, using a histogram.
(b) Estimate the mean number of hours of overtime per employee using the frequency table. Calculate the mean exactly from the raw data. Compare the two results.
(c) Find the median for the data, using two different methods. Compare your results. Comment on the appropriateness of the mean and the median as measures of average for these data.
(d) Estimate the standard deviation of the data, using the frequency table.
(e) Using an ogive, estimate the quartiles and the eightieth percentile for the data. Find also the percentage of employees who exceed 5 hours of overtime.

3. List the three approaches to calculating the national income.

4. Why is the numerical value of the residual error not a reflection of the accuracy of the national income accounts?

5. What are the three main sources of statistics used in compiling the national income accounts?

6. Explain the difference between 'factor cost' and 'market price'.

7. Why is 'capital consumption' included in the accounts and what are the major problems encountered in its estimation?

8. What is meant by the term 'per capita income' and how useful is this measure?

9. Why is it that the national accounts can only give a partial view of 'living standards' in the economy?

36

Assignment questions—Part One

1. The following observations have been made about the U.K. economy over the past decade:

> ... there is no doubt that the increase in public sector spending has grown enormously when compared with other sectors of the economy.
> ... it is no use 'knocking' our export performance; in fact there has been a great deal of stability in exports and imports.
> ... our main trouble has been a relative decline in the level of investment.

(a) For each of the above three propositions prepare a brief report outlining the results of your examination based on Table 1.1 of the Blue Book over the past 10 years. Illustrate each report with suitable graphs and/or diagrams.

(b) What is the mean of the balance of trade over this period?

(c) What is the standard deviation of the balance of trade over this period? What significance, if any, can be attached to your result?

(d) For your work on the above three questions you will have selected data at either 'market price' or 'factor cost'. Justify in a short paragraph the basis for your choice.

2. An insurance company has collected the following information on the claims costs of its motor insurance policies, and the percentages of policies in different categories:

Region	Claims cost/policy (£)	Percentage of policies
Inner London	49	7.3
Outer London	35	7.1
Glasgow	48	2.7
Other Scotland	35	7.1
South	35	15.7
North	30	20.5
East Midlands	26	9.1
West Midlands	33	17.3
East Anglia	27	2.1
West Country	35	5.7
Wales	34	4.8
Northern Ireland	35	0.6

Age of policyholder	Claims cost/policy (£)	Percentage of policies
17–20	82	1.8
21–25	56	6.3
26–30	41	9.3
31–35	34	10.8
36–40	32	11.8
41–50	32	25.7
51–70	28	32.1
Over 70	22	2.2

Note. Claims cost is the average cost of all policies in the category over a year.

(a) Draw appropriate diagrams to illustrate the variation in claims cost and the variation in percentages of policies both by region and by the age of the policyholder. Comment briefly on what your diagrams show.

(b) Estimate the mean claims cost over all policies. Calculate appropriate measures to indicate the difference in the variability of claims cost over regions compared to the age of the policyholder. Comment briefly.

(c) Stating any assumptions you feel are appropriate, make an estimate of the average claims cost you would expect for each of the following cases:

A driver aged 22 in Inner London
A driver aged 32 in East Midlands

Present your results in the form of a brief technical report. Include brief comments on any other factors you would expect to influence the claims cost.

Part Two

Chapters 4 and 6 deal with published sources of data on production and prices. These are key areas for both the management and trade union representatives in the individual firm. They also include discussions of a number of points which bear generally on the collection and measurement of statistics.

Many published data series are shown in the form of an index. This is particularly true of the two areas discussed in this part, the retail price index being the most famous example. Chapter 5 deals with the main methods in use for constructing indices and some of their advantages and disadvantages. The techniques are quite simple, but as will be seen there are many practical difficulties in applying the techniques. The most important considerations in the calculation of an index number are its value in interpretation and the difficulties encountered when collecting the required data. This should be amply demonstrated when the methods of index numbers are viewed in the present context.

Part Two concludes with some questions to test understanding and some suggested assignments.

4. Production and productivity

The importance of statistical data on production lies in the fact that 'living standards' and 'wealth' can thereby be inferred. It should be recalled from Chapter 3 that economists generally define living standards as the amount of commodities and services available for consumption (although noting environmental aspects discussed in that chapter). It is one element of these, namely goods, which are being measured in production statistics.

Since most of the data are broken down into defined industrial classifications they lend themselves to a number of analytical tests to help us to understand more fully how the economy functions and to provide the basis for policy measures. For example, by discovering the output of commodities that each industrial group contributes to the total we would be describing the industrial structure of the economy and by analysing these values over time we would be saying something about the changing nature of the industrial structure over time. This information might then be used as a basis for formulating, say, regional policy, where the 'growth' industries would be identified and, through policy measures, encouraged to relocate to the less prosperous areas of the country. In more general terms production statistics would be vital for the implementation of planning policies, particularly where such data can be used to establish interindustry linkages (i.e., where the output of one industry is used as an input in another industry). Finally, data on output are an essential piece of information for productivity measurements since productivity involves the relationship between inputs and the resulting output. The problems and techniques of productivity measurements will be dealt with towards the end of this chapter, together with a discussion of its importance and usefulness for companies, organized labour, and government industrial policies.

Since production data are presented in terms of defined industries and defined regions it would be appropriate to specify and explain these classifications. The reader should note that apart from production statistics many of the other indicators examined later in the text (incomes, unemployment, etc.) are also published on an industrial and regional basis.

4.1 The standard industrial classification

The standard industrial classification (SIC) was established in 1948 to provide a more systematic and detailed breakdown of economic activity. In 1968 substantial changes in the industrial classification took place, resulting in the establishment of the 27 industrial categories, known as the SIC 'order level', shown in Table 4.1.

For some analyses it may be convenient to think of the 27 groups as forming three distinct types of economic activity: the extractive or primary industries being order levels I and II, the secondary or manufacturing industries being order III to XIX inclusive, and the service or tertiary sector being orders XXI to XXVII. Order level XX, construction, does not fit neatly into any of these categories and is therefore generally treated separately. You should recall from Chapter 3 that something along these lines was adopted for the production approach in the summary tables of the Blue Book, where only one figure was given for all the manufacturing industries.

41

Table 4.1

Order level	Categories
I	Agriculture, forestry, and fishing
II	Mining and quarrying
III	Food, drink, and tobacco
IV	Coal and petroleum products
V	Chemicals and allied industries
VI	Metal manufacture
VII	Mechanical engineering
VIII	Instrument engineering
IX	Electrical engineering
X	Shipbuilding and marine engineering
XI	Vehicles
XII	Metal goods not elsewhere specified
XIII	Textiles
XIV	Leather, leather goods, and fur
XV	Clothing and footwear
XVI	Bricks, pottery, glass, cement, etc.
XVII	Timber, furniture, etc.
XVIII	Paper, printing, and publishing
XIX	Other manufacturing industries
XX	Construction
XXI	Gas, electricity, and water
XXII	Transport and communication
XXIII	Distributive trades
XXIV	Insurance, banking, finance, and business services
XXV	Professional and scientific services
XXVI	Miscellaneous services
XXVII	Public administration and defence

However, for certain uses and analysis the order level may be inappropriate because each order is too widely defined; the level of aggregation is too large and a 'finer' classification is required. This is provided for in the SIC, with a sub-classification of many of the order level categories in what is termed the 'minimum list heading' (MLH). In total there are 181 MLH,

Table 4.2

Order level	Minimum list heading	Industrial classification
XIII		*Textiles*
	411	Production of man-made fibres
	412	Spinning and doubling on the cotton and flax systems
	413	Weaving of cotton, linen, and man-made fibres
	414	Woollen and worsted
	415	Jute
	416	Rope, twine, and net
	417	Hosiery and other knitted goods
	418	Lace
	419	Carpets
	421	Narrow fabrics (not more than 30 cm wide)
	422	Made-up textiles
	423	Textile finishing
	429	Other textile industries

industries with several of the order level categories having as many as 10 to 15 component industries. Of course, for any data the MLH industries within an order level should total up to the value given for the industry as a whole, i.e., at the order level.

Thus production data (and other indicators) can be presented at the SIC order level as well as the finer MLH classification. As an example, order level XIII, textiles, has the MLH industries shown in Table 4.2.

4.2   The 'standard regions'

In addition to the industrial classification certain elements of production (and other) statistics are also disaggregated into areas of Great Britain (or the United Kingdom if Northern Ireland is included). These are referred to as 'standard regions' and although established for statistical purposes they do coincide with 'economic planning regions'. The latter owe their importance to the emphasis attached to planning by the Labour Government in the mid 'sixties and the view that a national plan should incorporate plans at a sub-national level. Even where national planning is not in favour by a particular administration, a regional breakdown of national data (on incomes, employment, unemployment, production, etc.) will be of considerable importance to the regional analyst and for certain types of decision-making, including marketing and location.

As will be discussed later, regional boundaries of standard regions are occasionally altered, but at the present time consist of the 10 regions of Great Britain given in Table 4.3.

Table 4.3

Regions	Counties
South East	Greater London, Bedfordshire, Berkshire, Buckinghamshire, Sussex, Essex, Hampshire, Hertfordshire, Isle of Wight, Kent, Oxfordshire, Surrey
East Anglia	Cambridgeshire, Norfolk, Suffolk
South West	Avon, Cornwall, Devon, Gloucestershire, Somerset, Wiltshire
West Midlands	Hereford, Worcester, Salop, Staffordshire, Warwickshire, and the metropolitan county of West Midlands
East Midlands	Derbyshire, Leicestershire, Lincolnshire, Northamptonshire, Nottinghamshire
Yorkshire and Humberside	South, West, and North Yorkshire, Humberside
North West	Greater Manchester, Merseyside, Cheshire, Lancashire
Northern	Tyne and Wear, Cleveland, Cumbria, Durham, Northumberland
Wales	Mid, South, and West Glamorgan, Clywd, Dyfed, Gwent, Gwynedd, Powys
Scotland	The mainland plus Orkney, Shetland, and the Western Isles

4.3   The system of collecting production data

Until 1970, production statistics were derived from a detailed census taken approximately every 5 years and a sample enquiry in the intercensal years. The usefulness of the resulting data has been questioned on two major grounds. First, the five-year interval between censuses has been too long, particularly when the economy is altering very rapidly over time. Second, and inevitably as a result of this long intercensal period, some of the definitions and classifications adopted have altered from one census to another. The resulting lack of consistency creates difficulties for long-term comparisons and analysis and therefore reduces the usefulness of the published data.

As a result of these shortcomings a new approach was taken in 1970, and is the system currently in operation. It consists of:

1. An annual census of production.
2. A quarterly inquiry into product sales.

It should be noted that many of the definitional and classification problems still remain, and are discussed in some depth later, but the change to an annual census and the introduction of a little more consistency has been a marked improvement on the system operating prior to 1970.

Annual census of production

The census of production, conducted annually since 1970 by the Business Statistics Office, is obligatory (under the Statistics of Trade Act, 1947) for all those establishments covered by the census. It is concerned only with the SIC order level industries II to XIX and XXI, and therefore includes all the manufacturing sector, plus one extractive industry (mining and quarrying) and the public utilities (gas, electricity, and water—order XXI). Within these industries only those establishments with 20 (previously 25 until 1973) or more full-time employees are included in the census. However, for some industries the 'small' firm may predominate and therefore to avoid the danger of under-representing output those firms with 11 or more full-time employees would be approached.

The census contains a series of questions from which the following information is obtained:

1. Details of business.
2. Number of working proprietors.
3. Number employed.
4. Wages and salary bill.
5. Value of stocks.
6. Capital expenditure.
7. Other items of expenditure.
8. Total purchases.
9. Total value of sales and work done.

Just why this information is required in a production census and the problems involved in compiling production statistics will be investigated after we have dealt with the second component.

Quarterly sales inquiry

Like the production census, the quarterly sales inquiry is based on the establishment and covers 165 MLH industries in manufacturing, mining and quarrying, and gas, electricity, and water (i.e., the same categories as the production census). Generally only those establishments with 25 or more full-time employees will be included, except where smaller employing firms are important contributors to the total sales of an industry. Approximately 30 000 establishments are covered.

44

As the name implies, the inquiry asks establishments to provide sales data for calendar quarters and therefore annual totals for sales would be the addition of the four quarters of the calendar year. The major question asked refers to the total value of sales during the quarter in terms of the *individual products* of the establishment. Additional questions occasionally relate to exports, total production, and specialized sales questions.

As we shall see during the course of this book, the period around 1970 appears to have been something of a watershed in the collection and provision of most published data. Major changes took place, sometimes out of necessity due to administrative changes, but more often resulting from a desire to improve the detail, validity, and therefore usefulness to decision makers of the data provided. The inevitable result has been a plethora of enquiries, surveys, and censuses such that spokesmen for private companies have expressed some concern about the increased burden of form-filling in the last few years. Most government departments responsible for collecting and providing data are conscious of this complaint and are attempting to minimize the burden. An interesting example is given in the quarterly sales inquiry where, from the first quarter of 1979, establishments received 'personalized' or 'custom-built' forms.[3] It is claimed that this will simplify the task of contributors since most of them will receive a one-page form compared with the previous forms which had anything from 4 to 24 pages.

The published data

The information obtained from the annual census allows the Business Statistics Office to publish[4] national figures for defined industries covering: (1) gross output, (2) purchases, (3) sales of individual commodities, (4) total sales, and (5) stocks.

In addition, information on (1) employment, (2) capital expenditure, and (3) net output is provided for industries and the standard regions. Students should note from this that the regional breakdown of production data is much more limited than that provided nationally, which reflects practical classification difficulties and will be referred to later.

The quarterly sales inquiry[5] together with a non-statutory (and sample) monthly inquiry and production information from certain public service industries are used to calculate and publish monthly the so-called 'index of industrial production'. In essence, this index serves to indicate the movement in net output in the industrial sector, i.e., in manufacturing, mining and quarrying, public utilities, and construction. The importance of this index lies in the fact that it refers to current trends in production and can therefore be taken as an early indicator to changes in economic activity.

Difficulties and problems with production statistics

The major problems can be conveniently (if artificially) separated into definitional and classification difficulties. In addition, the official industrial and regional classification has occasionally been changed, as we have already seen, and therefore presents a further interpretation difficulty. We will take each of these in turn.

Definitional and measurement difficulties   One can see from the published data, and appreciate, the importance attached to measurements of both gross output and net output; however, both

45

are nevertheless difficult things to measure in practice. In theory gross output could be defined as:

> The value of sales and work done in a year
> *less* the value of stocks and work in progress at the beginning of the year,
> *plus* the value of stocks and work in progress at the end of the year.

(In other words, gross output would be sales adjusted for changes in stocks.)

Net output would then be gross output less the cost of materials, services, etc., purchased from other industries. If all raw materials, semi-manufactured goods, and services purchased outside the industry can be accounted for and deducted from gross output, then our resulting net output figure would be equivalent to the 'value added' by the industry. An alternative way of measuring value added is, of course, to take the sum of incomes generated in the industry; it would therefore include, wages, salaries, and profits. You should recall from Chapter 3 that for national income purposes (published in the Blue Book) net output is estimated in this way, i.e., by summing incomes and profits, and is therefore identical to value added.

In practice, however, the Business Statistics Office are unable to measure net output by simply summing incomes and profits, since details of the latter cannot be obtained from the production census. The result is that net output is computed by adding and subtracting elements from the basic information collected. Two things should be realized. First, because net output is calculated in this 'roundabout' way it will not be identical to 'value added' (and, incidentally, is not therefore the same as the net output used in the Blue Book), although it is claimed, by BSO officials, to be the best possible proxy for it.[6] Second, the elements added and subtracted have occasionally changed, which means that, in practice, the definition of net output would have altered from time to time.

Since 1973 net output for census purposes is defined in the following way:

Sales of goods produced
>   + receipts for work done and industrial services rendered
>   + value of capital goods produced for own use
>   + sales of goods merchanted or factored
>   + receipts for non-industrial services rendered
>   + increase in value of stocks of goods on hand for sale
>   + increase in value of work in progress

= Gross output

>   − purchases of materials for processing and packaging and fuel
>   − purchases of goods for merchanting or factoring
>   + increase in value of stocks of fuel and raw materials
>   − payments for industrial services received (including work given out)
>   − net amount of any duties, etc., payable

= Net output

The major differences in the definition of net output prior to 1973 is that payment to other organizations for transport was previously deducted to arrive at net output, but since 1973 it has not been possible to deduct for this item, since the direct question on transport expenditure has been dropped from the census forms. This exclusion stems from the necessity to comply with EEC directives concerning annual industrial statistics, and had the effect of increasing the information required from business units. In order to reduce the burden of form-filling, certain questions not required by the EEC were dropped, including the question of transport costs.

Consequently, net output in the census of production is greater than value added because transport payments and certain 'bought-in' services (e.g., payments for advertising) have not been deducted.

Classification difficulties   As pointed out above, the reporting unit for both the census and quarterly sales inquiry is based on the 'establishment'. This is defined as the smallest unit which could provide the information normally required for an economic census. What this means in practice is that each establishment should, as a minimum, be able to provide information on employment, turnover, and capital expenditure.

For approximately 75 per cent of manufacturing concerns the reporting unit presents no real problems. These would be single-unit businesses producing a narrow range of similar commodities at only one locality. However, multi-unit businesses, though smaller in number, are the major contributors to total economic activity, and with the wide range of commodities produced in a wide range of localities it is with these concerns that major classification problems are found. In essence we have a locational classification problem and an industrial classification problem, a reflection of the growing complexity of economic activity where the two traditional types of integration, horizontal (where mergers take place of companies at the same stage of production) and vertical (mergers of companies involved in different stages in the industrial process), have to some extent been overshadowed by the emergence, in the last decade or so, of what have become known as 'conglomerates' (i.e., mergers of companies in diversified markets—tobacco companies producing potato crisps, for example).

The locational classification problem centres on the likelihood that multi-unit companies are unable to provide the detailed information required in the census for each of its branch factories located throughout the country. Presumably, whether these companies can provide the detail required will depend on their administrative and organizational system and the degree of sophistication of their accounting process. For example, some multi-unit concerns may collected their products from a number of establishments within the company and market them centrally—perhaps from the head office of the whole group. Likewise, there may be a practice of purchasing the necessary inputs centrally and despatching them to the branch factories. In the very large concerns one generally sees a compromise between central and local control by establishing regional or area control, in which area head offices may very well market the commodities and purchase supplies for a number of branch factories within their own areas.

In the event, given that many companies cannot give the required data for each of their localities, they are asked to provide, as a minimum, localized data for employment, capital expenditure, and net output, with the result that only these three elements are published on a regional basis.

For those firms producing a wide range of commodities the industrial classification into MLH and order level categories also presents problems. Consequently, the convention is adopted of allocating the whole of the output of an establishment on the basis of its 'principal product'. Thus if an establishment had a range of five products with the following sales profile:

Commodity	Percentage of total sales
A	75
B	10
C	5
D	5
E	5

47

then the whole of the output of this establishment would be allocated to the industry in which commodity A is one of the principal products. The weakness of this convention is obvious, i.e., if the remaining four commodities are so distinct from commodity A that they should legitimately be allocated to other industries then these industries are being undervalued in output terms while the output of the one industry is being exaggerated. It is possible, for example, that a firm mainly concerned with producing plastic materials may diversify into producing plastic toys and games. On the 'principal product' convention total output would be allocated to SIC order level V, chemicals and allied industries (MLH 276), while the toys and games part of output should have been allocated to SIC order level XIX, other manufacturing industries (MLH 494). Similarly, a firm mainly producing rubber may also produce rubber shoes. Therefore, although the latter part of output should be allocated to the footwear industry (SIC order level XV, clothing and footwear, MLH 450) it is likely that the whole of output would be allocated to the rubber industry (SIC order level XIX, other manufacturing industries, MLH 491).

Just how limiting this convention is will depend on three factors. First, it would depend on the degree of product-mix diversification there is in practice (and this may be increasing over time, though not necessarily on an 'establishment' basis). Second, it would depend on whether the products relate to different SIC order level classifications or simply different MLH industries within one order level. If the latter, then, clearly, the order level output would not be affected even though the individual MLH industries would show incorrect (but compensating) figures. Third, and perhaps most important, it would depend on what the data are being used for or what type of analysis is being undertaken. It has been pointed out,[7] for instance, that using production census data for calculating concentration ratios (which is aimed at identifying whether output is being produced by a small number of large firms or a large number of small firms, and how this changes through time) could be meaningless where under- or over-recording takes place because of the 'principal product' convention. This might occur where an establishment's major activity accounts for only a relatively small proportion of its total output.

Official industrial and regional classification changes When using production data we must be aware of the conventions that have been adopted for the problems outlined above and the possibility that these conventions may introduce limitations for certain types of analysis and tests. An additional difficulty arises from the fact that the industrial and regional classifications have been altered periodically. This clearly presents problems for the analyst concerned with establishing long-term production trends on an industrial and regional basis, and raises the question of why these changes were made.

As we have seen earlier, the industrial classification was altered in 1968 resulting in 27 SIC order level categories being established with 181 MLH industries. This replaced 24 order level and 152 MLH categories that had been effective since 1958. What should be realized is that while the industrial classification remained unaltered for a decade (many industries had been unchanged for two decades) the actual economy, like all economies, showed considerable adjustments over time as new growth industries developed and older established industries declined. Recognition of the changing structure of industry by altering the industrial classification is therefore seen to be necessary in order to avoid the danger of published statistics becoming meaningless. It is a moot point whether these changes should be made on a minor but more frequent basis, thus probably militating against long-term analysis or fairly major changes (on the 1968 scale) at more infrequent intervals.

48

It should be noted that plans are well under way for a substantial revision of the SIC, which is expected to be introduced in 1983. Opportunity is being taken to bring it more in line with the industrial classification of the EEC so that greater Community consistency will be obtained.

Alterations in the regional classification have largely reflected shifts in policy and administrative changes. The emphasis placed on national and regional planning in the mid 'sixties resulted in substantial alterations in the defined regions, presumably on the grounds that the newly established regions were more appropriate spatial areas for planning purposes. Additionally, boundary alterations were made to some regions following the reorganization of local government and the establishment of new counties in April 1974.

In summary, then, certain weaknesses are apparent with published data on production and reflect definitional and classification problems. Whether these weaknesses are significant will depend, as constantly stated, to what use the data are put and how they are handled.

4.4 Productivity

A productivity measurement relates input(s) to associated output and therefore says something about how efficient the inputs are. As such productivity is central to the economics discipline which studies the allocation of scarce resources (inputs) to satisfy demand (through output), it may therefore also play a part in explaining economic growth differences over time and between countries. At the company level productivity measurements are almost certain to be made when planning production through, for example, establishing target levels. A more familiar use of productivity estimates is in the field of collective bargaining where company representatives attempt to tie wage increases to improvements in efficiency and where trade union negotiators attempt to justify wage claims (if only partly) based on their estimates of past productivity achievements. The phrase 'self-financing' awards has become familiar to us all in recent years. Finally, both Labour and Conservative administrations have been vitally concerned with encouraging improvements in productivity, particularly since the late 'fifties when commitment to achieving faster overall economic growth became a consistent and major macroeconomic objective. Specifically, productivity 'deals' were encouraged between employers and worker representatives and during any period of rigorous income control wage awards in excess of that laid down in the incomes policy were invariably allowed if productivity improvements could be proven. Productivity measurements are therefore utilized by economic and political analysts, are used by both sides of industry as an element in decision-making, and are used by governments in certain policy decisions and measures.

Having established the importance and wide application of this particular measure it is now appropriate to consider some of the difficulties associated with the provision of data. Before we do, however, it should be noted that productivity measurements are based on net output since we are concerned only with the efficiency with which value is added at each stage of the production process. Consequently, it is conventional for the value of raw materials and semi-manufactured parts to be excluded as a factor input, as we shall see below.

Clearly, in any productivity calculations, we require information on output (numerator) and input (denominator). Let us look at these in turn.

Output

Data for individual industries and totals could be obtained from the annual census of production. However, one should be aware of the classification and definitional problems outlined earlier and the fact that the census only covers, by and large, the manufacturing sector and therefore may be inappropriate for some purposes.

Alternatively, the production part of the national income accounts could be utilized, particularly if national productivity measurement is the objective. GDP or GNP could be used and output could be valued at factor cost or market prices. Just what valuation is taken will depend on the purpose of the productivity measurement, but one important rule is to maintain, as far as possible, consistency of definition between the elements being compared (i.e., between industries, between countries, and over time). In terms of international comparisons of productivity the reader should recall the previous chapter where it was emphasized that many inconsistencies of definition, coverage, and treatment of national accounts make international comparisons particularly hazardous.

Input

The problem of acquiring data on input is altogether more complex and difficult. This reflects the fact that we should be including all those factors that could influence efficiency and productivity. Such a list would be rather extensive but might include the following:

1. Labour input.
2. Capital input.
3. Organizational factor (i.e., how the factors of production are combined).
4. Technical 'know-how'.
5. Industrial relations.
6. The shop-floor layout, etc.

The difficulty with elements (3) to (6) (and indeed many other factors the reader may feel are important, e.g., general health, working conditions, etc.) is that they do not readily lend themselves to quantitative measurement. Nevertheless, they may, in practice, have a substantial impact on productivity levels and changes in those levels.

Some estimates of the capital stock are available but are rarely used in estimating productivity because of the suspect nature of the data. This reflects the practical difficulties involved in obtaining the information and the realization that there is no universally accepted way of measuring capital stock. What definition is used and how it is measured will depend on the purpose of such estimates. Thus a company in a take-over bid will place a different valuation on its capital equipment than the bidding company; asset-strippers will have their own view of the value of assets; the valuation of shareholders may differ from the managers, etc.

What we are left with then is labour as our only input element in productivity measurements. As stated above, this does not mean that labour is the only or even the most important factor in determining productivity performances but simply reflects the difficulty or impossibility of obtaining numerical values for the other determinants of productivity. Clearly, what is therefore being derived is a measure of 'labour' productivity. The inherent danger, of course, is in the implication that any output improvements are the result of the employed labour force alone when, in reality, improvements in the capital stock with which labour works, or one or more of the other factors, may have been responsible or contributory.

However, even with our labour input a measurement difficulty is still encountered. This is because the labour force is composed of a wide variety of talents, skills, and characteristics, and the precise 'mix' is likely to differ between industries, regions, countries, and over time. Whether this presents a problem will depend on the type of analysis undertaken. A very general productivity measurement based on taking total output and total population (to get a measure of the relative efficiency of an economy) would ignore such differences in labour composition, but where interindustry, intercountry, or time comparisons are being made allowance should be made for differences in the proportion of skilled to unskilled workers; the age composition; the sex composition; the ratio of 'operatives' to 'non-operatives'; the proportion of part-time to full-time workers, etc. If these compositional differences are ignored then the resulting lack of consistency could seriously undermine the value of the measures obtained.

What is required in these circumstances is to present the labour force data in terms of 'standardized (or equivalent) labour units'. Thus the number of women equivalent to men or non-operatives equivalent to operatives could be calculated and the resulting labour force figure would represent 'male' equivalents or 'operative' equivalents, i.e., a standard unit of labour. This immediately raises the question of the basis on which such equivalents can be established. The most common procedure is to take average earnings of defined groups of labour as a means of establishing this equivalence. An example is given in Table 4.4 in which a standardized labour unit is constructed for the vehicle and mechanical engineering industries (SIC order levels XI and VII, respectively) based on the male/female composition.[8,9]

Table 4.4   Average employment and earnings in SIC orders VII and XI, April 1977

	Average employment[1] (000s)			Average earnings[2] (£)		Standardized units	
	Total	Male	Female	Male	Female	Female	Total (male equivalents)
Vehicles	756.5	665	91.5	77.3	53.4	63.1	728.1
Mechanical engineering	923.6	780.4	143.2	74.0	49.7	95.9	876.3

Reproduced from: (1) *Employment Gazette*, 'Employees in employment', January 1978. (2) *New Earnings Survey*, 'Average gross weekly earnings for full-time manual men and full-time manual women', April 1977. Both with the permission of the Controller of Her Majesty's Stationery Office.

In Table 4.4, the ratio of female to male earnings in the vehicle industry is 53.4/77.3, which equals 0.69. According to relative earnings, therefore, one female worker is equivalent to 0.69 male workers. Therefore, total females expressed as male equivalents would be 91.5×0.69, which equals 63.1 females when measured on the same basis as males. Total employment when expressed as male equivalents therefore becomes 728.1 thousands (i.e., 63.1 male equivalents plus 665 males). The reader is advised to carry out a similar exercise using the figures given for the mechanical engineering industry.

The advantage is that if a productivity comparison was being made between these two industries the final column would provide a more appropriate measure of labour input because of its consistency, rather than the initial column which simply 'counts heads' and therefore ignores compositional differences. However, the major criticism of this procedure is the implicit assumption made that relative earnings differences exactly reflect productivity differences (i.e., one female is equivalent to 0.69 males in the vehicle industry in the example

51

given above), which, in practice, is unlikely to be true. Nevertheless, it is difficult to think of any other more satisfactory method of estimating equivalence, although presumably for 'in-company' measurements efficiency differences between individuals or recognized groups of workers could be determined by time and motion study.

Finally, the time period over which productivity comparisons are being made has to be carefully considered since it would affect the type of productivity being measured and, indeed, the usefulness of any results. Taking annual data, for example, would result in a measure of 'productivity per employee year', which may be suitable for some analyses but is questionable when used for international comparisons. The reason, once again, centres on the lack of consistency, for the 'employee year' is likely to differ from one county to another. Before Britain joined the Economic Community we had substantially fewer paid weeks holiday than, say, Italy, and therefore any productivity comparison between Britain and Italy on the basis of employee year would be of doubtful validity. The most useful and commonly used technique is to measure productivity on an hourly basis (i.e., productivity per employee hour) which would avoid differences in total hours and total weeks worked and therefore provide a common scale for comparison.

5. Theory of index numbers

5.1 Simple indices

The statistical techniques so far discussed are useful in describing data referring to a particular point in time. Very often, however, we want to describe changes over time. Rather than presenting a series of observations or measurements as they arise at different points in time, it is often clearer to present them in index number form. This simply means expressing each value as a percentage of some base value. As a simple example we look at two possible index number series that a cake manufacturer could use to track changes in his production (Table 5.1).

Table 5.1

| | 1980 | | | | 1981 | |
Quarter	Jan.–Mar.	Apr.–June	Jul.–Sep.	Oct.–Dec.	Jan.–Mar.	Apr.–June
Cake production (£'000s)	60	62	65	68	72	76
Index (quarter 1, 1980 = 100)	100	103.3	108.3	113.3	120.0	126.7
Index (quarter 1, 1981 = 100)	83.3	86.1	90.3	94.4	100	105.6

In the first series, each number is expressed as a percentage of 60 (the quarter 1, 1980 production figure). Thus, for instance, the index for the second quarter of 1980 is calculated as

$$\tfrac{62}{60} \times 100 = 103.3$$

The index number shows clearly the *relative* changes in production. Any period can be chosen as the base, and over a long period of time it would be normal to occasionally re-base the index series. There are no rules about this, it is simply a matter of clarity and convenience. It would obviously be unwise to pick as a base a period which was in some way untypical; e.g., in this case, a quarter when there had been a strike or an exceptional amount of overtime working. In the above example a series with a different base is shown for comparison.

When there is a change in base, it is a simple matter to relate the old series to the new base. In the above example, the second series can be obtained from the first by multiplying the first indices by 100/120, the ratio of the new to the old index for the new base period.

Although in this chapter we will be concentrating on the calculation of index numbers, it should be borne in mind that they, in common with other statistical measures, are only of value insofar as they measure something meaningful. There are many practical and definitional problems to overcome while arriving at the data to calculate a production index, for instance. Some of these were discussed in the previous chapter in connection with the index of industrial production. To mention again just one important problem: how do we measure production? When a range of different products are made, we need a common unit. Monetary value is usually chosen, but of what? Do we take the gross value of the goods produced or the value added? Refer to Chapter 4 for a fuller discussion of these and other problems.

Index numbers are useful in showing relative changes in a simple time series, but their main importance lies in their application to summarizing changes across a range of time series. Thus the index of industrial production is an attempt to indicate production trends across the whole of industry. The retail prices index shows price changes across a wide range of consumer goods (see Chapter 6). We next examine some ways of doing this by way of a simple example.

5.2 Price/Cost indices

Table 5.2

Material	Unit	1979		1980		Price relatives
		Quantity	price (£/unit)	Quantity	price (£/unit)	
Flour	ton	72	95	80	105	110.5
Fruit	ton	110	720	150	700	97.2
Sugar	ton	60	210	70	220	104.8
Eggs	1000	950	20	1100	25	125.0
Butter	ton	70	700	60	950	135.7

Suppose that the cake manufacturer's main ingredients are those shown in Table 5.2, together with their usages and prices for 1979 and 1980. We shall use these data to illustrate some of the ways the manufacturer could construct an index of his raw material costs. The same principles apply to the construction of price indices.

Mean of price relatives

The price relatives shown in Table 5.2 are simply the 1980 prices expressed as a percentage of the 1979 prices. In other words, they are simple indices of price for each material based on 1979. The arithmetic mean of these indices (P_M) is the simplest overall index of price changes. Thus:

$$P_M = \tfrac{1}{5}(110.5 + 97.2 + 104.8 + 125.0 + 135.7) = 114.6$$

The problem with this as an overall measure of price change is that equal weights are given to each item. This is rarely a reasonable assumption. For instance, in the above example, the changes in fruit and butter prices are given equal weights, although a change in fruit prices will clearly have more impact, with substantially larger quantities used.

Weighted mean

One way of getting round the problem just mentioned is to weight the price relatives according to their importance. The weighted mean price index (P_W) for the above example, using 1979 quantities as weights, is

$$P_W = \frac{72 \times 110.5 + 110 \times 97.2 + 60 \times 104.8 + 950 \times 125.0 + 70 \times 135.7}{72 + 110 + 60 + 950 + 70} = 121.4$$

The main problem with this approach is that it tends to overstate the effects of a price rise, as it ignores the fact that a rise in price may be accompanied by a reduction in consumption— as is the case with butter in the example. Another problem is the choice of weights. Quantities do not necessarily reflect importance, as is the case with the eggs the cake manufacturer uses. They are given a very much larger weight than anything else, which is not reasonable in view of their much lower unit price. Of course, we could adjust the units to allow for this (e.g., by using a unit of 10 000), but there clearly are problems in finding a single measure to accurately reflect importance. Usually, a more satisfactory approach to weighting is that used in the Laspeyres or Paasche indices, to be discussed later.

Geometric mean

Another way of reducing the effect of relatively large (or small) price changes on the overall average index is to use the geometric mean instead of the arithmetic mean. The geometric mean of n items is defined as the nth root of their product. Thus the geometric mean of the price relatives (P_G) for the above example is

$$P_G = (110.5 \times 97.2 \times 104.8 \times 125.0 \times 135.7)^{1/5} = 113.8$$

Equivalently, we could arrive at the same result by finding the arithmetic mean of the logarithms of the price relatives and taking the antilogarithm of the result (we defined the geometric mean in this way in Chapter 2). This latter approach is necessary when there are a large number of price relatives to average, since otherwise their product would overflow the capacity of the calculator or computer used, or at least lead to significant rounding errors when the root is taken. Many modern calculators can cope with the calculation given above, however.

As can be seen, the result is not very different from the arithmetic mean of the price relatives, although it will always be smaller (113.8 as compared to 114.6 in the above case). The main advantages of the geometric mean for an index are largely theoretical, and in practice it is not very often used, since it is more difficult to interpret and more troublesome to calculate. The best known examples of its application are the share indices published by *The Times*.

Laspeyres index

The Laspeyres index (named after its inventor) is the most commonly used approach to calculating a price index. The arithmetic or geometric means give all items equal weighting, and, as we saw, the simple weighted mean using quantities as weights does not make allowance for possible interactions between prices and quantities used. The Laspeyres index goes some way to avoid these problems. There are two ways of viewing its calculation. The simplest is the aggregative method. A 'bundle' (or aggregate) of items is considered which reflects demand or usage in the base year. The total value of this bundle is found for the base year and the same bundle is then evaluated in subsequent years. The index for any year is then calculated by expressing the value for that year as a percentage of the base year.

Expressed as a formula, the Laspeyres price index, L_p, for a particular year is

$$L_p = \frac{\sum q_0 p_1}{\sum q_0 p_0} \times 100 \tag{5.1}$$

55

where

$$q = \text{quantity}$$
$$p = \text{price}$$
$$\text{subscript } 0 = \text{base year}$$
$$\text{subscript } 1 = \text{current year}$$

The quantity price multiples are summed over all items in the index.

Table 5.3

Material	q_0	p_0	p_1	$q_0 p_0$	$q_0 p_1$
Flour	72	95	105	6 840	7 560
Fruit	110	720	700	79 200	77 000
Sugar	60	210	220	12 600	13 200
Eggs	950	20	25	19 000	23 750
Butter	70	700	950	49 000	66 500
				$\sum q_0 p_0 = 166\,640$	$\sum q_0 p_1 = 188\,010$

As an example, consider again the data given in Table 5.2 for the cake manufacturer. The base year (subscript 0) is 1979 and the current year (subscript 1) is 1980. From the calculations shown in Table 5.3:

$$L_p = \frac{188\,010}{166\,640} \times 100 = 112.8$$

This indicates a 12.8 per cent increase in prices for the year. Although this is less than the values obtained using the previously described methods, this will not necessarily be so. In fact, the Laspeyres index tends to slightly overestimate the effect of price rises, since it does not reflect any reduction in quantity which may arise from an increase in price.

Paasche index

The Paasche index (also named after its inventor) is calculated in a similar way, except that the bundle of goods is valued at *current* year quantities. Using the same notation as before, the formula for the Paasche price index, P_p, is

$$P_p = \frac{\sum q_1 p_1}{\sum q_1 p_0} \times 100 \tag{5.2}$$

Table 5.4

Material	q_1	p_0	p_1	$q_1 p_0$	$q_1 p_1$
Flour	80	95	105	7 600	8 400
Fruit	150	720	700	108 000	105 000
Sugar	70	210	220	14 700	15 400
Eggs	1100	20	25	22 000	27 500
Butter	60	700	950	42 000	57 000
				$\sum q_1 p_0 = 194\,300$	$\sum q_1 p_1 = 213\,300$

The data from Table 5.2 is again used as an example. From the calculations in Table 5.4:

$$P_p = \frac{213\,300}{194\,300} \times 100 = 109.8$$

The Paasche index uses current year quantities in an attempt to overcome the problem of overestimation mentioned for the Laspeyres index. In doing so, however, it has a tendency to *underestimate* the effect of price rises. In general, as in this example, its value will be less than that of the Laspeyres index. (It is possible for the Paasche index to be greater than the Laspeyres index, but only when both prices and quantities are increasing over time, which is comparatively unusual.)

In practice, the two indices will usually give very similar results, since quantities will not vary violently from year to year. Indeed, if they do, the usefulness of any overall index is questionable. The above example is not typical in this respect and was chosen to make more obvious the characteristics of the different methods.

A major disadvantage of the Paasche index is the requirement for current quantity data each year. This may be costly to provide, where, for instance, a survey is necessary.

Weighted price relatives form of Laspeyres and Paasche indices

Algebraically, the Laspeyres and Paasche indices are equivalent to weighted means of price relatives. The weights are, respectively, base year quantities valued at base year prices and current year quantities valued at base year prices.

Since $q_0 p_1 = q_0 p_0 (p_1/p_0)$, the Laspeyres price index, L_p, can be expressed as

$$\frac{1}{100} L_p = \frac{\sum q_0 p_1}{\sum q_0 p_0} = \frac{\sum q_0 p_0 (p_1/p_0)}{\sum q_0 p_0} \tag{5.3}$$

Similarly, the Paasche price index, P_p, can be expressed as

$$\frac{1}{100} P_p = \frac{\sum q_1 p_1}{\sum q_1 p_0} = \frac{\sum q_1 p_0 (p_1/p_0)}{\sum q_1 p_0} \tag{5.4}$$

This form of the formulas is not generally convenient for calculation purposes, unless the price relatives are needed. Compared to the weighted mean discussed above, it can be seen that these indices use values as weights instead of quantities. This tends to be a better indicator of importance, and is why these indices are generally preferred.

5.3 Quantity indices

Some of the problems of providing a meaningful index of quantities were mentioned at the beginning of the chapter. Where groups of items are to be indexed, much the same considerations apply as those for price indices. The additional complication for quantity indices is that the quantities must be measured in the same units. As we have seen, this generally means monetary units, unless some other common unit makes sense. For instance, a measure of heat output could be used for comparing consumptions of different types of energy.

The arithmetic, geometric, and weighted means of quantities suffer from the same disadvantages as was the case for prices. For a Laspeyres or Paasche index, p is replaced by

q, and vice versa, in the above formulas. The Laspeyres index is more often preferred of the two, and the formula for the Laspeyres quantity index, L_q, is

$$L_q = \frac{\sum p_0 q_1}{\sum p_0 q_0} \times 100 \qquad (5.5)$$

Table 5.5

Material	p_0	q_0	q_1	$p_0 q_0$	$p_0 q_1$
Flour	95	72	80	6 840	7 600
Fruit	720	110	150	79 200	108 000
Sugar	210	60	70	12 600	14 700
Eggs	20	950	1100	19 000	22 000
Butter	700	70	60	49 000	42 000
				$\sum p_0 q_0 = 166\,640$	$\sum p_0 q_1 = 194\,300$

Table 5.5 shows the calculations for the cake manufacturer's 1980 quantity index. From the calculations in Table 5.5:

$$L_q = \frac{194\,300}{166\,640} \times 100 = 116.6$$

The Laspeyres quantity index can be viewed as a weighted mean of quantity relatives, just as the price index was shown in (5.3) to be a weighted mean of price relatives. The weights for the quantity index will be the same—base year quantities valued at base year prices. In this form it is

$$L_q = \frac{\sum p_0 q_0 (q_1/q_0)}{\sum p_0 q_0} \times 100 \qquad (5.6)$$

5.4 Further calculations with index numbers

Chain-basing

Indices, especially for groups of items, are often based on the previous year. In order to relate the indices so produced back to an earlier year, the chain base method is used. This is simple to do and is best illustrated with an example.

Suppose 1975 is the base year for some index series, I, thus:

$$I_{1975} = 100$$

Suppose that for 1976 we have:

$$I_{1976} = 105.0$$

The 1977 index is based on 1976; suppose we have:

$$I_{1977} = 104.0 \text{ (based on 1976)}$$

We re-base the 1977 index on 1975 as follows:

$$I_{1977} = 104 \times \frac{105}{100} = 109.2 \text{ (based on 1975)}$$

Similarly, if the 1978 index was:

$$I_{1978} = 106.0 \text{ (based on 1977)}$$

The re-based index would be:

$$I_{1978} = 106 \times \frac{109.2}{100} = 115.8 \text{ (based on 1975)}$$

The principle is thus the same as that discussed in Sec. 5.1 for relating indices based on different years. It should be noted that where the indices are calculated using weighted means, as, for instance, for the Laspeyres or Paasche indices, the resulting chained indices will *not* be the same as if they had been calculated on the required base year in the first place.

Several published series are calculated in this way, for instance, the retail prices index. This is calculated monthly, based on January of the current year. The resulting index is then chained back to January of the base year (currently 1974).

Deflating an index series

Any index series which measures money values will to some extent include the effect of inflation. In fact, in recent years any increase in such a series is likely to be very largely accounted for by inflation. A good example is the indices of wages and earnings. In order to show changes in real terms, an index series can be deflated by dividing each index number by the value of a deflator index for the same year. The retail price index (RPI) is often used as a deflator series, and is used in the example given in Table 5.6.

Table 5.6

	1976	1977	1978
Index of average earnings (all industries and services)	100	115.6	130.6
Retail price index (monthly averages, all items)	157.1	182.0	197.1
Deflator index (RPI/1976 RPI)	1.0	1.158	1.255
Deflated index of earnings	100	99.8	104.1

The deflator series is effectively re-based to the base year of the earnings series, but is expressed as a proportion instead of the usual percentage in order to form the deflator index. As can be seen, deflation has a dramatic effect on the earnings index. For a discussion of wages and earnings data, refer to Chapter 12.

5.5 Indices in practice

In practice, published index series are often calculated using modified versions of the methods described above. This is because it may be difficult or even impossible to collect the data in the precise form required by any particular formula. We next look briefly at two series, discussed extensively in other chapters.

Index of industrial production

This is a quantity index and essentially indicates changes in net output for the economy. For details of how this is done and some of the associated problems, see Chapter 4. It is essentially a Laspeyres index, calculated in the form given in (5.6). The weighting factors, base year quantities valued in monetary terms, are the value added (or £ net output) estimates arrived at in the census of production for the base year (currently 1975).

The quantity relatives for subsequent years are, where possible, calculated using the same data. This is not always possible and in some cases these ratios have to be estimated using some appropriate indicator. The quantity relatives are published by sector of industry, as are the related weighting factors. One further slight complication which will be noted if reference is made to the published data, is that the weights have all been re-scaled so as to add to 1000.

Retail prices index

The construction of this index is described in detail in Chapter 6. This is, of course, a price index for a selection of consumer goods. These prices are arrived at on a monthly basis, and the index tracks month-by-month changes. The quantities are the amounts of each item purchased, which are found once a year at the beginning of the year. A Laspeyres index is calculated each month based on the January of the same year. The index is then chained back to a base month (currently January 1974). Again, the relatives form of the formula is used (5.3) since the price relatives are themselves of interest. The weighting factors, the items valued at their base month prices for their base month consumption, are re-scaled so as to add to 1000. In fact, the consumption and price data are based on samples, so technically we have only an estimate of the Laspeyres index.

As will be seen from Chapters 4 and 6, many difficulties of classification, definition, and measurement are encountered in arriving at the data necessary to calculate indices such as those above. This should be borne in mind when interpreting published index series or constructing, say, company-based indices.

6. Prices

Interest in, and concern for, rising prices is shared by everybody in the community—from the housewife budgeting her weekly shopping and the union negotiator aware of rising living costs facing his members, to the purchasing manager of a business concern dealing with increased charges for necessary raw materials and other inputs. Indeed, it is likely that more people are aware of the official estimates of price changes each month than any other published statistic.

This greater awareness, of course, stems from the very rapid increase in prices during the 'seventies where rates of increase on an annual basis reached well into double figures for all industrialized countries, with Britain invariably inflating faster than comparable countries. It is interesting to note, however, that economic commentators and governments in Britain have been concerned with inflation (defined by economists as a rise in commodity and factor prices) throughout the period since 1945, as witnessed by the many anti-inflationary policies implemented periodically since that time. Until the early 'seventies the continuous, but small, price increases were called 'creeping inflation' by economists but were still of major concern to British governments principally because of the adverse effects on our foreign trade position. Even with annual rates as low, by modern standards, as $2\frac{1}{2}$ per cent, in a situation where our main foreign rivals were inflating at less than this our exports were clearly becoming uncompetitive in world markets. Internally, inflation has other economic as well as social and political ill-effects which adds to the resolve of governments to control the inflationary process. It tends to redistribute incomes from the non-unionized or weakly unionized labour force to the strongly unionized workers who will be able to force wages up, at least in line with rising prices; it tends to lower the real income for those people whose incomes are fixed (pensioners, students, those who depend on the returns of fixed interest securities); and it tends to redistribute incomes from savers to borrowers and thereby discourage savings. Indeed, if inflation reaches massive proportions it can impoverish whole sectors of the community and bring about the collapse of established order and institutions, as the German experience in the inter-war years well illustrates.

Having established the importance of inflation, the remainder of this chapter examines the way in which inflation is measured in the United Kingdom and also its weaknesses, strengths, and uses. We first turn to the most familiar of these measures.

6.1 The retail prices index

The retail prices index (RPI) is produced by the Department of Employment and is published monthly in the *Employment Gazette* (formerly the *Department of Employment Gazette*). It is designed to represent the changes in prices from some base date in the average or representative basket of goods and services. To be meaningful it takes account of the fact that items have differing degrees of importance—a 5 per cent increase in the price of a commodity that everybody purchases regularly will be more significant that a 50 per cent price increase in something that is bought by very few people. The index is therefore in weighted form and at this point readers who are unsure of the construction, or meaning, of a weighted index should refer back to Chapter 5 where the theory of index numbers is dealt with.

Since the RPI is a weighted index it is clear that its construction involves two component parts: (1) collecting the information on prices and (2) applying the appropriate weights. We will look at these in turn before dealing with the construction and interpretation of the RPI.

Collecting the information on prices

The first thing to realize is that in a period of, say, one month, there must be millions of individual transactions taking place in the economy in which goods and services are purchased and paid for. It would clearly be impossible to monitor the price of every item purchased and therefore a selection, or sample, of commodities is established on which price information may be sought. At the present time this list includes the following 11 main categories:

> Food
> Alcoholic drink
> Tobacco
> Housing
> Fuel and light
> Durable household goods
> Clothing and footwear
> Transport and vehicles
> Miscellaneous goods
> Services
> Meals bought and consumed outside the home

The majority of these main categories are subdivided into individual commodities; the food category, for example, has as many as 31 items, ranging from butter, eggs, milk, to types of meat and fresh and tinned vegetables. Even with this restricted list of items it is nevertheless still too extensive to include every commodity, and therefore something like 350 are selected for detailed price investigation every month.

The price recordings are obtained by Department of Employment officials from 200 local offices spread throughout the United Kingdom on one day each month, normally the Tuesday nearest to the 15th. The retailing outlets visited range from large superstores down to small corner shops so that a broad, representative picture of price movements can be obtained. For many individual items at least five price quotes are obtained (again from a range of stores), although for the more expensive durable goods, particularly in smaller towns, it may not be possible to obtain this number of price quotes. In each case the price recorded is that charged at the till—since this is what the purchaser would have to pay. Consequently, genuine price reductions and special offers would be taken into account, although where these discounts are due to commodities being damaged or 'seconds' they are excluded from the survey.

It should now be apparent that the whole exercise of collecting information on prices is based on a sample approach, i.e., a sample of goods and services are selected each month; a sample of prices are obtained for each item; a sample of retailing outlets are used; a geographical sample is taken, representing different sizes of communities (from large cities to small villages) spread throughout the country; and a sample of one day is taken each month for the actual recording. The resulting index could therefore be described as a partial 'snap-shot' of prices in the economy at a particular point in any month and is invariably compared with the previous partial snap-shot in order to infer something about price movements from one month to another and over longer time periods.

Recording problems Clearly there are interpretation problems where published data are based on a sampling approach, but we will reserve a discussion of these points until the RPI has been more fully described. However, one practical difficulty that warrants discussion at this juncture is the problem of eliminating, as far as possible, quality differences of the same commodity over time.

The reader should recall from Chapter 5 that one important consideration in index construction is to measure only that for which the index is being constructed. Thus for a price index only prices should be recorded. This might seem a rather spurious and obvious point but in practice it is rather more difficult than is often appreciated. For example, an item of clothing may have been increased in price by, say, 10 per cent from one month to another but if the quality of material had improved then part of this 10 per cent mark-up would have been due to quality differences and only the remainder would be the true price increase. An index which took no account of these quality differences would clearly be measuring not just prices over time but quality over time and would therefore not be a true price index. We have already seen that damaged and shop-soiled goods sold at a discount are excluded from the survey. The reason is now clear; it is because these goods are of different (inferior) quality.

However, damaged goods form only a part of quality differences taking place continuously and raises the question of how the Department of Employment officials discount for quality changes in practice. The answer is that no hard and fast rules are adopted; instead, a pragmatic but commonsense approach is taken. In some cases quality differences are obvious; in other cases a discussion with the retailer may elicit information necessary to judge these differences. For certain seasonal foodstuffs only those items in season are included. This is partly for quality reasons but also reflects the fact that the average household is unlikely to buy expensive, out of season, commodities. For beer, with differing degrees of potency (quality?), an averaging process is made.

One must assume that with many years of experience the Department of Employment are able to allow for these quality differences reasonably accurately, although some room for doubt must remain and it would be inconceivable that all quality differences have been allowed for in the construction of the index.

The weighting system

The application of weights to individual items and to the eleven main group headings mentioned earlier is an attempt to reflect the fact of differing degrees of importance these items have in the representative shopping basket. The items themselves and their relative importance have therefore to be established. How is this done? The answer is rather obvious, namely, a survey of spending patterns is undertaken, known as the family expenditure survey (FES).[10]

The family expenditure survey This survey was established in 1957 on a regular basis and replaced a larger, but less frequent, household expenditure enquiry. Although the Department of Employment is ultimately responsible for the survey it is actually conducted by the Social Survey Division of the Office of Population Censuses and Surveys. The sample of households is based on a random selection from the electoral register, but care is taken to spread the sample (1) throughout the United Kingdom, (2) in rural and urban communities, and (3) in prosperous and less prosperous areas. Since 1967 the sample of addresses used has been approximately 11 000 each year, which has resulted in about 7000 households per year actually cooperating. It is important to realize that the survey is conducted continuously throughout the year, rather than at one specific point in time, mainly because considerable variations in spending patterns occur during the year due to the seasonal characteristics of many goods and services.

The information obtained can be conveniently broken down under three main headings:

1. *Household schedule*. This refers to regular recurring household expenditure, i.e., rent and other housing costs, gas, electricity, telephone charges, season tickets, insurance premiums, motor vehicles, etc.
2. *Income schedule*. This would include information on income from employment and other sources (interest, dividends, social security benefits, pensions, etc.) for each adult member of the household. Income is defined in 'normal' terms to counter the effects of unusual circumstances such as sickness, short-time working, etc., at the time the information is requested. In addition, details of direct taxation and insurance contributions are also obtained.

   Both the household expenditure and income details are obtained by interviews with the skilled staff of the Office of Population Censuses and Surveys.
3. *Diary record book*. Members of households are additionally requested to keep a detailed record of their daily expenditure during 14 consecutive days. For all those cooperating a nominal payment of £2 is made.

Despite the fact that only about 65 per cent of households cooperate fully, which means that the annual results are based on something like 7000 households, it is felt by officials that this is sufficiently high to establish the major components of spending, particularly bearing in mind its main purpose of aiding the construction of the RPI.

The published annual data provide an analysis of spending patterns according to the composition of the household (i.e., single people; man, woman, and one child; man, woman, and two children; etc.) and according to household income. With regard to the latter, it is noticeable, but hardly surprising (although significant for RPI purposes), that marked variations in spending patterns among different income classes occur. Thus 'one and two person pensioner households' spend a considerably higher proportion of their total household expenditure on housing, fuel, light and power, and food than the 'high income households' or the average of all households. On the other hand, they spend considerably less than other income groups on such things as transport and vehicles and durable household goods. The most prosperous households spend proportionally more on services and durable household goods.

However, it is not the annual data that determine the weights in the RPI but information over a 12-month period ending in June. The reason, of course, is to allow time for collating and analysing the results so that the new weights can be established in January each year.

Constructing the RPI

The RPI is therefore constructed from the prices information collected by Department of Employment officials on one day each month and the appropriate weights attached to each class of goods and services as determined mainly, but not entirely, from the family expenditure survey[9]. They are not entirely due to the FES results because two types of modification are made.

64

First, given the fact that 'pensioner' and 'high income households' show a markedly different pattern of spending from the 'average household', it is felt desirable to exclude their spending behaviour when establishing the weights, otherwise the results for the average household would be distorted. This effectively means that 10 per cent of the population, at the high and low income ends of the spectrum, are ignored when constructing the weights. The precise definition of low income households is where at least 75 per cent of total income is derived from pensions or state benefits; high income households are those whose head earns an income above a certain limit which is frequently being changed to allow for inflation, i.e., in the second half of 1978 the limit was set at £180 per week, which was raised to £195 for the first half of 1979. The remaining households in the FES are referred to as 'index households' and it is their spending patterns that are analysed and form the weights used.

Second, it is recognized that there is some under-recording of expenditure in the FES, particularly for alcoholic drinks, cigarettes, sweets, and chocolates, and in these cases the FES results are either modified or replaced by values from alternative sources including HM Customs and Excise and manufacturers' sales information.

Conventionally the total weights used for all items is 1000, made up of the 11 major categories listed earlier and further sub-divided into specific types of goods and services. Thus for 1980 the food category was given a weighting of 214 out of the 1000 units (in other words, expenditure on food accounted for 21.4 per cent of total expenditure); this is made up of the 31 individual items in the food category.

The complete weights used in 1980 for the major categories are given in Table 6.1. The importance of these weights in constructing the RPI can now be seen.

Table 6.1

Major categories	Weights
Food	214
Alcoholic drink	82
Tobacco	40
Housing	124
Fuel and light	59
Durable household goods	69
Clothing and footwear	84
Transport and vehicles	151
Miscellaneous goods	74
Services	62
Meals bought and consumed outside the home	41
	1000

Suppose a 10 per cent price increase in one month is noted for meals bought and consumed outside the home. How much would this add to the total index? The calculation would be as follows: 10 per cent of 41 (the weight for this item) equals a price change of 4.1 units out of 1000 (the total weight) or, in other words, 0.41 out of 100. What this means, therefore, is that the one-month price change of 10 per cent for this item has added almost a half of one per cent (0.41 to be precise) to the index as a whole for this month. (Calculated as follows: $10/100 \times 41/1000 \times 100 = 0.41$.)

This process is continued for all commodities, gradually aggregating them into groups of items, the major categories, and finally the so-called 'all items' index. The result for any month would show the effect of price changes based on weights established in January of that particular year. For example, the RPI for 1979 (based on 16 January = 100) is as follows:

1979	
January	100
February	100.8
March	101.6
April	103.4
May	104.2
June	106.0
July	110.6
August	111.4
September	112.5
October	113.7
November	114.7
December	115.5

Clearly, prices rose by 15.5 per cent in 1979.

However, the Department of Employment publish the index in such a form that current year price movements can be linked back to previous years; in this way a continuous series of index values are presented. At the present time the base year taken is 1974, and since new weights would have been established in January of that year and price records taken on the 15th of that month, the precise base date is 15 January 1974, which is given the base value of 100.

The technique for converting the values within a year to a common base year is known as 'chain-basing' or 'chain-linking'. Quite simply, the value for, say, July 1979 based on January 1979 would be multiplied by the value for January 1979 based on January 1974 and divided by 100. Given the value of 207.2 for January 1979 (based on January 1974 = 100) the calculation would be

$$\frac{110.6 \times 207.2}{100} = 229.1$$

The actual published data for 1979 (based on 15 January 1974 = 100) are as follows:[8]

1979 (January 1974 = 100)	
January	207.2
February	208.9
March	210.6
April	214.2
May	215.9
June	219.6
July	229.1
August	230.9
September	233.2
October	235.6
November	237.7
December	239.4

Reproduced from *Employment Gazette*, March 1980, with the permission of the Controller of Her Majesty's Stationery Office.

It should be realized that the movement of 32.2 points from January to December 1979 (207.2 to 239.4) does not mean that the annual inflation for 1979 was 32.2 per cent. The rise in prices would, in fact, be 32.2 as a percentage of 207.2, or in other words 15.5 per cent, which is the annual rate of inflation indicated in the earlier table where the December value, based on January equalling 100, was 115.5.

An alternative way of looking at these data is to use the RPI to indicate how much purchasing power has changed from one time period to another. Assuming we wished to estimate this change for December 1979 compared with January 1979, taking £1 (100p) as our common measure, we would then have

$$100 \times \frac{207.2}{239.4} \quad \begin{matrix} \text{(RPI for January 1979 where January 1974} = 100) \\ \text{(RPI for December 1979 where January 1974} = 100) \end{matrix}$$
$$= 86.5$$

In terms of purchasing power, 100p in January 1979 had fallen to 86.5p by December 1979.

It is clear from all the foregoing that the RPI is a chain-based index with weights changing annually. It is sometimes referred to as a chain Laspeyres index since weights are established, as we have already seen, at the beginning of each year (i.e., a base-weighted index). It should also be appreciated that when linking back to a base year no attempt is made to recalculate the whole series on the weights established in the base year (i.e., January 1974), and therefore both prices and weights would have changed. Care must therefore be taken in interpreting the published data. The value of the index for December 1979 (239.4) represents the average change in prices since January 1974 of a representative basket of goods and services in 1979 compared with a *different* but still representative basket of goods and services in 1974.

Interpreting the RPI

The two most common mistakes made in interpreting the published RPI are to infer a degree of accuracy which is both touching and specious and to put it to uses for which it was never really designed. Its major purpose, of course, is to give some measure of the rate of inflation, but possibly because of its treatment by the media one gets the impression that the majority of people accept that this is a precise measure of price inflation felt equally by everybody in the community. The Department of Employment, however, point out that the RPI is representative for about 90 per cent of the population, bearing in mind that very low and very high income households are excluded when determining the weights. In terms of an economist's definition of inflation, a rise in all commodity and factor prices, it becomes apparent that the RPI is really a measure not of inflation as such but the *effect* of inflation on consumers' purchasing power since price changes are multiplied by commodity weights. Even here, however, it must be realized that the index refers to a 'typical' household buying a 'typical' basket of goods and services and is based on data collected nationally.

To the extent that households are not typical in the sense that they normally purchase a different basket of commodities than that assumed in the index or have different shopping habits, then these households could suffer more, or less, from inflation than is indicated by the RPI. The fact that the major categories of commodities display substantially different inflation rates, as Table 6.2 illustrates, emphasizes this particular point.

Certain groups of people could easily be identified as not being typical, e.g., students, pensioners, company directors, etc., and for these the index is likely to be very misleading. However, it should be recalled that the RPI is not intended to represent the effects of inflation for these income groups and even with the remaining 'typical' households considerable variability around the RPI average could occur. It is not hard to suggest examples. An

Table 6.2

Major categories	Percentage change over 12 months, ending 12 February 1980
Food	13
Alcoholic drink	22
Tobacco	17
Housing	26
Fuel and light	19
Durable household goods	16
Clothing and footwear	12
Transport and vehicles	24
Miscellaneous goods	20
Services	24
Meals bought and consumed outside the home	24
All items	19

Reproduced from *Employment Gazette*, March 1980, with the permission of the Controller of Her Majesty's Stationery Office.

agricultural worker, for instance, with relatively low pay and living in a small community may have difficulty in being able to 'shop-around' and therefore will tend to purchase most commodities from the local village shop. Given that these shops are unlikely to offer many bargains the weekly shopping bill may be somewhat higher than a person able to choose between alternative retailing outlets in larger towns. An additional complicating factor is that regional and area disparities in inflation rates occur whereas the RPI measures the average national rate of inflation.

It could, with some justification, be argued that all these points are not really weaknesses of the RPI, but reflect instead a common misuse of a measure whose concept and compilation is generally misunderstood. However, not all the difficulties of the RPI can rest on this argument. Accepting that the index is attempting to measure inflation, several weaknesses are apparent.

First, by using a Laspeyres (base-weighted) index the rate of inflation may be overstated, since it takes no account of the adjustment by consumers of their spending patterns (by substituting relatively cheaper goods for relatively more expensive ones) during a time when the weights are being held constant at the base period. Since the base weights are changed each year, serious overstatement may be avoided, although it should be recalled that the weights are determined principally by a one-year FES result ending in the previous June and therefore the RPI for December in any year would have been based on spending patterns at least one and a half years earlier. It should be noted that the alternative, the Paasche (current weights) index, would tend to understate the rate of inflation and therefore there is no easy solution to this problem.

Second, as has been pointed out,[11] the RPI, by concentrating only on consumer spending, omits other categories of spending in the economy such as government expenditure and company investment; therefore inflation is only being monitored for part of the total economy. However, this may not be as serious an omission as at first seems since, to some extent, price changes in these omitted categories will eventually filter down to retail prices where they will be accounted for.

Finally, the shift in emphasis from direct to indirect taxation by the Conservative Government in 1979 has recently focused attention on the validity of the RPI as a measure of inflation and its effects on living standards.[11] By raising value added tax (VAT), the RPI was automatically increased since retail prices were immediately effected, but since income tax was reduced by about the same total amount then living standards, by and large, remained unaltered. The point is that even if the index does measure inflation (and this contention has been somewhat qualified in all the foregoing) it is highly dangerous to assume that it also measures changes in living standards. In the event the Government felt it necessary to meet this inadequacy by introducing a new index in August 1979, the tax and price index (TPI), a discussion of which will be left until later.

The foregoing points illustrate the fact that the RPI has to be used with some care and considerable caution. It would clearly be a mistake to assume that the index gives a precise measure of inflation. However, in practice, given its major use in the collective bargaining process, it is unlikely that these reservations are ever considered. Groups of workers, represented by union wage negotiators, may in fact be suffering a lesser or greater rate of inflation than that shown by the RPI. Moreover, where *national* wage agreements are made, *regional* disparities around the published figure are almost certain to exist but are largely ignored in the negotiation process.

Despite all these qualifications, the RPI still remains the best single measure of the effect of inflation that we have—indeed, most commentators agree that it is almost certainly the most sophisticated and the most accurate of any country in the world. The real problem is one of misuse and misunderstanding.

6.2 Other consumer price indices

The previous section described the most familiar price index which is sometimes referred to as the 'all-items' index. Price indices for specific categories that make up the all-items index are also published. These include food, seasonal foodstuffs, items mainly manufactured in the United Kingdom (from home-produced raw materials and imported raw materials), items mainly home produced for direct consumption, items mainly imported for direct consumption, and all items except food.

The advantage of this detailed breakdown is that some insight into the inflationary forces at work in the economy can be gauged. For example, by January 1980 the RPI (all items) had reached 245.3 based on 1974 = 100, while manufactured items from imported raw materials had risen to 277.7. By contrast, items that show significant seasonal variations in prices had only risen to 223.6 and imports for direct consumption only rose to 218.3 during the same period. The implication of these figures suggests that domestic inflation is markedly influenced by what is happening to inflation in the rest of the world.

In addition to this commodity breakdown of the RPI, two particular types of household are also identified with the construction of their own quarterly indices: the 'one-person' and 'two-persons' pensioner households. The special treatment reflects their markedly different weighting pattern compared with the average household (spending proportionately more on food and fuel and light, and less on transport and vehicles, durable goods, and alcoholic drink, as mentioned earlier), and plays a major part in determining government pensions policy.

6.3 The tax and price index

This index was introduced in August 1979 and published monthly thereafter. The Central Statistical Office is responsible for its publication although the Inland Revenue do the actual calculations in consultation with the CSO and the Department of Employment (the Department responsible for the RPI).

The need for such an index, as briefly outlined earlier, reflects the fact that the ability to buy goods and services will depend not just on the prices of these commodities but also on the amount of income consumers have after all direct deductions have been made (i.e., income and national insurance contributions), whereas only the former is monitored through the RPI.

The reason why this gap in information has received little attention in the past is because the broad tax regime (i.e., the relative importance of direct and indirect taxation) has remained substantially unaltered for many decades. However, the new Conservative Government in 1979 shifted the emphasis appreciably by raising indirect taxes (VAT) and lowering income tax, and in these circumstances the short-fall in information became more serious, particularly where the RPI is used in collective wage bargaining as a measure of changes in living standards. It is clear that the Government must also have felt embarrassed, given its commitment to lowering the rate of inflation, since the effect of VAT changes was to raise inflation as recorded by the RPI. For these reasons, the new index was quickly introduced.

The tax element of the new index is based on the information provided by the Inland Revenue survey of personal incomes[12] (see Chapter 13 for more detailed treatment), and is therefore calculated from the tax records of 'tax units' which means single persons or married couples. Clearly, non-taxpayers are excluded from the analysis, but also excluded are the higher income groups, defined as those with over £10 000 a year at January 1979. There are two reasons for the exclusion of this latter group. First, the changes in tax liability was not uniform across the income ranges. With proportionally more going to high income groups they were therefore unrepresentative for the majority of taxpayers. Second, it should be recalled that high income groups are also excluded from the expenditure patterns used in the construction of the RPI, and therefore the TPI coverage is comparable to that of the RPI.

Given these exclusions, the tax records of about 80 000 tax units are used to determine the tax component. This is then combined with the RPI and is weighted 25 per cent (approximately) for changes in direct taxes and national insurance contributions and approximately 75 per cent for price changes as given by the RPI. The resulting index is therefore a composite of changes in direct tax and changes in prices and is claimed to be a more meaningful, since more complete, indicator of changes in the purchasing power of incomes for taxpayers, while the RPI would still remain the best indicator of changes in purchasing power for non-taxpayers.

Like the RPI, the Inland Revenue recognize that there will, in practice, be some variation around the one published TPI figure each month, although by excluding the high and low income earners it is claimed that the resulting spread of experience is so narrow that it does reasonably represent changes in purchasing power for the majority of the population, which, in Inland Revenue terms, means those currently earning between £2000 and £10 000 a year.

6.4 The wholesale price index

Finally we turn to the wholesale price index, which refers to the prices that producers have to pay for inputs such as materials and fuel used in the production process. It is therefore a producer's price index as opposed to a consumer's price index given by the RPI. Clearly, since the price of these inputs will eventually influence the prices in the shops for the finished commodities then this index is seen as giving an early warning of changes in the level of inflation. In addition, some commentators claim that the wholesale price index is a better guide to underlying inflation since VAT is excluded from the calculations, although revenue duties for some commodities are included.

The index is published each month in *British Business* (formerly *Trade and Industry*) and records wholesale price movements under three headings: (1) materials and fuel purchased, (2) output (home sales), and (3) commodities wholly or mainly imported into the United Kingdom.

Both the input and output series are published by major sectors, i.e., totals for manufacturing industries, but they are also broken down into broad sectors of industry, normally at the SIC order level. Additionally, data are published for commodities produced in the United Kingdom (home sales) covering industries II to XIX in greater detail than even the MLH level. The index covering commodities imported into the United Kingdom is presented under 15 main headings with many subdivisions.

The basic information on price movements comes from enterprises in the manufacturing sector, covering approximately 11 000 individual and well-defined materials and products. Each month the contributors provide prices for these commodities together with the date when any price change becomes effective. The prices recorded refer to quotes for current orders but reflect differences in trade practice. For example, some industries conventionally provide quotes on a 'delivered' basis, i.e., delivery charge is added while other industries traditionally provide quotes on an ex-works basis. The calculation of the index is therefore based on some prices that include a delivery charge and some that do not, although the prices of imported goods are measured, as far as possible, on a delivered basis.

The index itself is base weighted (Laspeyres) with the weights determined, at the present time, at 1974 from information provided by the quarterly sales enquiry, and therefore the index numbers refer to the cost of a basket of goods as a percentage of what the same basket cost in 1974.

The usefulness of the wholesale price index is not simply confined to commentators interested in analysing underlying inflation; businesses find the data particularly useful in many areas of decision-making. For example, it can be helpful in allowing for inflation when estimating the replacement cost for capital equipment or establishing contract prices for long-period contracts.

Self-assessment questions—Part Two

1. What are the three principal sets of published information on production?

2. What is the distinction between gross output and net output?

3. Why is the measure of net output in the census of production different from that in the national income accounts?

4. Explain the reporting unit problems associated with multi-unit businesses.

5. Why is labour conventionally taken as the only input in productivity measurements?

6. Of what importance is published information on price changes?

7. Since the RPI is a weighted index, how are the weights established and how frequently are they altered?

8. What effect on the all-items index would a 2 per cent increase in alcoholic drinks have, where this is given a weight of 82 out of 1000?

9. On what grounds has it been argued that the RPI fails to measure inflation?

10. What is the distinction between the RPI and the TPI?

11. In what ways can the wholesale price index be more useful than the RPI?

12. An index series is based on 1974 and gives the following indices up to 1977:

Year	1974	1975	1976	1977
Index	100	103.1	110.2	109.0

It is decided to re-base the series on 1977=100. Recalculate the indices from 1974 so that they can be compared to the new series. If the index for 1978 is 105.3, based on 1977, find the percentage increase in 1978 compared to 1976.

13. The following table shows the total U.K. inland energy consumption, measured in millions of tonnes of coal equivalents, for coal, petroleum, and natural gas in the years 1971 and 1979:

	1971	1979
Coal	139.3	129.6
Petroleum	151.2	139.0
Natural gas	28.8	71.3

Calculate the quantity relatives for these three sources of energy for 1979 based on 1971. Hence calculate an appropriate index of energy use for 1979 (1971=100).

14. The average wage rates for a firm's workforce, by category of employment, were as follows for 1979 and 1980:

Employment category	1979		1980	
	Numbers	Average weekly earnings (£)	Numbers	Average weekly earnings (£)
Unskilled	153	74.3	140	79.2
Skilled	65	88.5	66	94.6
Clerical	52	63.0	54	66.5
Managerial and technical	24	132.4	28	143.2

The firm require an index of earnings for 1980 (1979 = 100) as an indicator of their wages costs. Calculate a Laspeyres index and a Paasche index and comment on their appropriateness for this purpose.

15. A chain of restaurants collects the following information on their meat purchases over a three-year period:

	1978		1979		1980	
	Price (£/ton)	Quantity (tons)	Price (£/ton)	Quantity (tons)	Price (£/ton)	Quantity (tons)
Beef	1165	43	1224	45	1346	46
Lamb	914	32	933	38	980	42
Pork	928	24	974	26	1043	35

(a) Calculate a Laspeyres index for 1979 prices (1978 = 100).
(b) Calculate a Laspeyres index for 1980 prices (1979 = 100).
(c) Chain-base the 1980 index to a base of 1978 = 100 and compare with the 1980 index as directly calculated to this base.
(d) Calculate a Laspeyres quantity index for 1980 (1978 = 100).

16. Repeat question 15, parts (a), (b), and (c) for a Paasche index.

17. For the data of question 15, calculate a Laspeyres price index for 1979 and 1980 (1978 = 100) deflated by the wholesale price index for the same years. Comment on the effect of this.

Assignment questions—Part Two

1. You are required to calculate an index of productivity for the vehicles industry over the most recent five-year period which would be suitable for making international comparisons. The data provided include:

(a) Index numbers of output at constant factor cost from the Blue Book.[1]
(b) Industrial analysis of employees in employment from the *Employment Gazette*.[8]
(c) Industrial analysis of earnings and hours worked from the *Employment Gazette*.[8]

2. (a) Calculate a food price index for old age pensioners for 16 December 1980. Clearly explain all the stages required for such an index. The relevant information is contained in tables found in the *Employment Gazette*.[8]

(b) Compare your index with that for the total food price index. Comment on your results.

(c) Summarize the procedure involved in calculating the general index of retail prices in terms of obtaining prices information and establishing the weights.

Part Three

Chapters 7 and 8 extend statistical techniques from the single-variable analysis dealt with earlier to a consideration of relationships between two variables. The two most familiar techniques which test association, correlation, and regression are developed in Chapter 7, where procedures for their calculation are explained as well as their use and interpretation. The regression technique is then used, and others introduced, in Chapter 8, which deals with time series analysis and forecasting.

The techniques developed in these two chapters are frequently applied to published data on employment and unemployment which form the subject matter of Chapter 9 under the heading of manpower statistics. Much of these data have seasonal characteristics and are therefore seasonally adjusted, with trend analysis and forecasting also being common. The chapter explains the collection and provision of data and emphasizes their usage and problems of interpretation.

Once again we include self-assessment questions and suggested assignment topics on the areas covered by these three chapters.

7. Association, Correlation, and Regression

We have concentrated so far on the statistical description of sets of data relating to the same measurement or observation—what statisticians call 'single-variable' data. A further step in statistical analysis is to compare one set of data with another to see if there is any relationship between the two variables represented by the data. Two topical examples of possible relationships we could investigate in this way are the incidence of lung cancer and the level of smoking, and money supply compared with inflation rate.

The sort of relationship we can look for is when high values of one variable tend to be associated with high values of the other variable, and vice versa. Thus across a series of observations the two sets of numbers tend to go up and down together. When this happens the two variables are said to be *correlated*. Sometimes we see the reverse effect, when high values of one variable are associated with low values of the other; in this case we have *negative* correlation. For example, when discussing the construction of index numbers, we have suggested that price levels and quantities purchased are often negatively correlated.

7.1 Scatter diagrams and linear relationships

In order to measure the strength of a correlation, we must first be more precise about the nature of the relationship we are investigating. A good starting point is the *scatter diagram*, a simple graphical means of examining a relationship between two variables. Suppose, for instance, that a transport manager was comparing the delivery costs of a group of customers with their round-trip distances from a warehouse. Costs and distances for 10 customers are given in Table 7.1.

Table 7.1

Delivery cost (£)	Round-trip distance (miles)
5.4	20
7.7	24
8.6	31
10.7	35
12.4	44
11.4	46
15.1	58
16.1	65
18.7	80
17.6	82

Each pair of values can be represented as a point on a graph, with the two variables measured along the two axes. A scatter diagram is the plot of these points, and is illustrated for the data of Table 7.1 in Fig. 7.1 with delivery costs measured along the vertical axis and distance measured on the horizontal axis.

It is clear from Fig. 7.1 that cost and distance are strongly correlated. A straight line has been drawn through the points, and it can be seen that the points lie close to it. This indicates a *linear* relationship between the variables. We shall only be dealing with the case where this is a reasonable assumption.

It may happen that the points seem to lie more closely on a curved line. When this happens, either transform the variables by, for instance, taking logarithms of one or both of the variables—this often 'straightens out' the relationship—or it may be possible to define some other relationship between the variables such as a quadratic curve. The first of these methods is straightforward, since we proceed exactly as with a linear relationship except that the variable(s) is used after transformation. The second method, which is not often necessary, goes beyond the scope of the present text.

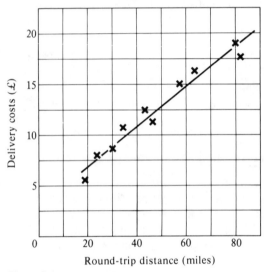

Figure 7.1

Correlation, therefore, is defined in terms of how closely the relationship between two variables is approximated by a linear relationship; in other words, it describes how closely the points on the scatter diagram lie on a straight line.

A scatter diagram will show whether two variables are correlated, and we shall see later how to arrive at a measure of the strength of the correlation, so as, for instance, to compare different relationships. We consider first the problem of finding the equation of the staight line which gives the 'best fit' to the data points. This will be useful where we want to predict the value of one variable from the values of the other variable. Thus, for instance, in the above example it may be much easier for the transport manager to measure the distance of a customer from the warehouse than it would be to cost out a delivery. He could use the equation to estimate the cost of a delivery from the distance. In other cases, it may be possible to control the value of one variable and the equation can then be used to estimate the resulting value of the other variable. The government essentially uses this approach when it sets targets for certain variables it can control (e.g., the money supply), which according to its prediction equation will give desirable results for some other variable (e.g., the rate of inflation). It should be noted that it is not always clear-cut which of two variables is the controllable one. Some, for instance, would argue that the government can control inflation by appropriate policies and that this would lead to a prediction of the resulting money supply.

Let us suppose, however, that we are examining the relationship between two variables, x and y say, with a view to being able to predict y from x. We will stick to the convention of plotting y on the vertical axis and x on the horizontal axis of the scatter diagram. The equation of the straight line which relates y to x can be put in the form:

$$y = a + bx \qquad (7.1)$$

where
  $a = y$ axis intercept
  $b =$ slope of line

As an example, Fig. 7.2 illustrates the line whose equation is

$$y = 2 + 0.5x$$

It can be seen from Fig. 7.2 that a (the y intercept) is 2 and b (the slope) is 0.5.

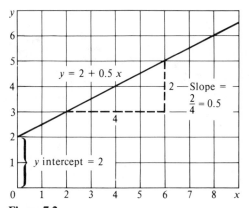

Figure 7.2

The problem of fitting a straight line through a set of points resolves to finding the values of a and b in Eq. (7.1). This can be done by fitting the line by eye and estimating a and b from it. As people will vary, however, in fitting a line that looks best to them, there are advantages in using a method which is reliable and consistent. Such a method is described in the next section.

7.2 The regression method

This is the most commonly used method for fitting a straight line through a set of points. It is based on the assumption that we are using the line to predict y values from x values and want to minimize the errors in y that will result.

These errors can be estimated by comparing the actual values of y that we have with the values that would be predicted from their paired x values if we used a straight line equation. Thus, for a particular pair of values (x_i, y_i), the predicted value of y would be

$$\text{Predicted } y \text{ value} = a + bx_i$$

and the prediction error would be

$$\text{Error} = y_i - (a + bx_i) \tag{7.2}$$

This error could be positive or negative. The two cases are illustrated in Fig. 7.3 (a) and (b).

The regression method finds the values of a and b which define this line such that:

1. The sum of the errors is zero, i.e., positive and negative errors cancel out. This is to ensure that the line equation gives unbiased predictions, where over-prediction (positive errors) is no more likely than under-prediction (negative errors).
2. The sum of the squared errors is minimized. The errors are squared to remove their sign, which is a means of minimizing error, regardless of sign.

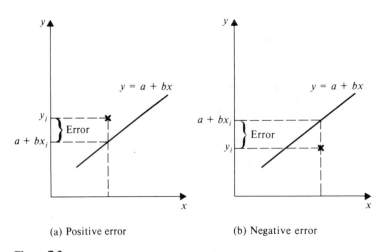

(a) Positive error   (b) Negative error

Figure 7.3

The problem of finding a and b to meet these requirements is solved using differential calculus. The derivation is omitted here, but may be found in many statistics texts. The results can be stated as follows:

$$b = \frac{\sum xy - (1/n)(\sum x)(\sum y)}{\sum x^2 - (1/n)(\sum x)^2} \tag{7.3}$$

$$a = \left(\frac{1}{n}\right)\sum y - b\left(\frac{1}{n}\right)\sum x \tag{7.4}$$

where there are n pairs of values of x and y available.

To illustrate the method, we use the data given in Table 7.1. The variable to be predicted, y, is delivery cost and the predictor variable, x, is round-trip distance. The calculations for finding the equation of the regression line are as follows:

y	x	x^2	xy
5.4	20	400	108.0
7.7	24	576	184.8
8.6	31	961	266.6
10.7	35	1 225	374.5
12.4	44	1 936	545.6
11.4	46	2 116	524.4
15.1	58	3 364	875.8
16.1	65	4 225	1046.5
18.7	80	6 400	1496.0
17.6	82	6 724	1443.2
123.7	485	27 927	6865.4

Calculations for b—see formula (7.3)

$$\sum x^2 = 27\ 927 \qquad\qquad \sum xy = 6865.4$$
$$\left(\frac{1}{n}\right)(\sum x)^2 = \underline{23\ 522.5} \qquad\qquad \left(\frac{1}{n}\right)(\sum x)(\sum y) = \underline{5999.45}$$
$$\text{Denominator} = 4\ 404.5 \qquad\qquad \text{Numerator} = 865.95$$

$$b = \frac{865.95}{4404.5} = 0.197$$

Calculations for a—see formula (7.4)

$$a = (\tfrac{1}{10})123.7 - 0.197(\tfrac{1}{10})485$$
$$= 2.82$$

Regression equation   Putting the values of a and b we have obtained into the general form of the regression equation, we have

$$y = 2.82 + 0.197x$$

It is a good idea to draw this line on our scatter diagram as a visual check on whether or not we have carried out the calculations for a and b correctly. The line drawn on the scatter diagram for these data (Fig. 7.1) is, in fact, the regression line for these data. Another useful check is given by the fact that a regression line always passes through the point defined by the mean of the y values and the mean of the x values—12.37 and 48.5, respectively, in this example. If the $\bar{x}$ value is substituted in the above equation, it will be seen that the $\bar{y}$ value results.

We can now use the regression equation to predict delivery costs (y) for given round-trip distances (x). For instance, suppose a customer was a round-trip distance of 50 miles from the warehouse. If we substitute $x = 50$ in the equation we get

$$y = 2.82 + 0.197 \times 50$$
$$= 12.67$$

The delivery cost is therefore estimated as £12.67.

7.3   Accuracy of the regression equation; coefficient of determination

A regression equation can only be used with any confidence within the range of x values used to find its equation. In the example we have been considering, the x values (round-trip distances) range from 20 to 82 miles, and the straight line equation we found appears to give a good fit within this range. Outside this range, there is no guarantee that a straight line relationship will still hold. Considered over a much wider range of values, the relationship may be curved—a small segment of a curve can be closely approximated by a straight line.

To determine how accurate predictions will be using the regression equation, we can compare our actual y values with those that would be predicted from the regression equation from their paired x values. This will provide an estimate of the error to be expected in using the regression equation. An analysis of the errors for the example we have been looking at is as follows:

x	Actual y	Predicted y	Error	Squared error
20	5.4	6.76	−1.36	1.85
24	7.7	7.55	0.15	0.02
31	8.6	8.93	−0.33	0.11
35	10.7	9.71	0.99	0.98
44	12.4	11.49	0.91	0.83
46	11.4	11.88	−0.48	0.23
58	15.1	14.25	0.85	0.72
65	16.1	15.62	0.48	0.23
80	18.7	18.58	0.12	0.01
82	17.6	18.97	−1.37	1.88
			−0.04	6.86

The sum of the errors should be zero, which is nearly true for this example—the discrepancy is due to rounding errors. It follows that the mean error is zero. The variance of the errors can therefore be simply determined from the sum of the squared errors; we then have:

$$\text{Variance of errors} = \frac{6.86}{10} = 0.686$$

$$\text{Standard deviation of errors} = \sqrt{(0.686)} = 0.828$$

If we want to estimate the error involved in using the regression equation for predicting other y values, we are effectively using a *sample* of errors to do so. As indicated in Chapter 2, the above results will be slightly underestimated. There are in fact some other complications which arise in estimating the error when applying a regression equation, depending on the precise assumptions we make about the data (a further discussion of this problem is contained in Chapter 11, sec. 11.8). A reasonable approximation is to multiply the standard deviation as obtained above by the factor $\sqrt{[n/(n-2)]}$. For this example we get

$$0.828 \times \sqrt{(10/8)} = 0.926$$

It is usually also a reasonable assumption to make that the errors are approximately normally distributed. We will be looking in more detail at this distribution in Chapter 10, but as already indicated in Chapter 2 this gives us a simple interpretation of the standard deviation. For instance, we saw that 95 per cent of normally distributed values lie in the range:

$$\text{Mean} \pm 2 \text{ standard deviations}$$

Thus, using the above result, it is *approximately* true that the prediction error when using the above regression equation is, with 95 per cent confidence:

$$0 \pm 2 \times 0.926 \qquad \text{or} \qquad \pm 1.66$$

In fact, in our example all 10 errors lie within this range.

An overall indication of how well a regression equation fits a set of data is given by the *coefficient of determination, R*. This is a measure of the proportion of variability of y which is 'explained' by the regression equation, and is defined as

$$R = 1 - \frac{\text{variance of errors}}{\text{variance of } y}$$

Putting this in symbols, if we represent errors by e, we have

$$R = 1 - \frac{(1/n)\sum e^2}{(1/n)\sum (y - \bar{y})^2}$$

For computational convenience, we can cancel the $1/n$ factors and use the more easily calculated version of the variance formula to give

$$R = 1 - \frac{\sum e^2}{\sum y^2 - (1/n)(\sum y)^2} \qquad (7.5)$$

For the above example, we have found that

$$\sum e^2 = 6.86$$

Some further calculations (given in the next section) show that

$$\sum y^2 - (1/n)(\sum y)^2 = 177.121$$

Hence we have

$$R = 1 - \frac{6.86}{177.121} = 0.96$$

Since R is a proportion, it must lie between 0 and 1, and the nearer to 1 it is, the better the fit of the regression equation. In the example above, the fit is clearly very good, with $R = 0.96$. We can interpret this as meaning that 96 per cent of the variation in y is explained by the regression line.

7.4 The correlation coefficient and its interpretation

The previous two sections have concentrated on finding the equation for the best fitting linear relationship between two variables and on using it to predict the value of one variable from a value of the other variable. Sometimes, we only want to know how good a relationship is, and we are not interested in finding an equation to describe it. We could use the coefficient of determination for this purpose, but most commonly the (product moment) correlation coefficient is used. In fact, the two measures are closely related, as we shall see.

There are several reasons why we may only require a single measure to indicate the strength of a relationship, such as a correlation coefficient. For instance, in exploratory work we may be examining a number of possible relationships and simply want to single out the more promising ones for further study. Correlation coefficients are also widely used where the interrelationships between *many* variables are being studied. In cases such as these, even quite low levels of correlation may be of interest, although the two-variable regression equation would be quite useless.

Several measures of correlation have been proposed, all of which have the property that they measure on a scale from 0 (for no correlation) to 1 (for perfect correlation) or from 0 to −1 (for negative correlation). They differ in how they define these two extreme cases. The product moment coefficient due to the statistician Karl Pearson is by far the most often used, and is the one we next define.

The correlation coefficient, r, for n pairs of values of the two variables x and y is found from the following formula:

$$r = \frac{\sum xy - (1/n)(\sum x)(\sum y)}{\sqrt{\{[\sum x^2 - (1/n)(\sum x)^2][\sum y^2 - (1/n)(\sum y)^2]\}}} \qquad (7.6)$$

To illustrate the calculation of a correlation coefficient, we again use the data of Table 7.1. In fact, the numerator and the left-hand part of the denominator have already been found, when we calculated the slope of the regression line in Sec. 7.2. We will repeat these calculations here for convenience. All but one of the necessary summations are shown in tabular form in that section and we will simply repeat their totals here—check back if in any doubt as to how to arrive at them. The exception is the summation $\sum y^2$. This is found for the y values in exactly the same way as $\sum x^2$ was found for the x values, and the quoted figure of 1707.29 is easily confirmed. The calculations for r can be set out as follows:

$\sum x^2 = 27\,927$	$\sum y^2 = 1707.29$	$\sum xy = 6865.4$
$(1/n)(\sum x)^2 = 23\,522.5$	$(1/n)(\sum y)^2 = 1530.169$	$(1/n)(\sum x)(\sum y) = 5999.45$
Difference $= 4\,404.5$	Difference $= 177.121$	Numerator $= 865.95$

$$\text{Denominator} = \sqrt{(4404.5 \times 177.121)}$$
$$= 883.25$$

$$r = \frac{865.95}{883.25} = 0.9804$$

The correlation coefficient of 0.9804 found in this case is clearly very high, and indicates a strong linear relationship between the two variables.

As indicated, the correlation coefficient and the coefficient of determination are closely related. In fact:

$$\text{Correlation coefficient} = \sqrt{(\text{coefficient of determination})}$$

or, in symbols:

$$r = \sqrt{R} \qquad (7.7)$$

Use of this result with formula (7.6) is usually an easier way of calculating the coefficient of

84

determination than the method given in the previous section, since it saves having to find all the errors. From formula (7.7) we have

$$R = r^2$$

so for the above example:

$$R = (0.9804)^2$$
$$= 0.96 \quad \text{(correct to two decimals)}$$

This is the same answer as before. A proof of this relationship between r and R is not included, but is a fairly straightforward algebraic manipulation of the two formulas.

We turn finally to the interpretation of the correlation coefficient. At the beginning of the chapter it was stated that correlation between two variables simply means that observed pairs of values for the two variables tend to go up and down together. More specifically, the points on their scatter diagram will lie close to a straight line. This is a statement about numerical values; on its own it tells us nothing about the *meaning*, if any, of the relationship between the two variables represented by these numbers. It may be the case that changes in one variable are causing changes in the other variable. If so, this must be established on other grounds; the correlation coefficient can only indicate the possibility. Thus, for instance, studies have shown a high statistical correlation between smoking and the incidence of lung cancer. This *suggests* that there is a causal link, but a *proof* depends on a demonstration of the physical link between the two—experiments on the action of carcinogens, for instance, are aimed at providing this kind of evidence.

The reason for this caution is that it is easy to find examples where two variables are correlated but where it patently is not the case that changes in one are causing changes in the other. Three possible reasons for this are:

1. Each variable may be quite independently related to the same third variable. This is often the basis for the many quite meaningless correlations which have been found. For instance, someone reputedly found a high correlation between stork populations and birth rates! In this example (as with many other cases of this type of spurious correlation) the third variable is time—both variables were increasing approximately linearly with time.
2. A more subtle problem arises where the action of one factor may affect another via one or more intermediate variables. A study carried out some years ago in one English university compared degree results with a number of other factors; the highest correlation was found with the age of the candidate. It does not make sense to suggest that age in itself was causing exam success, but we might hypothesize that, for instance, older students tend to have more commitments, which in turn would encourage a greater motivation, which in turn would cause better exam results.
3. The correlation may arise purely by chance. This is especially likely to happen when the coefficient is calculated for a small sample of values. We will look at sample errors in more detail in Chapter 11. A common instance of this problem occurs when the values of one variable are compared to the values of several other variables. The more comparisons that are made, the more likely it is that at least one high correlation will arise by chance. This may happen when the results of a survey are analysed, for instance. Thus, a tobacco firm compared the incidence of lung cancer with many other factors and found a high correlation with the consumption of cornflakes—it must be said that they had their tongue firmly in their cheek at the time!

In summary, then, correlation coefficients must be interpreted with caution, and are at best only suggestive of a possible relationship between two variables. Nevertheless, they are widely used, and may provide the best if not the only evidence for a relationship between variables. This is often true, for instance, in the analysis of economic problems. Usually, though, there are other grounds for supposing that a relationship exists (otherwise why would we be doing a correlation analysis?), and results are viewed with caution until confirmed by several different studies.

8. Time series analysis and forecasting

A time series is simply a sequence of observations or measurements taken over a period of time, with each data point usually relating to a 'chunk' of time such as a week, a month, or a year. We have already encountered such data series in, for instance, the chapter on index numbers. Also, much economic data are published in the form of a time series. In this chapter we shall be looking at some statistical approaches to analysing the variation that will typically occur over time in a data series.

The object of this type of analysis is to try to find some consistent pattern in the way data vary over time. This is useful both in interpreting the current level of the variable we are interested in compared to its past levels and also in providing a basis for forecasting future levels by extrapolating any pattern we find.

Time series can be loosely divided into long term and short term. In a business context, annual sales and annual capital expenditure are examples of long-term time series. Such data are used in the overall control of the company via the annual budget and in strategic planning for several years ahead. Short-term time series include, for instance, daily orders received, weekly or monthly sale, and production, etc. This sort of data gives a picture of how things are going and is useful in the tactical planning of the company's operations over the next few months. A similar division occurs for similar reasons in the data the government collect. Of course, there is no rigid distinction between the long term and short term, but the distinction is nevertheless useful because of the uses the data are put to and the statistical methods that are likely to be most appropriate in each case.

We shall be concentrating on the estimation of two factors, the trend and the seasonal or cyclical fluctuation. These occur in reasonably consistent patterns in many time series and can be analysed with some success using simple techniques. The trend is the overall upward or downward movement of a series; seasonal fluctuations are regular variations about the trend. We begin by looking at methods for determining the trend.

8.1 Trend—regression techniques

We start by looking at the problem of estimating the trend in long-term time series. Figure 8.1 shows the total inland energy consumption in the United Kingdom for the years 1960 to 1974. Although there are some ups and downs, the data show a fairly consistent upward movement over the period. As suggested by the graph, the trend can be approximated by a straight line. We have already seen in Chapter 7 the use of regression in fitting a straight line through a set of points; estimating a trend for data of this type can be seen as essentially the same problem. Although, as is the convention for a time series graph, we have joined the data points with lines, this graph can be viewed as a scatter diagram with energy consumption as the y variable and time as the x variable. To simplify the arithmetic we count x as 1 in 1960 and increase it

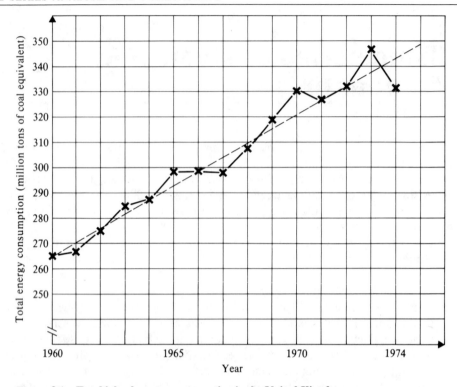

Figure 8.1   Total inland energy consumption in the United Kingdom

by one for each subsequent year. The data for Fig. 8.1 and the necessary calculations for the regression line estimate of the trend are shown in Table 8.1.

Table 8.1

Year	Year (1960 = 1), x	Energy consumption, y
1960	1	265
1961	2	266
1962	3	274
1963	4	284
1964	5	286
1965	6	297
1966	7	298
1967	8	297
1968	9	307
1969	10	318
1970	11	330
1971	12	326
1972	13	331
1973	14	346
1974	15	331
	$\sum x = 120$	$\sum y = 4556$

Calculations for *b*—see formula (7.3)

$$\sum x^2 = 1240 \qquad\qquad \sum xy = 38\ 026$$
$$(1/n)(\sum x)^2 = \ 960 \qquad (1/n)(\sum x)(\sum y) = 36\ 448$$
$$\text{Denominator} = \ \overline{280} \qquad\qquad \text{Numerator} = \ \overline{1\ 578}$$

$$b = \frac{1578}{280} = 5.64$$

Calculations for *a*—see formula (7.4)

$$a = (\tfrac{1}{15})4556 - 5.64(\tfrac{1}{15})120$$
$$= 258.6$$

Regression equation

$$y = 258.6 + 5.64x$$

The regression calculations suggest that there is a steady increase in the trend for energy consumption of 5.64 (million tons of coal equivalent) per year. The dashed line showing the trend in Fig. 8.1 is in fact the line of the regression equation we have found. Extending the line, it can be seen from the graph that the forecast trend for 1975 is just under 350. Since we have identified no other consistent pattern in the figures, an extension of the trend line can be used as a forecast for the data in future years, accepting that the actual figures are likely to vary slightly and, as far as we are concerned, also randomly from the trend. The arithmetic equivalent to extending the trend line is to substitute the value of x for the year in question into the equation for the line. For 1975, $x = 16$, and putting this into the regression equation from Table 8.1 we have

$$y = 258.6 + 5.64 \times 16$$
$$= 349 \quad \text{(approximately)}$$

This confirms the estimate made by eye above.

There are, of course, problems with extrapolating trends, particularly with long-term time series. We are making the assumption that all the factors influencing the variable are going to continue, on balance, to exert the same influence in the future. This may not be so, and the assumption is more hazardous the further we go into the future. This is well illustrated by the example of energy consumption, where in recent years there have been some dramatic changes in the factors influencing energy consumption, notably the very large increases in the price of oil. With the benefit of hindsight we might guess that extrapolating the trend in consumption seen in the years our data covers would be unlikely to give a very accurate forecast of current energy consumption. This is indeed so, and using the equation (with $x = 20$) to forecast 1979 would give a figure of 371, compared to the actual of about 356. Where such changes can be foreseen, an extrapolated forecast can be adjusted. In any case such methods need to be used with caution.

Trends often show an upward *curve* rather than a straight line. This happens when a variable increases by a constant percentage amount, for instance, with each year's increase thus being slightly greater than the previous year's. This type of trend is called an *exponential trend* and represents the growth of many biological organisms as well as many economic time series. This type of curve is easy to fit using regression methods, since the logarithm of the

89

variable will show straight line growth over time, and we simply base our regression calculations on the logarithms instead of the original values. The trend values found by the equation are then changed back, using antilogarithms; an example of fitting this type of trend is given in the self-assessment questions with some explanation of the principles involved. Other types of curve may occur, and in particular any upward moving trend (especially an exponential one) is likely to eventually level out or even start coming down. There are statistical methods for fitting these more complicated shapes of trend, but they are of somewhat specialized application and beyond the scope of the present text.

8.2 Trend—moving average techniques

For short-term time series, although regression methods can be used, other techniques are usually more successful. This is because, in the short term, the trend is likely to change slightly from time to time. Thus, within an overall upward long-term trend, there may be short-term downward trends, perhaps extending over several months. The method of moving averages enables us to track these short-term fluctuations in the trend.

To illustrate the idea, suppose we want a simple three-monthly moving average for a sequence of monthly data. A part of the data might be as follows:

Month	Jan.	Feb.	Mar.	Apr.	May	June
Data	10	12	8	13	15	8

To find the average for the first three months we take the mean of the values $= \frac{1}{3}(10+12+8)=10$. The middle of the period is February and so we take our trend estimate as 10 for February. We then move the average forward one month and find the mean of the three months from February to April; these give an average of 11. This will be the trend estimate for March. Similarly, the moving average trend estimates for April and May are, respectively, 12 and 12, and then we run out of data. Calculation of a five-monthly moving average would follow much the same lines. First we average the five months from January to May to arrive at 11.6, which estimates the trend at the mid point, in this case March. Next we drop January from the average and include June to get an average of 11.2, the trend estimate for April; again we then run out of data for any further calculations. Clearly, for any period of moving average we will not get trend estimates for the first few and last few months of data available, with more estimates missing the longer the period of the moving average—this is one problem with the simple moving average method.

Another problem occurs if we take an even number of months for the moving average period. Suppose, for instance, that we took a four-monthly period with the above data. The average for January to April is 10.75, but the mid point of the period falls in between February and March, so effectively we have a trend estimate for the month running from the middle of February to the middle of March, which is not very convenient. The usual way round this problem is to take the mean of two successive moving averages. Thus the next four-monthly average would cover February to May and is 12. This average is centered midway between March and April, so taking the mean of the successive averages we obtain a trend estimate for March of $\frac{1}{2}(10.75+12)=11.375$. Strictly speaking, we no longer have a simple moving average, which is one where each month has an equal weighting. In fact, in this case, we have a five-month moving average where the first and last months have half the weighting of the other months. This is illustrated by restating the arithmetic as follows:

90

$$\tfrac{1}{2}(\text{first moving average}+\text{next moving average})=\frac{1}{2}\left(\frac{10+12+8+13}{4}+\frac{12+8+13+15}{4}\right)$$

$$=\frac{10+2\times12+2\times8+2\times13+15}{8}$$

$$=11.375$$

Since the period taken for a moving average is normally fairly long (typically 12 months), this does not present much of a problem. For shorter periods it is probably best to stick to odd periods.

The correct period to choose for a moving average depends on the data. It needs to be long enough to cancel out most of the random variations in the data but not so long that we lose significant changes in the short-term trend. For monthly data a reasonable compromise is usually about 12 months. This also has the advantage that any seasonal fluctuation (see later) is cancelled out. In general, if there is any regular cycling movement in the data about the trend, the moving average should be taken over a period which covers one complete cycle (e.g., from one peak to the next) or a multiple of this period.

To conclude this section we give an example of the application of this method to some sales data for a particular company. The calculations are shown in Table 8.2 and Fig. 8.2 illustrates the results. For simplicity we use quarterly data. Table 8.2 shows a suggested way of setting out the calculations and gives another illustration of the calculation of an even period (in this case four-quarterly) moving average. A twelve-monthly moving average would follow much the same lines.

Table 8.2

Year	Quarter	(1) Sales of chemical ('000 tons)	(2) Four-quarterly totals (at end points)	(3) Sums of successive totals	(4) Four-quarterly moving average (at mid points)
1968	1	15.1			
	2	15.0			
	3	17.6			15.9
	4	15.4	63.1		15.9
1969	1	15.9	63.9	127.0	15.9
	2	14.2	63.1	127.0	16.3
	3	18.2	63.7	126.8	16.9
	4	18.3	66.6	130.3	17.4
1970	1	17.5	68.2	134.8	17.8
	2	17.3	71.3	139.5	17.9
	3	18.2	71.3	142.6	17.9
	4	18.7	71.7	143.0	18.2
1971	1	17.2	71.4	143.1	18.8
	2	20.3	74.4	145.8	19.4
	3	20.1	76.3	150.7	20.0
	4	21.6	79.2	155.5	20.0
1972	1	18.4	80.4	159.6	19.7
	2	19.4	79.5	159.9	19.4
	3	18.7	78.1	157.6	
	4	20.4	76.9	155.0	

Notes. Column (1) gives the original data. Four-quarterly totals are given in column (2) positioned against the last quarter of the period to which they refer. Successive totals are summed to give column (3), and these are divided by eight to give the averages in column (4) (correct to one decimal), positioned at the months for which they give trend estimates. The brackets and arrows show the route by which the first moving average is calculated.

Figure 8.2 shows how the moving average tracks the trend through the data. The overall long-term trend seems to be upwards, but over the last few quarters the short-term trend is downwards. A major disadvantage of the moving average method is the difficulty in extrapolating the trend into the future. It can be done by eye, but this is not a very reliable method. Simply extending the last section of the trend would not always give a sensible forecast either. For instance, in this example it would seem to imply an underestimate, as there are signs that the trend may be starting to increase again. At any rate, there is no reliable automatic method for extrapolating a moving average; experience and judgement are the only real answer. This disadvantage can be surmounted to some extent by using a form of weighted moving average, as we shall see later. As a final note, the method of moving averages can be used for long-term data, but this approach is mainly used where there are clear fluctuations in the long-term trend. For cases where the trend appears to be fairly consistent, regression methods are usually preferable—especially where extrapolation is required.

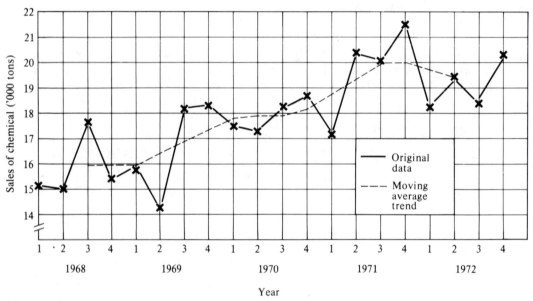

Figure 8.2

8.3 Trend—exponentially smoothed moving average

It is quite common to use *weighted moving averages*, where the data points making up an average are given unequal weights, although the weights must always add up to one. For determining the historical trend in some data, we might, for instance, give more weight to data near the middle of the period averaged. For forecasting purposes, however, a method that gives an estimate of the current trend would be more useful for extrapolation purposes. A simple way of doing this is to take as an estimate of the current trend a weighted average of the latest and preceding data values, with the weights decreasing as the data get older. This makes sense, as it seem reasonable to suppose that the older the data, the less influence they have on the current trend. This current trend estimate can then be used directly as a forecast for the next time period. The *exponentially smoothed moving average* employs this idea and also leads to a very simple method of calculating the trend.

We start by choosing a weighting factor, a, which lies between 0 and 1. The weights are then in sequence from the latest backwards:

$$a, a(1-a), a(1-a)^2, a(1-a)^3, \ldots$$

This forms a geometric progression, and can be shown to add to one, as required. If x_t, x_{t-1}, x_{t-2}, $x_{t-3}, \ldots$ are the latest and preceding data points for time periods $t, t-1, t-2, t-3, \ldots$, then the current trend estimate and forecast for time $t+1$ is written $\hat{x}_{t+1}$ and is found from

$$\hat{x}_{t+1} = ax_t + a(1-a)x_{t-1} + a(1-a)^2 x_{t-2} + a(1-a)^3 x_{t-3} + \cdots$$
$$= ax_t + (1-a)[ax_{t-1} + a(1-a)x_{t-2} + a(1-a)^2 x_{t-3} + \cdots]$$

The expression in square brackets is the forecast we would have made *last* period for the current period, that is, $\hat{x}_t$, so

$$\hat{x}_{t+1} = ax_t + (1-a)\hat{x}_t$$

Rearranging:

$$\hat{x}_{t+1} = \hat{x}_t + a(x_t - \hat{x}_t)$$

Putting this in words we have:

Forecast for next period = last forecast + a (error in previous forecast)   (8.1)

To illustrate the method we use the first few quarters of the chemical sales data given above, with $a = 0.2$ (see Table 8.3).

Table 8.3

(1) t	(2) x_t	(3) $\hat{x}_t$	(4) Error $(x_t - \hat{x}_t)$	(5) a × error $(a=0.2)$
1	15.1	15.1	0	0
2	15.0	15.1	−0.1	−0.02
3	17.6	15.08	+2.52	+0.50
4	15.4	15.58	−0.18	−0.04
5		15.54		

Notes. (1) $t=1$ is 1968 quarter 1. (2) The actual sales data for 1968. (3) To start off, we take the first forecast as equal to the first actual. (4) This is (2)−(3). (5) This is $0.2 \times (4)$, and is added to (3) to obtain the next entry in (3).

It is a worthwhile exercise, left to the reader, to continue this example up to the end of the data and find a forecast for the first quarter of 1973. A plot of the trend estimates given [column (3)] compared with the original data will show how this method tracks the trend. The particular advantage of this method is that it gives an automatic one-period-ahead forecast. Also, it is only necessary to retain the last actual and forecast figures to do so, which makes it particularly useful for computer applications, especially where many time series need to be forecast. For these reasons the method is very popular for business forecasting, for instance, of sales for stock control purposes.

One problem has been glossed over: the problem of choosing a value for the weighting factor *a*. Too large a value will cause the forecast to swing about too much unless the original data do not vary much from time to time. Conversely, too small a value will cause the trend estimate to respond slowly to real underlying changes. A value of about 0.2 is often used as a reasonable compromise. A common practice is to try several values on an historical run of data and see which seems to give the best results, for instance, by comparing the variances of the errors (see Chapter 7 for an example of this type of calculation).

Finally, it must be noted that the method as described is only suitable for data which show no seasonal fluctuation and for which there is no consistent upward (or downward) trend. In this latter case the method will give increasingly large under(over)-estimates as the forecast tries in vain to catch up with the data as they get further and further away. As an example use the method to forecast a simple increasing time series such as: 1,2,3,4,5, ... More sophisticated (but still simple to implement) methods exist to deal with these cases. There are also methods for automatically monitoring the forecasts, to ensure that they do not go out of control if, for instance, there is a sudden upward surge in the data leading to a sequence of underestimates, or the reverse. The interested reader is referred to one of the several excellent texts on forecasting methods to follow these up. This body of methods, based on the idea of the weighted moving average, has proved to be the most successful in many business applications, especially when the advantage of simplicity is taken into account.

8.4 Seasonal factors—additive and multiplicative methods

Many short-term time series display a regular cycling pattern about the trend over the course of the year, with some parts of the year always being above the trend and other parts always being below the trend. This is often, at least indirectly, influenced by the seasonal fluctuations in weather—this, for instance, would explain the marked seasonal variation in sales of such things as ice creams or umbrellas. Figure 8.3 illustrates quarterly energy consumption in the United Kingdom and shows a clear seasonal pattern, again influenced by the weather. Other time series are influenced by other factors which vary regularly with the seasons; examples are new car registrations, sales of turkeys, and house purchases. In most of the examples quoted the pattern is obvious, as are the reasons for it, but a surprising proportion of all short-term time series display some seasonal variation, for reasons that are not always at all obvious, although one might suspect that the weather and related natural cycles often play some part.

There are two main ways of estimating seasonal factors from historical data. The *additive model* assumes that each season has a constant difference from the trend; the *multiplicative model* assumes that each season has a constant ratio to the trend. We next illustrate the calculation of seasonal factors using both of these methods. The energy consumption figures relating to Fig. 8.3 are given in Table 8.4, which also includes a trend estimate using a centered four-quarterly moving average (the moving average derivation follows exactly the same lines as the example given in Table 8.2). For each quarter where a trend estimate is available the consumption figures have been differenced from the trend to give the seasonal differences.

To calculate the seasonal factors, the simplest method is to average the seasonal differences for each quarter as shown in Table 8.5. Averaging the seasonal differences for each quarter gives the mean figures shown. The positive and negative seasonal factors should cancel out over the year, but in general these means will not, as indeed is the case here. It is necessary to correct them, therefore, so that they do. Since in this case the means sum to -1.7, a correction

94

Table 8.4

Year	Quarter	(1) Total energy consumption (million tons coal equivalent)	(2) Centered four-quarterly moving average (trend)	(3) Seasonal differences (1)−(2)
1971	1	96		
	2	76		
	3	65	80.7	−15.7
	4	89	80.3	8.7
1972	1	90	80.9	9.1
	2	78	81.9	−3.9
	3	68	83.6	−15.6
	4	94	85.1	8.9
1973	1	99	87.7	11.3
	2	81	86.3	−5.3
	3	70	85.0	−15.0
	4	96	83.1	12.9
1974	1	87	82.9	4.1
	2	78	82.9	−4.9
	3	71		
	4	95		

Table 8.5

	Seasonal differences				
	Quarter				
	1	2	3	4	
Year 1971			−15.7	8.7	
1972	9.1	−3.9	−15.6	8.9	
1973	11.3	−5.3	−15.0	12.9	
1974	4.1	−4.9			
					Sum
Mean	8.2	−4.7	−15.4	10.2	−1.7
Correction	0.4	0.2	0.7	0.4	+1.7
Seasonal factor	8.6	−4.5	−14.7	10.6	0

of +1.7 is apportioned across the means, roughly in accordance with their magnitude (ignoring signs). This gives the seasonal factors in the bottom row which have the required property of summing to zero. The interpretation of these factors is that we estimate quarter 1 energy consumption to be 8.6 million tons above the trend, quarter 2 to be 4.5 below trend, and so on, on average. We can gauge how well our model fits the data by adding the seasonal factors to the trend estimates and comparing with the original data. This is done in Table 8.6, Fig. 8.3 giving a visual comparison. The difference between the model (trend + seasonal factor) and the original data is the *residual*, which as we have seen before stands for all the variation in the data (assumed random) that is not accounted for by our model. The variance of the residuals would give a numerical measure of the fit of the model to the data.

It is clear that the additive seasonal model fits these data very well. One notable discrepancy is the significant overestimate for the first quarter of 1974. It may be that there is a good reason

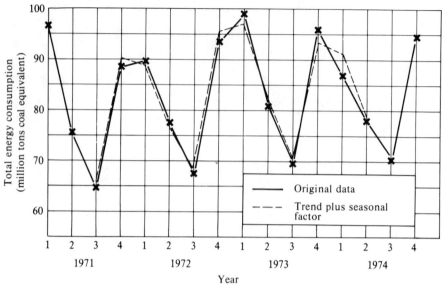

Figure 8.3

Table 8.6

Year	Quarter	(1) Original data (energy consumption)	(2) Trend	(3) Seasonal factor	(4) Model of data (2)+(3)	(5) Residual (1)−(4)
1971	3	65	80.7	−14.7	66.0	−1.0
	4	89	80.3	10.6	90.9	−1.9
1972	1	90	80.9	8.6	89.5	0.5
	2	78	81.9	−4.5	77.4	0.6
	3	68	83.6	−14.7	68.9	−0.9
	4	94	85.1	10.6	95.7	−1.7
1973	1	99	87.7	8.6	96.3	2.7
	2	81	86.3	−4.5	81.8	−0.8
	3	70	85.0	−14.7	70.3	−0.3
	4	96	83.1	10.6	93.7	2.3
1974	1	87	82.9	8.6	91.5	−4.5
	2	78	82.9	−4.5	78.4	−0.4

Note. The first two and the last two quarters of the data given in Table 8.4 have been omitted, since no trend values are available for these quarters.

for the abnormally low energy consumption of that quarter—e.g., unusually mild weather or a sharp rise in fuel costs. Where a discrepancy like this is explainable and not just random, allowance can be made in fitting the model so as not to bias the estimates in other quarters. This point will be discussed further in Sec. 8.6.

The multiplicative model for estimating seasonal factors assumes that seasonal variations from the trend are a constant percentage above or below, rather than a constant difference. Thus, as the trend increases, the seasonal swings get larger. To estimate the seasonal factors we take the *ratios* of the original data to their related trend values and average them out. To illustrate the method, we again use the energy consumption data and start by finding these

96

ratios. Using Table 8.4 we divide the figures in column (1) by the trend figures in column (2); thus the first quarter 3 ratio (for 1971) is $65 \div 80.7 = 0.81$, and so on. The calculation of the seasonal factors is then as shown in Table 8.7. In this case, since we are going to multiply by

Table 8.7

	Seasonal ratios				
	Quarter				
	1	2	3	4	
Year 1971			0.81	1.11	
1972	1.11	0.95	0.81	1.10	
1973	1.13	0.94	0.82	1.16	
1974	1.05	0.94			
					Sum
Mean	1.10	0.94	0.81	1.12	3.97
Correction	0.01	0.01		0.01	0.03
Seasonal factor	1.11	0.95	0.81	1.13	4.00

the seasonal factors, we must ensure that they average out at 1. In this example there are four factors, so they should sum to 4; a small correction apportioned across the means ensures that this is so and we arrive at the seasonal factors given in the bottom row of the table. The interpretation of the factors is that quarter 1 energy consumption is 11 per cent above trend, quarter 2 is 5 per cent below trend, and so on. As before, we can examine the fit of the model by combining the trend and seasonal factor estimates (this time by *multiplying* them) and comparing them with the original data. This is done in Table 8.8. A visual comparison is not given since it would be much the same as Fig. 8.3 for the additive model—the reader is encouraged to confirm this.

Table 8.8

Year	Quarter	(1) Original data (energy consumption)	(2) Trend	(3) Seasonal factor	(4) Model of data $(2) \times (3)$	(5) Residual $(1) - (4)$
1971	3	65	80.7	0.81	65.4	−0.4
	4	89	80.3	1.13	90.7	−1.7
1972	1	90	80.9	1.11	89.8	−0.2
	2	78	81.9	0.95	77.8	0.2
	3	68	83.6	0.81	67.7	0.3
	4	94	85.1	1.13	96.2	−2.2
1973	1	99	87.7	1.11	97.3	1.7
	2	81	86.3	0.95	82.0	−1.0
	3	70	85.0	0.81	68.9	1.1
	4	96	83.1	1.13	93.9	2.1
1974	1	87	82.9	1.11	92.0	−5.0
	2	78	82.9	0.95	78.8	−0.8

Note. It can be assumed that the residual is also a multiplicative factor, in which case it is found by *dividing* (1) by (4), and should average close to 1.

Again it is clear that this model gives a good fit to the data. In fact, comparing the residuals for the additive and multiplicative models, there is very little to choose between them. This is not surprising given the relatively short run of data over which they are being compared and the fairly modest changes in the trend over the period. Differences are only likely to be apparent if the time series includes a marked change in trend, which may require a long series of data.

We have not yet mentioned the use of seasonal factors in forecasting. The simplest method is to arrive at a trend estimate for the future period, using the appropriate method as discussed in previous sections, and correct it by adding (or multiplying by) the related seasonal factor. Thus, if we forecast a trend value for quarter 1 of 1975 as, say, 83.0, the seasonally corrected forecast would be $83.0 + 8.6 = 91.6$, using the additive model, or $83.0 \times 1.11 = 92.1$, using the multiplicative model (in case you are wondering, the actual figure was 93, so we are not far out!).

Just as with trends, we can also estimate seasonal factors using *weighted* averages. Thus, instead of taking the arithmetic mean of the available seasonal differences or ratios, we can take a weighted average. In some cases it is better to give more weight to the middle of the data; in other cases the more recent data are given a higher weight. As with trends, this latter approach is often used for forecasting, and again the method of exponentially smoothed moving averages can be applied to seasonal factors.

In this section we have concentrated on short-term data, but long-term data may also exhibit regular variations about the trend. These are usually referred to as *cycles*, and are analysed in much the same way as seasonal variation. As well as showing regular short-term variations the weather also has regularities in its long-term variation, often linked to the very regular variation in sun spot activity; this is likely to have an influence on some long-term series of data. There is also thought to be some regular cyclic behaviour in a number of economic time series, the result of the so-called 'business cycle'. However, the existence of these cycles is difficult to establish, since such a long series of data is necessary (perhaps a minimum of 30 years), and over such a long period there are likely to be many other short-term influences that will disturb any pattern. For this reason, the existence of such cycles in long-term time series is often a matter of controversy.

8.5 De-seasonalizing time series

One special use of seasonal factors occurs when the latest figure in a time series is regularly reported to give an idea of how things are currently going—in other words, to indicate the current trend in the series. Management regularly need this kind of information for controlling their business, and so do the government, who have the additional requirement to inform the public of what effect their policies are having. Merely reporting the latest figure as it arises may be seriously misleading in this respect, if it is part of a time series which shows a marked seasonal pattern. For this reason, such figures are often seasonally adjusted. The rationale for this is as follows:

$$\text{Let} \quad \begin{aligned} X &= \text{original data} \\ T &= \text{trend} \\ S &= \text{seasonal factor} \\ R &= \text{residual} \end{aligned}$$

Then, for the additive model:

$$X = T + S + R$$

So, given the latest value of X, an estimate of S, and assuming $R=0$ (the best we can do, given its randomness), we have:

$$T=X-S$$

This gives us a means of estimating the current value of T. For example, the quarter 1 energy consumption figure for 1975 was 93.0. At that time our estimate of the seasonal factor was 8.6, so we could have estimated the current trend as

$$T=93.0-8.6=84.4$$

Simply reporting that energy consumption for the quarter was 93 might have given the impression that there had been a dramatic increase, whereas the seasonally adjusted figure of 84.4 gives the truer picture of only a modest rise compared to 1974.

Similarly, if we use the multiplicative model, we have

$$X=T\times S+R$$

Thus, assuming $R=0$, we can estimate T from

$$T=X\div S$$

For example, our estimate of the multiplicative seasonal factor for quarter 1 is 1.11, so the current trend estimate would be

$$T=93.0\div1.11=83.8$$

The government use this type of approach in reporting several time series, for instance, the price index and the latest unemployment figures. The unemployment data are discussed in the next chapter; as explained there, what is essentially an additive approach is used in de-seasonalizing it.

8.6 Other factors

The trend and the seasonal or cyclic variation may not be the only explainable factors in a time series. Figure 8.4 illustrates some other types of variation which may occur in a time series.

Figure 8.4 (a) shows the impulse, the effect of an unusually high or low figure in a series. We saw the possibility of such a figure in the energy consumption data (quarter 1 of 1974). Impulses can be caused by unusual weather, strikes, special promotions, and many other factors which would be known. Where they occur, it is a good idea to smooth them out before analysing the data for trend or seasonal factors. This is often called 'prior adjustment', and can be done, for instance, by replacing the unusual figure by the average of the adjacent figures. This will prevent the trend or seasonal estimates from being biased by an atypical figure. It should be noted, however, that we ought only to do this when there is a reasonable explanation for the impulse—it could have arisen purely by chance, in which case it is questionable whether we should make such an adjustment. How, for instance, do we recognize an impulse if we have no reason for supposing that there might be one? There are sophisticated statistical techniques for detecting chance impulses which are unlikely to occur again, but in general it is a safer policy to err on the side of caution in making prior adjustments to data.

Figure 8.4 (b) and (c) illustrates a different type of variation which may occur in a time series. In practice there is not much difference between a step and a ramp; what we are

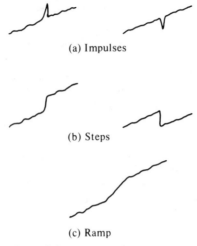

(a) Impulses

(b) Steps

(c) Ramp

Figure 8.4

observing is a fairly sudden uplift in the trend which then continues at the same rate as before but from a higher base. This type of phenomenon might be caused by a change in reporting method, the opening of a major new sales outlet, the negotiation of a major new contract, etc. With the same provisos as before, it would be a good idea to adjust the trend estimates to allow for the uplift when analysing the data. One problem with this type of change is that an upward step may be followed by a downward step. This regularly occurs, for instance, in the sales of alcoholic drinks, where a pre-budget or pre-Christmas uplift in trend is followed by a downward step. The reverse occurs when the taxes on tobacco are put up (this is sometimes known as the 'sulk' effect). It needs considerable experience of a time series to estimate the net effect of such shifts. In general, allowing for these kinds of variations is more subjective and calls for more judgement than is the case in estimating trend and seasonal fluctuation.

This concludes our coverage of some of the statistical methods available for analysing time series and forecasting. As a final word, we return to the statement made at the beginning of the chapter that time series analysis was useful in providing a *basis* for forecasting. As we have seen, subjective knowledge also plays a part, and the blind extrapolation of figures will not usually provide the best forecast. This is particularly true of long-term forecasting, where we are led to an even more fundamental criticism of extrapolation techniques blindly applied. It is, quite simply, why forecast at all? After all, if we are using a forecast for planning purposes, it only tells us what will happen if nothing changes, but planners in government and industry can take actions that will change the future. Should they not, therefore, be setting targets for what would be desirable in the future and making changes to achieve those targets rather than chasing trends?

9. Manpower statistics

Conventionally manpower statistics would include all data that relate to labour as a factor of production: such indicators as wages and earnings, labour productivity, employment and unemployment, etc. Much of these data is likely to serve as a basis for formulating company manpower policy which is generally taken to involve such things as recruitment, training, labour turnover, etc.

The present chapter, however, is concerned only with employment and unemployment statistics and related data, since the other measures have been dealt with elsewhere in the text. Section 9.1 deals with unemployment and vacancy statistics and Sec. 9.2 with employment data, concepts of the working population, and activity rates.

9.1   Unemployment and vacancies

Historically, unemployment figures have been taken as a general indication of the economic 'health' of a country and have played a significant part in determining national and regional economic policies. The economic impact of unemployment is, of course, the loss of potential output of goods and services due to one important factor of production (labour) being underutilized, together with the reduced spending (and therefore reduced demand) by those individuals and families affected by unemployment. However, the effects of unemployment are not simply confined to economic ramifications. At the personal level, for those people who find themselves out of work it is a very traumatic and distressing experience which, according to researchers, has many psychological side-effects for the individual and family, particularly where a person is unemployed for a long period of time. Politically, unemployment and the threat of unemployment is also significant since this, together with prices, are usually at the forefront of people's minds when voting takes place. Indeed, at the extreme, when mass unemployment occurs the whole of accepted institutions and democracy itself could be threatened as the mass of people become disenchanted with the economic and political system.

More specifically, the government and commentators will use the data for measuring the success or otherwise of national and regional economic policies, and as recent past experience shows, governments have changed both types of policy dramatically as a result of a marked upward trend in the official statistics of unemployment. Additionally, the statistics do fulfil an administrative function concerned with the employment and benefit services. The data are also likely to be used by businesses when determining manpower policy (recruitment, training, etc.) and are likely to be influential when relocation to another area is being considered.

In summary, then, the unemployment data reflect a desire to measure:

1. The social waste and distress associated with unemployment.
2. The economic waste associated with unemployment.
3. The excess labour capacity as a guide to economic policy by governments and manpower policy by companies.

Before the 'seventies most users of the information felt that the unemployment data were particularly 'hard' statistics, being both meaningful and reliable. However, during the last decade serious doubts and reservations have been expressed about the nature, reliability, and usefulness of the official published figures. This change in attitude may reflect two factors. First, there is a growing appreciation that with the establishment of a welfare state the full economic and social impacts of unemployment have been somewhat cushioned compared with the experience of the inter-war years. Second, and more importantly, the rapid rise of unemployment in the last few years has placed it, together with inflation, at the centre of the stage of controversy and concern. Naturally, in these circumstances a closer attention to the official estimates and a greater awareness of their shortcomings is the inevitable result.

Consequently, it is now suggested that unemployment data alone can only present a partial measure of the three problems outlined above. Thus, a measure of social waste will require, in addition to unemployment, such indicators as early retirement, low pay, health, etc., while economic waste will additionally require information on incomes, output, employment, and vacancies. As a measure of excess labour capacity, other statistics relating to labour hoarding, unfilled vacancies, etc., will also be required.

Despite this growing awareness that the unemployment data have to be qualified and, in most cases, have to be combined with other measures, nevertheless sufficient has been said to indicate the importance of unemployment statistics. It is the one key economic indicator. Its social, political, and physiological effects have been mentioned but cannot be developed any further in a book of this nature, although it does serve to illustrate the great importance attached to unemployment and the necessity of having as meaningful a measure as possible.

Recording and publishing the data

The complete range of unemployment statistics are collected by the Department of Employment and results are published in the *Employment Gazette*.[8] Essentially, the data are by-products of the administrative system since those people out of work would be encouraged to register as unemployed at local employment offices and youth employment offices, first, to increase their chances of obtaining work and, second, to obtain unemployment benefit. The published data therefore simply stem from analysing the records of those people who register as unemployed. Thus the most familiar unemployment statistic is the so-called monthly 'count' in which all the employment offices throughout the country total up the number of people who are registered as unemployed on the day of the count. However, two important qualifications have to be made. First, not all those who register will be included in the monthly count, although for certain recognized groups, separate figures are presented. Second, inclusion on the register and therefore in the count is not dependent on the payment and receipt of unemployment benefit. There will be some people therefore who will be included in the data even though they are not receiving unemployment benefit. Let us look at these two qualifications in more detail.

Those registered as unemployed but nevertheless excluded from the unemployment total are classified under several headings:

1. Those 'temporarily stopped'.
2. Those claiming unemployment benefit but registered only for part-time work (defined as less than 30 hours a week).
3. Severely disabled people.

4. Adult students seeking vacation work.
5. School leavers aged under 18.

Additionally, where an unemployed person is ill for more than a few days then he would be removed from the register and not included in the count since, although unemployed, he would not be available for work.

By making these exclusions the resulting unemployment total may be a more useful figure since it would refer to those people who are:

1. What might be called wholly unemployed.
2. Seeking full-time employment.
3. Not severely handicapped, which would otherwise present major difficulties in obtaining employment.

Figures are published separately for adult students, school leavers under 18, disabled persons, and those 'temporarily stopped'. The latter refers to those who are suspended by their employers (perhaps because of bad weather or industrial disputes), are claiming benefit, but who should resume work with the same employer shortly.

Additionally, there are a small proportion of unemployed who remain registered but have been disqualified from receiving benefit mainly due to the continued refusal to accept what is deemed as being suitable work.

The range of data provided tends to be on a monthly or quarterly basis. Monthly published information includes:

1. Total registered unemployed.
2. Temporarily stopped.
3. School leavers aged under 18.
4. Adult students seeking vacation work.
5. Disabled persons.
6. Duration of unemployment up to and over four weeks.
7. Married women.

Quarterly published data include:

1. Detailed duration of unemployment cross classified by age.
2. Industry in which last worked.
3. Occupation sought.
4. Minority group workers.

In addition, annual information is published for minority group workers by age and a detailed analysis of disabled persons by age and duration is also published annually. Finally, practically all this information is broken down into males and females and into local areas and standard regions.

The published statistics are in the form of absolute values and unemployment 'rates'. Although in the United Kingdom more attention is generally placed on the absolute total and changes in that total each month, where local area, regional, or international comparisons are being made it is more meaningful to use the unemployment 'rate'. The problem with this measure, however, is that it could differ, in some cases quite markedly, according to the definitions used for the numerator and denominator. This is clearly a serious problem where international comparisons are being made since it is unlikely that identical definitions would be used since each country would have its own customs, conventions, and practice. In the United Kingdom, for conventional rather than conceptual reasons, the unemployment rate is taken as the total registered unemployed (excluding the categories mentioned earlier), expressed as a percentage of the total number of employees in employment plus the registered unemployed, i.e.,

$$\frac{\text{Registered unemployed}}{\text{Employees in employment} + \text{registered unemployed}} \times 100$$

Not only is this practice likely to differ from other countries but it is presumptuous to assume that the U.K. definition is more accurate or meaningful. A whole range of alternative approaches could be justified as being more appropriate according to what uses the statistics are being put. However, a fuller examination of this difficulty will be left to the section dealing with interpretation problems later in the chapter.

The unemployment data, then, is a by-product of the administrative system which includes the employment offices (Jobcentres) and the benefit services. This system and the resulting data have remained substantially unaltered for many years but at the time of writing (1981) proposals have been made* which, if accepted by the Government, would alter the arrangements for payment of unemployed benefit and therefore the basis for the published data.

From the data viewpoint the most significant proposal is that entitlement to unemployment benefit, for those over 18, should not depend on registering as unemployed at Jobcentres; in other words, the introduction of voluntary registration. It follows that if this proposal is introduced then the monthly count from these employment offices would be less satisfactory since they would only have records of those who voluntarily register as unemployed. Consequently, the unemployment data will have to be based on the benefit side of the system, i.e., the records of the Unemployment Benefit Offices (UBOs). In this case the subsequent published unemployment data will relate only to those who are receiving unemployment benefit compared with the current system operating which is based on the unemployment register at employment and career offices as described earlier.

The result of this change would be to lower the unemployment totals, since there would be some currently on the unemployment register who are not receiving unemployment benefit. However, estimates suggest that the recorded total would be reduced by only about 50 000 compared with the present system.

Other effects would be that severely disabled people and the unemployed sick would be included in the recorded measure, since it would not be possible for the UBO to distinguish these groups. At present both these unemployment categories are excluded.

In terms of the detailed published analysis, information on unemployment by last industry will have to be discontinued and the occupational analysis and measure of the unemployed disabled people will be based only on voluntary registration at employment offices. The quality of these two sets of data will therefore be of a lower order than is currently available.

If these proposals become policy then there will clearly be a discontinuity in the recorded measure of unemployment and should be carefully noted by users.

Seasonal adjustment   The published figures for totals and rates of unemployment, excluding

---

* By a team of officials set up by the Secretaries of State for Employment and Social Services, whose report was published in March 1981.

school leavers, are further modified to take into account seasonal influences. This is referred to as seasonal adjustment and the modified figures are described as being seasonally adjusted.

Many economic and business indicators do have noticeable seasonal characteristics and it is common in these circumstances to eliminate, as far as possible, the seasonal element so that underlying trends can be more readily identified. With unemployment, for example, it is noticeable that higher levels are recorded in the winter months compared with the summer months and therefore when unemployment does rise in the winter we wish to know whether this reflects a real underlying upward trend in unemployment or simply reflects the normal seasonal characteristics.

Any seasonal characteristic involves two component parts: first, the pattern of events, i.e., the time period when values are high and when values are low (winter and summer months, for example, with regard to unemployment), and, second, the magnitude of that pattern, i.e., how high and low the values are. These can be derived statistically from past experience and then applied to the raw data. The standard technique used is moving average which is covered in Chapter 8. There it is noted that the method involves either the additive or multiplicative approach. The additive assumes the seasonal factor to be constant whatever the level of unemployment, while the multiplicative approach assumes the seasonal factor will vary according to the level of unemployment. The former is therefore measuring simply the seasonal differences, while the latter is measuring the seasonal ratios. In terms of U.K. published data the statisticians use the moving average technique to estimate the trend and for most data adopt the additive approach. However, two modifications to the basic technique are made.

First, although several years of data are analysed so that the seasonal factor can be estimated, the most recent years are felt to be more relevant and are therefore given more weight than the earlier years.

Second, some adjustment to the basic data is made when irregular events occur which distort the underlying pattern. The obvious examples here would be such things as abnormally bad weather or industrial disruption, strikes, etc.

Interpreting the published statistics

At the beginning of this chapter it was pointed out that two of the major reasons for collecting unemployment data are to measure the economic waste associated with unemployment and to indicate excess labour capacity. The critics of the published data argue that, by and large, they fail to measure either. Some commentators argue that the official measure of unemployment seriously understates the true situation, while others argue that the true level of unemployment is substantially lower than the official figures. This may, at first, appear to be a surprising dichotomy of views, but as in most cases involving the application of official statistics it may simply reflect differences in the usage of the data. These opposing views will first be presented.

The understatement assertion   This is based on the argument that the registered unemployed form only a part of total spare labour capacity. One would also have to include those workers who are not being fully employed, e.g., in a situation where two workers are actually doing the job of one worker. This is referred to as labour hoarding and the main economic justification would seem to be the cost and disruption associated with firing and then re-hiring labour as demand increases. Logically one of these workers should be included in the unemployed category but both would officially be employed. The second category of unemployed who

105

would not be included in the official register would be all those people who wish to obtain employment but do not actually go along to register, possibly because they feel there is little chance of obtaining employment. This is referred to as 'concealed unemployment', the major group affected being likely to be married women interested in part-time work.

Thus a measure of spare labour capacity should include (1) registered unemployed, (2) labour hoarding, and (3) concealed unemployment. Since only the registered unemployed are actually measured it follows that the true levels of unemployment in the economy are substantially higher than the published figures.

The overstatement assertion The counter argument to the above asserts that the official figures for unemployment overstates the true position. This case rests on a number of arguments.

First, the claim is made that many people on the register are virtually unemployable. This may reflect a conscious preference to remain out of work (the so-called 'work shy' case), although for others it may reflect the psychologically debilitating effect of long-term unemployment such that it may become extremely difficult to find employment for these people. Whatever the reasons, it is argued that even if the economy improved there would always be a hard core of unemployed who would be virtually impossible to place.

Second, it is pointed out that given all the provisions of the welfare state today the economic hardship associated with unemployment is far less, for example, than it was in the 'thirties and earlier. The welfare state has therefore cushioned the full economic effects of unemployment and along with it has lessened the associated social stigma. It is also claimed that there has been a substantial growth in recent years of people registered as unemployed but actually working in the so-called 'black economy' where employment and earnings are not declared. This, of course, is illegal and its extent is difficult to estimate, but its effect would again be to reduce the economic and social effects of unemployment. In summary, then, this second argument suggests that it is a distortion of the facts to equate the misery and hardship of unemployment in the 'thirties with unemployment in the 'seventies and 'eighties.

Third, the point is made that many on the unemployment register remain unemployed for only a relatively short period of time—a short interval between leaving one job and obtaining another. Economists describe this element as 'frictional' unemployment since it reflects the fact that the labour market (and indeed all other markets) is not a perfect one in the sense that instantaneous adjustments are not possible. It follows therefore that despite all governments in the United Kingdom making 'full' employment a major economic objective, at least since 1945, it is simply not possible to obtain zero unemployment. At any point in time there will be some people in between jobs. A proportion of the total registered unemployed should therefore be considered as a constantly changing 'pool' of unemployed with people entering and leaving the register. Moreover, it is suggested that the ill-effects of high levels of unemployment would be exaggerated if it was associated with a much more rapid turnover. It is a moot point whether higher unemployment levels and shorter average duration of unemployment is better or worse than a lower unemployment level but longer average duration of unemployment. One thing is certain, however, and that is the necessity to consider measures of unemployment other than the monthly count. On its own the count cannot shed much light on these other important characteristics of the labour market.

The contentious point with this third argument is the definition of 'short duration'. Just how short is short? Most analysts make the assumption that frictional unemployment is represented by those people who remain on the register for up to and including four weeks. Despite its

106

obvious arbitrariness, if we accept this view then at a recent count 15.9 per cent of total registered unemployed would refer to the frictionally unemployed.[13]

It is left to the reader to decide the merits and demerits of these two opposing views. It would seem that both sets of arguments contain some element of truth and the marked disagreement may simply reflect the published data being put to different uses. It is a constant theme in this book that the definitions used for official economic and business indicators may be suitable for some analyses but inappropriate for others. For the reader, the important lesson of this dispute is that the official measure of unemployment must be treated with some caution. The older view that the unemployment 'count' is a reliable and 'hard' statistic is seriously questioned.

Other weaknesses and interpretation difficulties associated with unemployment data are also apparent.

Flow statistics   It is clear that since the measure of registered unemployment takes place on one day each month then we have a series of 'stock' counts throughout the year. This static approach ignores the real dynamic nature of the labour market where each month many thousands of people would be entering and leaving the register. Possibly as a result of the pressure for additional information on this aspect of the labour market, in the early 'seventies the Department of Employment began publishing in the *Employment Gazette* so-called 'flow statistics', both for unemployment and unfilled vacancies.

Unemployment flow statistics record the new people joining the register since the last stock count (referred to as the inflow) and the numbers who have left the register since the last count (the outflow). Naturally the difference between the inflow and outflow would represent the differences in the stock count from one month to another. Thus if inflows exceeded outflows during any month by, say, 20 000, then the monthly count (the stock count) for that month would show an increase of unemployment of 20 000 compared with the previous month's stock count. In other words, the following identities are established:

$$\text{Inflow} - \text{outflow} = \text{net change in stocks} = \text{closing stock} - \text{opening stock}$$

which could also be presented in the following way:

$$\text{Inflow} + \text{opening stock} = \text{outflow} + \text{closing stock}$$

The value for the inflow comes from a direct recording of the total registration between the stock counts, while the outflow has to be derived from the available information. A consideration of the second identity above indicates how this is done. This could be rewritten as:

$$\text{Inflow} + \text{opening stock} - \text{closing stock} = \text{outflow}$$

Thus the outflow can be derived by summing the inflow and opening stock and subtracting the closing stock.

It should be apparent that some people would appear in the flow statistics but not in the monthly count if they joined and then left the register in the interval between two stock counts. Additionally, it should be noted that the inflow is measuring registrations rather than people entering the register since it is possible to register more than once between the count dates. In practice, the number of people who do just this is likely to be a small proportion of the total new registrations but its significance lies in the fact that there is a conceptual difference

107

between the flow and the stock measurements. The flow measurement refers to registration, while the stock measurement refers to people.

Two interesting aspects of the functioning of the labour market have been highlighted with the introduction of flow statistics.

First, it establishes that even with very high unemployment levels there are substantial numbers of people who are successful in obtaining employment. Moreover, the outflow figures show remarkable stability from one month to another and one year to another, despite marked difference in the unemployment totals. For example, the monthly outflows recorded during 1979 ranged from 254 700 (October 1979, the lowest outflow) to 278 900 (December 1979, the highest outflow), while in 1973 the range was 282 700 (October 1973) to 315 800 (January 1973), despite the fact that unemployment in 1973 was substantially less than in 1979. A similar constancy is found with the inflow statistics, where in 1979 they ranged from 257 100 (May 1979) to 290 600 (December 1979), compared with 269 000 (September 1973) to 289 000 (January 1973).

Second, it is noticed that on many occasions changes in the flow statistics have occurred just before an upturn or downturn in the unemployment levels. Just prior to an upturn in unemployment a rise in inflows are generally recorded, while a marked fall in inflows is a general indication of a fall in unemployment shortly afterwards. However, this relationship is not conclusive enough to be used as a definite predictor, although it may be used to confirm that a significant change in the underlying trend of unemployment has taken place.

Rates and levels   It was noted earlier that the unemployment data record both absolute totals and percentage rates, and despite the emphasis in the United Kingdom on totals, area, regional, and international comparisons are best made using unemployment rates since the size of the population or working population would differ. Although more appropriate, the difficulty with rates is that many alternative values could be calculated depending on how the numerator and denominator are defined. Again it was noted that in this country the numerator is based on those registered as unemployed, while the denominator includes employees in employment plus the registered unemployed. The assumption is therefore made that a reasonable measure of the total potential workforce would include those actually in employment and those seeking employment.

This might appear to be a reasonable approach and would be suitable for much analysis. However, alternative definitions could be used and may be more appropriate for some analyses. For example, one could include in the denominator either all or some of the following: the self-employed, the employers, members of the armed forces, and those unemployed but seeking part-time employment. This list indicates the difficulty of making international comparisons based on unemployment rates for the scope for differences in definition is quite wide. However, among Western industrial nations three definitions appear to be favoured: civilian labour force (the United States, Canada, Australia, Spain, Sweden, and Switzerland), total labour force (Denmark and Japan), and total employees and registered unemployed (the United Kingdom, West Germany, Netherlands, and Austria).

Additional comparison difficulties stem from different procedures in collecting the unemployment data. Many countries conduct labour force surveys (e.g., the United States), while others, including the United Kingdom, rely on the administrative system.

Finally, there is a wide variance internationally in the coverage of the unemployed (the numerator). The United Kingdom and the United States differ markedly in their treatment of (1) those unemployed but temporarily sick, (2) adult students seeking work, (3) those temporarily stopped, with the United Kingdom excluding these categories and the United States including them.

The problem with rates, particularly where international comparisons are concerned, can therefore be seen to include (1) possible differences in collection method, (2) possible differences in the numerator, and (3) possible differences in the denominator. It obviously follows that unemployment rate differences between countries could be partly explained by the difference in coverage, and any analytical treatment would have to carefully consider the coverage and definitions used.

Local area data Before the early 'seventies local area unemployment data were based on employment office areas, but for many the published data were probably misleading. This resulted from the growing tendency of people to travel further distances to their normal place of work, probably due to the increase in ownership of motor vehicles and a desire to live in a cleaner environment, well away from industrial connurbations. The difficulty arises when these people are made redundant, since they are likely to register at their local employment office which therefore inflates local unemployment figures although the redundancy occurred in another area. Moreover, it may be that with little local employment opportunities the individual expects to obtain employment outside the local area but for convenience registers locally. Clearly, in these circumstances, many local unemployment rates are likely to be distorted, with those from areas consisting mainly of dwellings being overstated and those from areas containing mainly offices and factories being understated.

To counter this weakness the Department of Employment introduced 'travel-to-work areas' for which unemployment rates are published. Each one of these areas would therefore include both residential and workplace such that they represent as far as possible local labour markets.

Unemployment and vacancies Finally, for most labour market analyses unemployment data on their own are insufficient since a 'market' includes both demand and supply. Thus both unemployment and unfilled vacancies are required, with the former indicating labour supply and the latter indicating labour demand. Thus the true level of excess labour supply would be total unemployment *less* unfilled vacancies, while excess demand for labour would be where unfilled vacancies exceed unemployment.

Although one can appreciate the logic of the argument that vacancies should be combined with unemployment to present a clearer picture of the total labour market there are, in practice, many difficulties with following this approach. We will examine these difficulties in the following section on vacancy statistics.

Vacancy statistics

These statistics are published in the *Employment Gazette*[8] from information collected by the Manpower Service Commission's local employment offices, the Professional and Executive Recruitment Offices, and the careers offices of Local Education Authorities. The monthly published data include:

> Notified unfilled vacancies at employment offices
> Notified unfilled vacancies at careers offices

109

while the quarterly data include:

> Occupational analysis (excluding vacancies at careers offices)
> Industry analysis at employment offices
> Industry analysis at careers offices

Regional breakdown of the data is also presented and, as mentioned earlier, flow statistics of vacancies are also published.

Interpreting the data   There are several problems involved in applying and interpreting the vacancy statistics. Undoubtedly, the biggest difficulty arises from the fact that the published data records only about one-third of total unfilled vacancies. The reason is that employers are not obliged to use the employment offices in order to obtain workers. Many jobs are filled through the work of private employment agencies, or through newspaper advertisements, or advertising at the factory gate, or even by 'word of mouth'.

The substantial under-recording might suggest that it would not be suitable for any sort of analysis, and certainly the suggestion earlier that a combination of vacancy and unemployment data would measure the excess demand for, or supply of labour must be held in considerable doubt. However, a case will be made out later that the statistics can still be useful although any conclusions would have to bear in mind this basic weakness.

There is also some ambiguity in the vacancy statistics which is not present in the unemployment data. Given the growing tendency in certain occupations for having to give notice before leaving an employer, one week, one month, or in some professions three months, then the employer could very well advertise the vacancy while the individual was serving out his notice. The result, of course, is that while this individual would be recorded as being employed his job would be recorded as a vacancy. Thus a person could be both employed and an unfilled vacancy, compared with the unemployment statistics where no ambiguity arises since a person would either be employed or unemployed.

This conceptual problem is further exacerbated by the growing practice of employers to forecast future labour turnover, which means that vacancies are advertised before the job becomes vacant. Further, as they are forecasts this implies that employers are not really certain how many jobs will require filling in the future although they advertise situations now. The fact that the data may not represent genuine vacancies or may under-report vacancies suggests a further interpretation problem, although the Department of Employment claim that such errors are not likely to be large.

Another limitation of the data would include the likelihood that some of the unfilled vacancies are virtually 'unfillable', or difficult to fill, because of low pay, unsocial hours, or poor working conditions, etc.

Some problems encountered reflect more a misinterpretation of the data rather than its limitations. For example, simply deducting unfilled vacancies from registered unemployment to arrive at a measure of excess labour demand or supply ignores the fact that the unemployed and vacancies may not 'match'. The unemployed could largely consist of unskilled labour while the unfilled vacancies require skilled workers (or the unemployed may not have the appropriate skills). In addition, even if they did match occupationally, the bulk of the vacancies may be in the south while the unemployed are likely to be found in the north of the country. Thus any 'mis-match' may reflect both occupational and spatial differences.

In these circumstances the correct procedure would be to analyse the regional, industrial,

110

and occupational breakdown of the total unfilled vacancies. As mentioned above, these data are available on a quarterly basis.

Uses of the data   Despite all these limitations the data may still serve a useful purpose in indicating the trends in unfilled vacancies and, when combined with unemployment, the overall trends in the labour market. The major noticeable trend established is the inverse relationship between unemployment and vacancies—when unemployment is low unfilled vacancies are generally high (representing a buoyant economy) and when unemployment is high vacancies are generally low (a depressed economy). However, it is certain that the absolute values given are inaccurate and therefore the results of any analysis using these measures must be held in doubt.

Once again, the warning is made that given these limitations one has to handle the data on unfilled vacancies with considerable caution.

9.2 Employment

Using data to establish employment characteristics of an economy can play an important part in many areas of decision-making and government policy. For example, identification of the employment growth industries would suggest the sort of industries that should be encouraged to relocate in the less prosperous areas as part of regional policy. The data can also serve as the denominator in productivity measurements. Thus the output of establishments would be related to the numbers employed. Such productivity measures, as we have seen, are relevant for incomes policies, collective bargaining, employment and regional policies, etc.

In more general terms, employment information can be used as a general indicator of the buoyancy of a country's economy, and in this sense is used as an alternative to production statistics or unemployment data. A country going into recession is likely to exhibit an upward trend in unemployment and a downward trend in full-time employment and production.

In addition, employment data are central to many debates, the most recent being the concern with the 'de-industrialization of Britain'. Here the claim by many commentators is that the fall, in recent years, of manufacturing employment reflects a permanent change rather than one associated with the temporary world-wide recession, and is linked to the very rapid introduction of technology—particularly the microchip. Clearly, in this debate employment information would be vital.

The published data

The range of employment data is published by the Department of Employment in the *Employment Gazette*[8] and records information under the heading, 'employees in employment'. However, a major change in the collection procedure took place in 1971, resulting from a change in the administrative system which did not alter the terminology (employees in employment) but effectively altered its definition. The significance of this change can best be established by considering both systems.

The system, 1948–1971: 'the card count'   Employment data in this period were obtained from a count of national insurance cards. All workers had these cards (with a few exceptions like

111

civil servants and post office employees) which showed the national insurance contribution made by each worker in the form of monthly national insurance stamps. In practice, the employing company would make the arrangements to purchase the appropriate stamp and maintain the card up to date. Since each card lasted for 12 months and were issued by the Department of Health and Social Security (DHSS) each quarter throughout the year, it followed that one in four cards would be exchanged at the DHSS each quarter (March, June, September, and December). It was when these cards were exchanged that the count was made, but since only a proportion of cards would be exchanged each quarter then the resulting published figures would clearly be estimates. The card count actually showed the total employees rather than the employees in employment, since some of those cards counted would actually relate to unemployed persons. Thus, from the card count the number of unemployed had to be deducted, the result being an estimate of employees in employment.

'Voluntary survey'   The data were therefore published on a quarterly basis, but not in a great deal of detail for the March, September, and December quarters. For the June quarter, in addition to the card count, a voluntary survey was conducted for all those employers with five or more workers. Among the information requested was the number of cards *held* by the employer at the beginning of June, thereby obtaining a more accurate measure. Greater detail was thus presented for this quarter, including an analysis of employment by sex, by industry, by local area, and by standard region.

The system since 1971   The new system introduced in 1971 resulted from a decision by the government in the late 'sixties to phase out national insurance cards and replace them with deductions at source in the pay as you earn (PAYE) scheme, with administrative responsibility being transferred from the DHSS to the Inland Revenue. Consequently, the source of employment data disappeared and a new system had to be established.

The decision was made to expand the previous voluntary survey held in June by introducing a more comprehensive and obligatory (under the 1947 Statistics of Trade Act) census of employment conducted in June each year. The first official census took place in 1971 after two 'pilot' surveys—a partial one in 1969 and a more complete trial in 1970.

The employment census   The census takes the form of a postal enquiry, with the Inland Revenue supplying the addresses from which employers send PAYE payments. For those companies with more than one factory or office, separate information is requested for each address. In the case where one address undertakes more than one kind of activity separate information is required for each type so that a proper industrial classification of employment can be made. These reporting unit difficulties have already been discussed in the chapter dealing with the census of production (Chapter 4) and therefore shall not detain us here.

At each address information is obtained for total employment, male and female, full time, and part time (defined as those normally employed for 30 hours or less per week). In addition, details of the business activity at each address is requested. Employers are asked to include all of their employees, under the above categories, who were working on the census day in June plus those workers who would normally be working but were absent due to such things as illness, holidays, stoppages, etc. Part-time workers who were not present on the day of the count but who would normally be working on other days in the census week were also to be included. The published data include the following:

Employees in employment:
Male and female:
Full-time
Part-time

Male:
Full-time
Part-time

Female:
Full-time
Part-time

An industrial and regional classification is also published.

Comparison of the two systems

It was asserted earlier that the change in procedure in 1971 effectively altered the definition of employees in employment. This resulted from a basic conceptual difference between the two systems and some differences in the coverage. Whether the published figures since 1971 are more accurate and meaningful is a debatable point, bearing in mind that the change was a result of the introduction of a new administrative system rather than an attempt to improve the quality of the published figures. Tentative answers to this question will be reserved until after a fuller discussion of the major differences of the two approaches.

Since each member of the workforce (including those unemployed) would have only one national insurance card it follows that the former card count system was actually measuring people in their main employment. This stands in contrast to the census approach because the Inland Revenue would have details of an individual's earnings and employer details in his main and any additional employment—always assuming that these additional (part-time) jobs are actually declared. Thus the former system would count each employee once only, and related to their main job of work, while the census would count each person in terms of the number of jobs they do. The difference, then, is that the card count measured people whereas the census measures 'jobs'.

This conceptual difference is unlikely, in practice, to have a significant effect on the total figures for employment, particularly since separate data are presented for full-time and part-time employees in employment. In addition, many supplementary jobs are unlikely to be declared and would therefore go unrecorded. However, for those industries and occupations which tend to employ people supplementing their full-time earnings with part-time work (many service sector categories, for example), the published data are likely to show an increase in the numbers employed; this might reflect a real growth in employment in these sectors or may simply reflect the new procedure which makes it possible for the first time to record these jobs.

Invariably a result of changes in procedure is some change in the coverage. This is so with employment figures, where from 1971 certain categories of employment have been excluded.

The major group affected are domestic servants in private households. The decision to exclude these workers from the census stemmed from the experience gained in the pilot

113

surveys conducted prior to 1971, which highlighted the difficulty of obtaining information from private households and the necessity of sending the forms to private addresses. The final card count in 1971 showed that there were approximately 90 000 of these domestic servants.

Other people excluded are those working in their own homes, pensioners who are working, self-employed, working proprietors, and directors; it should be noted that most of these would not have been included in the employees in employment category under the former system either.

However, a further group that would have been included formerly but are unlikely to be counted under the census are the so-called 'part-year' workers. This is because these workers had to exchange their national insurance cards whether they were working or not, whereas they are only included in the census if they are working during the census week. Many of these part-year workers are students doing seasonal jobs and are therefore unlikely to be working at the time of the census.

A further point that should be noted is that a complete census is not conducted every year; in some years those employers with less than three employees will not be approached for information, although the numbers involved are estimated using the most recent full census.

Given these differences in coverage, and to aid analysts attempting to make pre and post 1971 data comparable, it was decided that both approaches would be conducted and published in 1971. Thus in that year the last card count and first official census took place. In the event the estimates from the census were appreciably lower than the estimates based on the card count. This result was expected, given the exclusions mentioned above and despite the fact that jobs rather than people are being measured under the new system.

Interpreting the data

It is difficult to say conclusively which of the two systems produces more reliable and more useful results. The exclusion of certain categories from the census, particularly domestic servants, is an obvious weakness, although it is probable that many people not actually working would nevertheless have been included as employees in employment with the card count system (the 'part-year' workers, for example). It may be that while the census understates employment levels the card count almost certainly exaggerated the true levels.

Basically, however, the fundamental question is whether the card count or census produces more meaningful and useful results. Once again, there is, unfortunately, no definitive answer: for some analyses the older system would have been more appropriate, while for other analyses the census procedure is more suitable. This would clearly reflect the conceptual differences between the two approaches in which the card count measured people in employment compared with the census which effectively measures jobs being performed.

Accepting that we cannot state conclusively that the census is superior to the card count— it would depend on the type of analysis being undertaken—we can be rather more certain with regard to local area and regional figures. These are likely to be far more accurate, and perhaps therefore more useful, since 1971 than under the former system. The explanation is that under the former system there was a growing tendency of companies to exchange cards centrally (i.e., for all or most of their branch factories), which created difficulties for classifying employment on a regional and local area basis, while under the census system information on employment is required from each address.

114

Other published data on employment

Although the annual census is a comprehensive exercise, producing detailed information of employment on a regional and industrial basis, the fact that it is conducted just once each year may be limiting for certain types of analysis. Furthermore, given its comprehensive nature, a period of a year usually elapses between carrying out the census and publishing the results. Both the delay in publishing and the annual approach obviously presents difficulties for decision makers requiring more frequent and up-to-date information. Consequently, in addition to the annual census, quarterly and monthly estimates of employees in employment are also published.

The published estimates are based on sample enquiries and like the census they are obtained under the 1947 Statistics of Trade Act whereby selected firms are obliged to complete the questionnaire. In both the quarterly and monthly surveys a stratified sample approach is taken, which means that results are obtained from a range of different sized companies.

The published data include both regional and industrial analyses although the monthly estimates relate only to the index of production industries: the manufacturing sector plus mining and quarrying, gas, electricity, and water, and construction.

Naturally, where estimates are based on sample surveys there is some doubt about the degree of accuracy of the results—all the problems, in fact, of 'sample statistics'. Consequently, the quarterly and monthly published estimates are periodically revised as the results of the most recent annual census become known. Thus the annual census plays an important role in providing a 'benchmark' for the monthly and quarterly estimates.

The working population

For many types of analysis a wider measure of the workforce than is given by employees in employment plus registered unemployed may be required. An estimate of the working population may be more useful, for example, in calculating certain types of productivity measurements, or for calculating unemployment rates, or for measuring activity rates (defined and explained below). Estimates of the working population are published quarterly in conjunction with the annual employment census and the quarterly sample survey. It comprises the following categories:

> Employees in employment + self-employed persons (with or without employees)
>   = civil employment
> + HM Forces = employed labour force
> + unemployed = working population

The sub-totals shown could be used as alternatives to the working population in any analysis and their precise definition is evident. Thus the employed labour force would include employees in employment, the self-employed, and HM Forces. By adding the registered unemployed we would arrive at an estimate of the working population.

As noted, the employees in the employment category are obtained from the annual employment census and quarterly sample survey; the figure for HM Forces is provided by the Ministry of Defence; while the unemployment data are obtained from the appropriate monthly count of registered unemployed. The remaining category, the self-employed, presents the greatest difficulty since the only direct measure comes from the census of population which is infrequently conducted. Consequently, the estimates for this group are based on the most recent population census or some alternative survey (a labour force survey, for example). By way of illustration, the 1980 figure for the self-employed has remained unchanged since June 1975 in the estimates of the working population.

Activity rates

Much of the data discussed in this chapter can be used in the calculation of activity rates, which simply express the percentage of a defined group that is economically active, i.e.,

$$\frac{\text{The labour force}}{\text{Total population}} \times 100$$

The term 'defined group' implies that activity rates can be calculated for different age groups, for male and female, and for standard regions and local areas.

The claim is made that activity rates can provide a measure of the relative strength of economic activity and may also be able to indicate the magnitude of concealed unemployment, referred to earlier in this chapter.

In the former case (indicating relative economic strength) and using regional data, for example, we would expect the less prosperous areas of the country to exhibit lower activity rates than, say, the two Midland regions and the South East, reflecting their more depressed regional economies. This measure, together with other indicators (unemployment, outward mobility, etc.), could be used to determine the areas that would receive special financial assistance as part of regional policy. However, whether we can interpret the derived activity rates in this way will depend crucially on the coverage of the total population. The appropriate measure would be the regional population of working age since some regions (notably the South West and East Anglia) have a significantly higher proportion of their total population in the retirement age bracket, which would tend to lower their activity rates if the total population is taken as the denominator. Thus, for these areas, lower rates are likely to reflect demographic differences (i.e., a different age structure of the regional population) rather than (or in addition to) weak regional economies. This is not to suggest that age structure differences are unimportant—indeed, it is probable that those regions with a relatively large dependent population (children and retired persons) face particular pressures on their educational, health, and welfare resources, together with creating a somewhat different demand 'mix' for goods and services as indicated by the family expenditure survey results discussed in Chapter 6. If the aim of activity rates is to highlight these demographic differences regionally then the appropriate denominator would be the total regional population, but if the emphasis is on establishing the relatively weak and strong regional economies then clearly the regional population of working age would be a more suitable denominator measure to use.

In terms of providing some measure of concealed unemployment the crucial point would be the coverage of the labour force. Bearing in mind the meaning of the term 'concealed unemployment', it becomes obvious that the labour force should be defined as employees in employment (or possibly civil employment or the employed labour force) plus the registered unemployed, while the denominator would be the population of working age. This point is emphasized since many analysts calculate activity rates from information provided by the census of population, which defines everybody over 15 as 'economically active', with the exception of students, retired persons, and those permanently sick. It follows that the economically active would include all those in employment as well as those out of employment, whether they are registered as unemployed or not. Consequently, these data would actually include concealed unemployment as an element of the labour force figure, which is clearly inappropriate since the object would be to isolate and measure this element of spare labour capacity.

Figure 9.1 illustrates these points with five different activity rates for three selected periods covering the East Midlands standard region.[8,14] Each activity rate is defined differently and

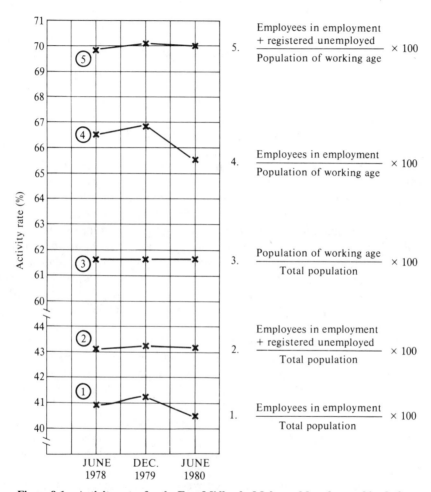

Figure 9.1   Activity rates for the East Midlands, Males and females combined; three time periods (Reproduced from *Employment Gazette*, March, July, September 1981, and from *Population Trends*, Autumn 1981, Table 3, with the permission of the Controller of Her Majesty's Stationery Office)

a quite remarkable spread of values is apparent, ranging between 41 and 70 per cent, depending on the components of the numerator and denominator.

Activity rate 1 measures employees in employment divided by the total population for the region. It gives the smallest value and shows that approximately 41 per cent of the total regional population were actually employed and, apart from the self-employed category, were responsible for the total output of the region. The large supported population (approximately 59 per cent) would include the registered unemployed, those of working age but not working, children, and those of retirement age.

Activity rate 2 measures employees in employment plus registered unemployed divided by total regional population. Apart from the self-employed, the numerator can be taken as an indication of the actual and potential workforce, at least as far as the official data are concerned. The slightly higher activity rate derived is, of course, the inclusion of the registered unemployed as part of the labour force.

Activity rate 3 measures the population of working age divided by the total population. The value of a little under 62 per cent would indicate not only the maximum potential workforce as a proportion of the total population but also the dependent population (children and people above retiring age), which in this case amounts to approximately 38 per cent of the total. This form of activity rate would be useful for establishing those regions with demographic differences, as described earlier. For example, the equivalent activity rate in 1980 for Northern Ireland is approximately 57 per cent, Wales 59 per cent, and Scotland just under 60 per cent. Note, however, that the constant value of 61.6 per cent for the East Midlands was obtained from the age distribution of the population in 1980, which was assumed to be identical for 1978 and 1979. In practice, the age distribution is likely to alter only marginally.

Activity rate 4 measures employees in employment divided by the population of working age. It would be tempting to interpret this rate (approximately 66 per cent) as indicating the measure of concealed unemployment, which would suggest a figure of some 34 per cent. However, this figure would be too high since it includes the registered unemployed, students, the self-employed, those of working age but not seeking employment, and finally those wishing to obtain employment but not registered as unemployed, which would be our concealed unemployment. It is noticeable that this activity rate shows the greatest variability, with a sharp fall between December 1979 and June 1980. This is mainly accounted for by a fall in employment and an associated rise in unemployment.

Activity rate 5 measures employees in employment plus registered unemployed divided by the population of working age. It is certainly the best of the measures for indicating concealed unemployment but since it includes students, self-employed, etc., it would still give an exaggerated value. However, of the five illustrated, this remains the best activity rate to use if we wish to indicate relative economic strengths of regional economies. This is because we have included the registered unemployed as an element in our numerator, which removes bias resulting from unemployment differences between regions, and because, by taking the population of working age as our denominator, we have reduced the risk of demographic characteristics influencing the result.

It is important to emphasize that these activity rates demonstrate different things and therefore each one could be appropriate for a specific type of investigation.

Finally, it should be appreciated that activity rate differences between areas, or countries, or over time, might reflect different social customs and conventions rather than economic or demographic character. For example, relatively low activity rates for females of working age in certain areas or countries may be due to the accepted convention that married women are not expected to go out to work, rather than being due to a lack of job opportunities for women. It must be admitted, however, that if job opportunities were improved it could help to break down this social convention (if present). Other features that would affect activity rate measurements but might reflect social changes include the movement towards earlier

118

retirement; the tendency for earlier marriages and child-bearing; and increasing the proportion of young people in full-time education.

It is clear from the foregoing that the analyst will have to define the numerator and denominator in the best way suited to the type of analysis being undertaken. Any general reader should be aware of the definitions used and avoid the danger of interpreting the results in economic terms when they may reflect demographic or social considerations.

Self-assessment questions—Part Three

1. The following indices have been extracted from *Economic Trends*:[15]

Year	Average price new dwellings (1975 = 100)	Earnings per person employed* (1975 = 100)
1969	39.3	42.3
1970	41.8	47.2
1971	48.1	53.1
1972	63.3	59.4
1973	86.2	65.4
1974	91.4	79.3
1975	100.0	100.0
1976	108.4	112.5
1977	119.0	124.9
1978	142.6	142.6
1979	183.2	165.4

* Derived from output per person employed × earnings per unit of output.

Reproduced from *Economic Trends*, with the permission of the Controller of Her Majesty's Stationery Office.

(a) Draw a scatter diagram for these data.
(b) Find the regression equation for predicting the average price of new dwellings from earnings per person employed.
(c) Find the coefficient of determination and comment on your results.
(d) If the index of earnings is 200 for 1980, estimate the index of average price for new dwellings. Comment on the accuracy of your result.

2. A retail organization is examining methods for predicting shop turnover. It collects the following information for a sample of 10 shops:

Turnover (£'000s)	150	140	120	140	120	160	140	140	140	100
Sales area (m²)	98	76	58	94	73	97	91	79	92	54
No. of staff	19	13	9	17	13	19	17	15	17	8

(a) Find the correlation coefficient for turnover compared to sales area.
(b) Find the correlation coefficient for turnover compared to number of staff.
(c) Deduce the best single factor for predicting turnover and mention any reservation you have about your result. Plot this factor against turnover on a scatter diagram.
(d) Find the equation of the regression line for predicting turnover from the factor determined in (c). Indicate the likely error in using this equation.
(e) Comment on your results and suggest any way that you feel the prediction of turnover could be improved.

3. Discuss briefly the reasons why a high correlation coefficient between two variables does not necessarily mean that there is a cause/effect relationship between the variables.

120

4. Fit a linear trend to the following data and hence forecast exports of cars for 1980. Check your equation graphically.

Year	1969	1970	1971	1972	1973	1974	1975	1976	1977	1978	1979
Exports of motor cars ('000s)	68.7	60.2	59.5	51.1	50.4	49.7	44.3	47.1	46.9	41.2	32.7

5. The following table shows the retail prices index by quarters for the years 1976 to 1979:

Year	Quarter			
	1	2	3	4
1976	110.9	114.9	117.6	123.0
1977	129.2	134.9	137.0	139.0
1978	141.4	145.3	147.8	150.3
1979	155.0	160.7	171.4	176.2

Plot the data, and on the same graph plot a four-quarterly moving average. Comment on your results. How useful would this approach be for forecasting purposes?

6. The following table shows the average exchange rate for the pound in U.S. dollars for the months of July 1979 to December 1980:

1979	Month	July	Aug.	Sep.	Oct.	Nov.	Dec.
	$ to £	2.260	2.238	2.200	2.145	2.133	2.198
1980	Month	Jan.	Feb.	Mar.	Apr.	May	June
	$ to £	2.266	2.290	2.206	2.216	2.304	2.336
1980	Month	July	Aug.	Sep.	Oct.	Nov.	Dec.
	$ to £	2.373	2.371	2.402	2.417	2.396	2.346

(a) Use the method of exponentially smoothed moving averages to forecast the series, starting in July 1979, assuming the forecast for that month equals the actual figure (2.260). Use a smoothing constant of $a = 0.4$.

(b) By considering the errors over this period, estimate the likely error in using this method. Give a forecast for January 1981. How useful do you think this method is for these data? Why might a company want such a forecast?

7. Table 8.2 of Chapter 8 gives quarterly sales figures for the sales of a chemical made by a certain manufacturer, and a four-quarterly moving average estimate of the trend. For these data:

(a) Find the additive seasonal factors.
(b) Find the multiplicative seasonal factors.
(c) Compare the additive and the multiplicative model for these data and demonstrate that there is a significant seasonal pattern.

8. A time series for an index of earnings per person employed is given in question 1.

(a) Plot earnings over time and show that the trend is curved.
(b) Plot the logarithm of earnings over time (or use log scale graph paper) and show that this gives an approximately linear trend.

(c) Find the regression equation for predicting the logarithm of earnings, i.e., the trend line. Hence predict the index of earnings for 1980.

Notes. 1. Logarithms to any base can be used.
2. If the equation found in (c) is:

$$\text{Log earnings index} = a + bx \quad (x = 1 \text{ for } 1969)$$

This is equivalent to the equation:

$$\text{Earnings index} = A \cdot B^x$$

where $a = \log A$ and $b = \log B$.

9. What categories of registered unemployed are excluded from the monthly count?

10. Why are these categories excluded?

11. Why might the percentage unemployment rate be more meaningful compared with the absolute total?

12. What purpose is served by seasonally adjusting the unemployment data?

13. The view that the unemployment data underestimate the true levels are based on what arguments?

14. On what basis is the opposing view taken?

15. How useful has been the introduction of flow statistics?

16. What are the major interpretation difficulties of vacancy statistics?

17. Is it meaningful to deduct vacancies from unemployment and arrive at a figure of spare labour capacity?

18. How is information on employment obtained?

19. How significant was the procedural change in the collection of employment data in 1971?

20. What must be borne in mind when interpreting activity rates?

Assignment questions—Part Three

1. Over the most recent three-year period, using seasonally adjusted quarterly data from the *Employment Gazette*,[8] establish a linear trend for both unemployment and vacancies. Plot the data and the linear trend for both on the same graph and discuss the relationship between both variables suggested by your analysis. How far, do you feel, your results are influenced by weaknesses in the data source?

2. Your company is producing a computerized system for providing price quotations for its products. Part of the problem is to estimate freight costs. These are based on a cost per unit per road mile. It would be difficult to store in the computer a list of road distances for all present and potential customers, so you decide to investigate the possibility of using straight line distances. Given a grid reference for a customer, it would be simple for the computer to calculate a straight line distance from the nearest depot.

Your problem is, then, to find a simple relationship between road distance and straight line distance. You obtain a sample of customer locations currently served from your company's Leicester depot as follows:

> Nottingham, Melton, Grantham, Peterborough, Cannock,
> Burton, Northampton, and Derby

(a) Estimate the quickest road distance and the straight line distance between Leicester and each of these locations.
(b) Plot a scatter diagram of road versus straight line distance for your sample. Find the regression equation for predicting road distance from straight line distance and add this to your graph.
(c) Comment on the fit of the regression line and give some indication of its likely accuracy and range of validity in predicting road distances.
(d) Illustrate the calculations the computer would need to perform to arrive at a road distance from a grid reference. Use as an example a possible customer whose location is 17 miles north and 26 miles west of Leicester.

Present your results clearly in the form of a brief technical report.

Part Four

Two sources chapters and two chapters dealing with techniques make up Part Four. Chapter 10 develops the area of probability theory leading to a discussion of frequency distributions, including the binomial and normal distributions. This serves as a basis for the final techniques chapter (Chapter 11) which covers the demanding, but nevertheless essential, topics of sampling theory and significance testing.

Attention has been drawn to the fact that much published data is based on a sample approach which inevitably involves some interpretation difficulties. This is seen most clearly in Chapter 12, which deals with published data on wages and earnings. The major source of information is obtained from the new earnings survey, which is a sample survey but with a 'matched' component. Chapter 13 examines the published data on income and wealth distribution and applies standard techniques developed earlier to the information. One new technique, the Lorenz curve, is explained and applied to the same data, while in an addendum to the chapter examples of other applications of the technique are illustrated.

Self-assessment questions and assignment topics on these four chapters complete Part Four.

10. Probability and theoretical frequency distributions

Probability theory provides the foundation for the methods of statistics. In this chapter we will look briefly at some of the key concepts of this subject, and their application to some of the main methods discussed in the book. Some understanding of probability theory is particularly important to the use of sampling, to be discussed in the next chapter, and we have already seen examples of the importance of sample data in statistical analysis.

10.1 Probability and some basic rules

In statistics we are concerned with analysing data generated by observation, measurement, or experiment. A single result of any of these processes is termed an 'event' for the purposes of probability theory, which is not concerned with practicalities of how data arise. Thus an event could be a month's sales, the height of a selected individual, or someone's answer to a question in a survey. The key point about all these processes is that they are *random*, which means that it is in principle impossible to specify what the event will be until it has occurred, although of course we know what the range of possibilities is. Instead, we can talk about the *probability* that a particular event will occur. As we have already seen (see Chapter 2, for instance), the result of an observation or measurement—an event—can be represented as the value of a *variable, x* say. Such variables are usually called *random variables* since they represent the outcomes of random processes, and the probability of an event can thus be thought of as the probability that a random variable takes a particular value. Strictly speaking, we are only dealing here with the simplest type of event, since probability theory allows this concept to cover more complicated cases where the event would cover a range of possible values for the random variable. Thus, for instance, if the random process we are interested in is the throw of a dice, we can talk about the probability of a simple event such as throwing a 6, or an event such as throwing an even number which combines the values 2, 4, and 6.

Probability is measured on a scale from 0 to 1, where 0 represents impossibility and 1 represents certainty. Events which do not come into either of these categories have probabilities somewhere between 0 and 1. *Mutually exclusive* events are two or more events such that if one occurs then the others are impossible. This will always be true of simple events, since a random variable can take only one value at a time. We make the assumption that the probability of *either* of two mutually exclusive events occurring is the sum of their individual probabilities. Thus the events 'throw a 2' and 'throw a 4' with a dice are clearly mutually exclusive for one throw, and if each has a probability of 1/6 of occurring, the probability of throwing a 2 *or* a 4 is $1/6 + 1/6 = 1/3$. Finally, we assume that if we divide *all* the results of some random process into a set of mutually exclusive events, i.e., list all the possible values of a random variable, then the sum of their individual probabilities will be 1. This makes obvious sense, for if we have listed *all* the possibilities then we are certain that one of them will occur; this is represented as 1 on our probability scale.

To summarize, we have made three assumptions:

1. Probability is measured on a scale from 0 to 1.
2. The probability of either of two mutually exclusive events occurring is the sum of their individual probabilities.
3. The sum of the probabilities of an exhaustive list of mutually exclusive events is 1.

These are the only fundamental assumptions (called 'axioms') of probability theory, which proceeds to work out the consequences of making these assumptions. It is surprising that such a simple seeming beginning can lead to a theory as rich and wide ranging in its application as probability theory.

10.2 The measurement of probability

We have said nothing so far about how to arrive at a measure of probability. Probability theory as such does not help us here, since it is unconcerned with how probability is measured, as long as the measures, however arrived at, meet the requirements listed above. Consider the following statements:

1. If I take the course, my probability of passing is 0.8.
2. The probability of getting heads if you toss a coin is 0.5.
3. The probability that *Sundancer* will win the Derby is 0.2.

The first statement might well have been arrived at by a consideration of past results on the course. If 80 per cent of those who have taken the course previously have passed, then I could assess my chances using the same relative frequency. One way of arriving at an estimate of the probability of an event, then, is simply to equate it to the relative frequency with which that event has occurred, compared to all other possibilities, in the past.

The second statement is different. Most people would agree with it, but not because they had counted the number of heads that came up in all their previous experience of coin tossing. It is rather because we have a theory about the way coins behave owing to their symmetric construction, which leads us to suppose that, approximately at least, there is an equal chance of getting a head or tail. We can arrive at a probability from a theoretical model then as well.

The third statement does not fit in with either of these ways of measuring probability. It cannot be based on past frequencies, since it refers to a unique event—the next Derby. Nor do we have any theoretical model about the way a particular horse behaves. It can only be based on a subjective estimate—no doubt based on our knowledge of *Sundancer*, our assessment of the rest of the field, our general knowledge about horseracing, etc. So a third way of arriving at a probability measure is by some subjective process.

All three of these approaches to measuring a probability can meet the requirements we have set out above. The third approach is of particular interest in the application of probability theory to decision-making, but is not one we will pursue here. We will concentrate on the measurement of probability from relative frequencies and the derivation of probabilities from theoretical models. The two are often linked when we can approximate an empirically derived probability using a theoretical model.

We will look first at the use of relative frequencies. Consider again Table 1.2 in Chapter 1 which records the number of accidents per week over a 50-week period for a large company. The results are shown in Table 10.1. We have added the relative frequency column, which was

Table 10.1

Number of accidents per week	Frequency	Relative frequency
0	6	0.12
1	17	0.34
2	12	0.24
3	8	0.16
4	5	0.10
5	1	0.02
6	1	0.02
	50	1.00

calculated by dividing each individual frequency by the total (50). If we use the relative frequencies as estimates of probability they meet all our requirements. Clearly, they must lie between 0 and 1. It makes sense to say that the probability of 0 or 1 accidents, for instance, is $0.12 + 0.34 = 0.46$, and the sum of all the probabilities is 1. An important point to bear in mind when measuring probability in this way is that a probability is a fixed quantity, whereas relative frequencies may vary. Thus, if we took another 50-week period, it would not be surprising if the relative frequencies of different numbers of accidents varied slightly from the above. It is necessary to have a sufficient number of observations to be sure that the relative frequencies are fairly stable, and thus a reasonable basis for estimating the (fixed) probability of their related events.

At this stage we introduce another important probability concept. From the above we can conclude that the probability of there being no accidents next week (for instance) is 0.12. What is the probability that there will be no accidents in the next two weeks? It seems natural to reply that it must be $0.12 \times 0.12 = 0.0144$. We are assuming that what happens in one week has no influence over what happens in the next week, just as we would assess the probability of throwing heads twice in succession with a coin as $0.5 \times 0.5 = 0.25$. In probability theory we define two events as being *independent* if the probability of them both occurring is the multiple of their individual probabilities. So in both of the above cases we are assuming that the two events are independent. In the case of the accident data we could empirically verify that this was a reasonable assumption. Let us assume that this is so.

The introduction of the idea of multiplying probabilities for independent events begins to lead us to some interesting results. For instance, what is the probability that in two weeks at least one of them is accident free? The only alternative is that in both weeks there is at least one accident. Now in any one week an application of the rules tells us that there is a probability of 0.88 that there is at least one accident. We arrive at this either by applying rule 2 and adding $0.34 + 0.24 + \cdots$, etc. Or using rule 3, we note that it must be $1 - 0.12$. If the probability of an accident in one week is 0.88 then the probability that in two weeks there is in each case an accident is $0.88 \times 0.88 = 0.7744$. The only alternative is that in at least one of the weeks there was no accident, so this must have a probability of $1 - 0.7744 = 0.2256$. We note in passing that this example could have been tackled using another probability rule.

It is possible to derive the following general rule. For any two events, call them A and B:

The probability that A or B occurs = the probability A occurs
+ the probability B occurs
− the probability both occur

129

In the above example, if the two events are no accidents in the first week (probability 0.12) and no accidents in the second week (probability 0.12), and as we have seen the probability of no accidents in both weeks is 0.0144, then it follows from the rule that the probability of no accidents in at least one of the weeks$=0.12+0.12-0.0144=0.2256$, exactly as we have already deduced.

As another example, consider the problem of finding how many weeks must go by for there to be a probability of more than 0.5 that in at least one of them there was no accident. The only alternative is that there is at least one accident in each consecutive week, so we want the smallest sequence of weeks that makes this probability less than 0.5. We have seen that the probability of accidents in both of two weeks is 0.88^2 (0.7744), by extension, the probability of three weeks all with accidents is $0.88^3=0.68$ (approximately), and so on. The solution is left for the reader to find and is perhaps less than might be initially supposed.

Incidentally, a rather more difficult application of this idea is to find the number of people necessary in a group for there to be a better than evens chance of two of them having a birthday on the same day. The answer is only 23 (assuming all birthdays are equally likely). For a group of 30 the probability is nearly 0.7 and for a group of 40 it is nearly 0.9.

The foregoing examples were something of a digression, and only intended to indicate that the application of the rules of probability can lead to 'interesting', i.e., non-obvious, results. We return now to the main thrust of the chapter, which is the development of the idea of a probability distribution. This will eventually lead us to results which are both 'interesting' and yield statistical methods of wide practical application.

A *probability distribution* is simply the set of probabilities associated with each of the possible values of a random variable. If we let the random variable x equal the number of accidents in a week for the company above, then the probability distribution of x is

x	0	1	2	3	4	5	6
Probability	0.12	0.34	0.24	0.16	0.10	0.02	0.02

Theoretical models of probability are called *probability distribution functions* (in statistical theory they are more correctly called probability *density* functions), and can be given in the form of a mathematical expression which generates the probabilities of a probability distribution. We have already met the simplest type—it simply assigns all values of the random variable equal probabilities. There are many others, but only a few are of wide applicability. To be of much use, a probability distribution function must generate probabilities which approximate to those that arise in practice in some set of circumstances. We shall be discussing two of the most useful in the next section, but to illustrate how they work we will now look briefly at one called the Poisson distribution.

The Poisson distribution makes the assumption that a particular event occurs independently and at random over a period of time. If we divide time up into a number of equal slices, e.g., weeks, and on average the event occurs m times per week, then it is possible to deduce (using probability theory beyond the scope of the present text) that the probability of r such events occurring in any one week is

$$\frac{e^{-m}m^r}{r!}$$

In this formula, e is the 'exponential constant' and equals approximately 2.718, while $r!$ is read

130

'r factorial' and means $r(r-1)(r-2) \cdots 1$. Thus $1!=1$, $2!=2\times1=2$, $3!=3\times2\times1=6$, and so on. By convention, $0!=1$.

If accidents occur independently and at random, which seems a reasonable assumption, we would expect this probability distribution function to give a reasonable approximation to the empirically derived probability distribution found above. Let us see if it does. We already know (see Chapter 2) that the mean number of accidents per week is 1.92, so this will be our value of m; thus, $e^{-m}=0.1466$ (approximately). If we let $P(r)$ stand for the theoretical probability of r accidents in a week, then

$$P(0)=\frac{0.1466\times1.92^0}{0!}=0.15$$

$$P(1)=\frac{0.1466\times1.92^1}{1!}=0.28$$

$$P(2)=\frac{0.1466\times1.92^2}{2!}=0.27$$

$$P(3)=\frac{0.1466\times1.92^3}{3!}=0.17$$

$$P(4)=\frac{0.1466\times1.92^4}{4!}=0.08$$

$$P(5)=\frac{0.1466\times1.92^5}{5!}=0.03$$

$$P(6)=\frac{0.1466\times1.92^6}{6!}=0.01$$

Theoretically we can continue for higher values of r, but the total probability of r being 7 or more is negligible (about 0.01). When compared with the empirical distribution the probabilities are not exactly the same, of course, but they are not far out, which suggests that the Poisson distribution is a reasonable model of the accident data. The Poisson distribution has a far wider application than we have indicated, and can be a good model of such phenomena as the number of people arriving in a unit of time at the end of a queue and the number of faults occurring in a unit length of material. In the next section, we develop the idea of a probability distribution function further, and look at two other widely useful models.

10.3 Probability distributions and their properties

As we have seen, if a random variable takes a range of possible values which are associated with a mutually exclusive and exhaustive set of events resulting from some random process, then the probabilities associated with the values of the random variable form a probability distribution. Their sum must be 1. Just as we found it useful to describe frequency distributions by a few characteristics, so do we with probability distributions; indeed, we use the same types of measure. If the random variable x takes the values $x_1, x_2, \ldots, x_n$ with probabilities $P(x_1)$, $P(x_2), \ldots, P(x_n)$, then we define the *mean* of the distribution as μ, where

$$\mu=x_1P(x_1)+x_2P(x_2)+\cdots+x_nP(x_n) \tag{10.1}$$

Thus for the probability distribution representing the accident frequency data:

$$\mu = 0 \times 0.12 + 1 \times 0.34 + 2 \times 0.24 + 3 \times 0.16 + 4 \times 0.10 + 5 \times 0.02 + 6 \times 0.02$$
$$= 1.92$$

This is, of course, exactly the same as the mean of the frequency distribution which we used to estimate the probabilities. The variance of a probability distribution, σ^2, is defined as

$$\sigma^2 = (x_1 - \mu)^2 P(x_1) + (x_2 - \mu)^2 P(x_2) + \cdots + (x_n - \mu)^2 P(x_n)$$
$$= x_1^2 P(x_1) + x_2^2 P(x_2) + \cdots + x_n^2 P(x_n) - \mu^2 \qquad (10.2)$$

Either version of the formula can be used. For the accident data:

$$\sigma^2 = 0^2 \times 0.12 + 1^2 \times 0.34 + 2^2 \times 0.24 + 3^2 \times 0.16 + 4^2 \times 0.10 + 5^2 \times 0.02 + 6^2 \times 0.02 - 1.92^2$$
$$= 1.87$$

Again, this is the same as the variance found for the original frequency distribution. These are the main characteristics we are interested in for probability distributions, although we often take the square root of the variance to obtain the standard deviation which we call σ, simply dropping the square. For the accident data, this would be 1.37.

Theoretical probability distributions, generated by probability distribution functions, can be described in just the same way. Thus, for the Poisson distribution, described in the previous section, we can show that the mean is m and in fact the variance is also m. The mathematics involved in proving these results is beyond our present scope and involves a knowledge of the infinite series from which the exponential constant, e, is derived. Note again that for the accident data the mean and variance are nearly equal, which was a sign that the Poisson distribution might give a good fit.

We next go on to describe the main properties of two important theoretical probability distributions, the binomial and the normal.

The binomial distribution

Consider a random process for which there are only two possible outcomes. We can represent this by a random variable which takes the values 0 and 1 only. For instance, we could consider the output of a manufacturing process as either producing an acceptable item or a defect. Providing defects are produced at random, we have just such a process as described. Another very important process of this type is attribute sampling, where we take a sample and determine whether or not it has some particular attribute; the attribute occurs at random across the population we are sampling. It could, for instance, be a political opinion survey where the attribute was 'intends to vote Conservative', a market research survey where the attribute was 'buys brand X', or it could be a financial audit sample where the attribute was 'entry checks correctly'.

In all the examples we have considered, we are interested in a series of repeated outputs from the random process. In probability terms, this is a sequence of 0 or 1 values for the random variable. The binomial distribution gives the probability of each possible number of 1's that can occur in a sequence of given length. It is, of course, quite arbitrary which outcome we classify as a 1 and which we classify as a 0, since having specified the number of 1's in the sequence, we have determined the number of 0's. Thus the distribution will give us either the probability of any possible number of defects in a batch of production or the number of individuals possessing some attribute in a sample of given size.

We need to make one further assumption—that the events in the sequence are *independent*. It is now possible to derive the probability distribution function for these assumptions. It should (and indeed does) show a good fit to the probabilities that we would observe in practice for the types of example we have described.

Consider a sequence of n values of the random variable. Suppose that, in each case, the probability of a 1 is p and the probability of a 0 is q (which must equal $1-p$). Let $P(r)$ be the probability of r 1's in the sequence. Since each event (value of the random variable) is independent, the probability of no 1's, $P(0)$, must be

$$P(0)=q \times q \times \cdots \times q=q^n$$

Consider next the case where there is just one 1. The probability of a sequence in which it occurs in the first place is $p \times q \times q \times \cdots \times q=pq^{n-1}$. The probability of a sequence in which the single 1 comes in the second place will be exactly the same: pq^{n-1}. The same will be true of any sequence in which 1 occurs just once. Altogether there are n such sequences, which together form a set of mutually exclusive ways of achieving one 1 out of a sequence of n possibilities. We can therefore simply add them to find

$$P(1)=npq^{n-1}$$

Applying the same idea we can find $P(2)$, $P(3)$, and so on. In fact, we can find a general formula for $P(r)$, where r takes any of the possible values from 0 to n. The probability of any particular sequence which contains just r 1's and therefore $n-r$ 0's will be $p^r q^{n-r}$. We now need to determine how many such sequences there are. The answer is the same as finding the number of ways of putting r 1's into n possible positions, because there will then be only one way of filling the remaining $n-r$ positions with the $n-r$ 0's. In other words, how many ways are there of selecting r out of n possibilities? This you may remember from school is the problem of finding r *combinations* from n (often written nCr). The answer is

$$\frac{n!}{r!(n-r)!}$$

Thus, for instance, the number of combinations of 8 from 10 (a familiar problem for those who do the football pools) is:

$$\frac{10!}{8!(10-8)!}=\frac{10!}{8!(2)!}=\frac{10 \times 9 \times 8 \times 7 \times \cdots \times 1}{8 \times 7 \times \cdots \times 1 \times (2 \times 1)}=\frac{10 \times 9}{2}=45$$

We can now write down the formula for $P(r)$, which is the probability distribution function for the binomial distribution; it is

$$P(r)=\frac{n!}{r!(n-r)!} p^r q^{n-r} \tag{10.3}$$

For example, suppose a production process produces 1 per cent defectives, i.e., the probability of a defect is 0.01. If we take a batch of 10 from the output:

$$P(0)=0.99^{10}=0.904 \qquad \text{(the probability of no defects)}$$
$$P(1)=10 \times 0.01 \times 0.99^9=0.091 \quad \text{(the probability of one defect)}$$

and so on. We can also deduce that, for instance, the probability of two or more defects is about 0.005, since the above probabilities sum to 0.995. This sort of result could be used in quality control sampling, since, if in fact we found two or more defects in a sample of 10, we could either conclude that a highly unlikely event has occurred or, much more reasonably, that our process is in fact producing more than 1 per cent defects and so ought to be investigated.

The mean of the binomial distribution is intuitively fairly obvious. If 1's occur with a probability of p, then we would expect that the mean number of 1's in a sequence of n would be np. This is in fact so, although the proof is beyond the scope of this text. We then have

$$\text{Mean of binomial distribution} = np \qquad (10.4)$$

It can also be shown that

$$\text{Variance of binomial distribution} = npq \qquad (10.5)$$

For example, for the case where $n = 10$ and $p = 0.01$ (our model for the production defects example) the mean is $10 \times 0.01 = 0.1$ and the variance is $10 \times 0.01 \times 0.99 = 0.099$. We could also deduce that the standard deviation was 0.315 (approximately).

Before concluding our coverage of the binomial distribution, we note that its main disadvantage as a model is that its application can lead to some horrific arithmetic! Try calculating the probability of getting between 35 and 45 1's in a sequence of 100, for instance. There are, it is true, tables of binomial probabilities, but they can of course only cover some of the possible cases. We could also use a computer—if one happened to be available every time we wanted it. Fortunately, there is a much simpler way for many cases—we can use an approximation method which is accurate and very much easier to calculate. There are several such methods, depending on the precise values of n and p involved, the most useful of which involves the normal distribution which we will be meeting next in this chapter.

The normal distribution

So far, we have discussed probabilities and probability distributions for cases where there are only a small number of possible events or, equivalently, a small number of values that the related random variable can take. Very often in practice we require a random variable that can take a large number of different values; e.g., the distribution of incomes or the distribution of order sizes. This will apply, in particular, to any variable which represents the result of a measurement on a continuous scale, e.g., height, weight, or temperature. In theory, any such measurement can take an infinite range of values between any two given points, no matter how close together on the scale they are. In practice this will not be so, since we can only measure to some degree of accuracy, i.e., to a finite number of decimal places, so again, in practice, we simply have a variable which can take a large number of values.

It is often convenient, however, to approximate such processes by using a *continuous random variable**—a variable which has the theoretical properties of a measurement as stated above. There are many mathematical functions which can be used to generate the probabilities of such a variable. The most important is the one used for the *normal distribution*. There is no point in quoting the formula for it here, since the required probability values cannot be found from it in any simple way; instead we use tables, as we shall see.

We cannot talk meaningfully of the probability that a continuous random variable takes any specific value; instead we can only consider the probability of it lying in a particular range. We saw in Chapter 1 how it was often convenient to treat empirical data in this way by forming a grouped frequency table. Graphically, as we saw, this can be represented by a

---

* The cases we have seen so far are called *discrete random variables*.

histogram or a frequency polygon. The simplest way of thinking of the probability distribution of a continuous random variable is as an approximation to the frequency polygon. We met this idea in Chapter 2 and it is repeated here, using the normal distribution as an example.

First let us represent the possible values of a random variable as points on a line:

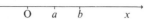

Thus the values of x are represented as points on the line measured as distances from the origin, O. Values in the range a to b would be points in the segment of the line indicated. We make this line the horizontal axis of a graph. The vertical axis through the origin is used for probability, the probability distribution of the normal distribution being as shown in Fig. 10.1.

The curve is drawn so that the total area underneath it above the x axis is one (in some convenient unit). The shaded area represents the probability of x lying between a and b. As

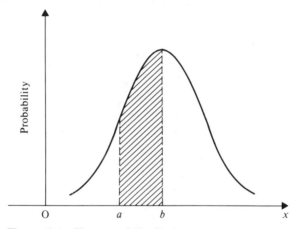

Figure 10.1   The normal distribution

noted before, the peak of the curve lies above the mean value of x and the curve is symmetrical about a vertical line drawn through that point. Thus the normal distribution represents a situation where x is equally likely to be above or below its mean and where the probability of some value diminishes the further away we get from the mean.

Figure 10.1 shows a typical shape for the normal distribution, but its shape for any particular case depends on two factors: the mean and the standard deviation of the random variable. Changing the mean simply has the effect of moving the curve sideways so as to keep the peak immediately above it. Increasing the standard deviation of x, i.e., making it more variable, has the effect of flattening the curve or making it less peaked. Reducing the standard deviation has the opposite effect. Since, as we noted above, there is no simple way of calculating areas under the curve of the normal distribution, it is fortunate that we can always calculate any required area by reference to a standard curve. The *standard normal distribution* is such that its mean is 0 and its standard deviation is 1; we shall call the random variable whose probabilities are distributed in this way z. Theoretically, z can take any value between plus and minus infinity, but the probability that z lies between -3 and $+3$ is more than 0.997, so we can virtually ignore the possibility of z lying outside this range.

The normal distribution is usually tabulated by giving the probabilities of z being less than given values. Table 10.2 shows a simple example. Since the mean of z is 0, as we have already

Table 10.2

z	Probability of less than z
0	0.5000
1	0.8413
2	0.9772
3	0.9986

noted, the probability of z being less than 0 must be exactly 0.5. From the table, we see that the probability of z being less than 1 is 0.8413, and so on. We can deduce that the probability of z being between 0 and 1 is $0.8413 - 0.5 = 0.3413$, and similarly for any other range of the values tabulated. Check, for instance, that the probability that z lies between 1 and 3 is 0.1573.

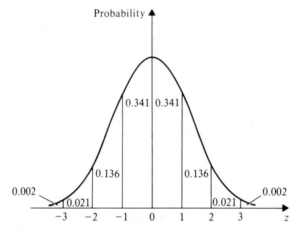

Figure 10.2   The standard normal distribution

Because of the symmetry of the curve, the probability that z lies between -1 and 0 must be exactly the same as the probability that z lies between 0 and 1, that is, 0.3413. It follows that the probability that z is less than -1 is $0.5 - 0.3413 = 0.1587$. We could also arrive at this by noting that the probability of z being less than -1 must be the same as the probability of z being greater than 1, which is $1 - 0.8413 = 0.1587$. These results are easier to appreciate when related to the curve of the normal distribution. The areas for ranges of unit width between -3 and $+3$ are shown in Fig. 10.2.

With a little practice, it is quite simple to find the probability that z lies in any given range. A more detailed table of the normal distribution will be found at the end of the book. All that is necessary is to use the symmetry properties of the curve, together with this table. At first, it may be found helpful to draw a picture of the distribution and shade in the area corresponding to the probability to be found.

To find probabilities for a general normal distribution, proceed as follows. For example, suppose x is normally distributed with a mean of 10 and a standard deviation of 2. We convert x to the standard normal variable by first subtracting its mean. As required, $x - 10$ will have a mean of 0. We then convert to units of standard deviation to ensure that it has a standard deviation of 1. We do this by dividing by the standard deviation; thus $(x-10)/2$ will be a standard normal variable, with a mean of 0 and a standard deviation of 1. Symbolically:

$$z = \frac{x-10}{2}$$

It follows that, for instance:

$$\text{Probability that } x \text{ is less than } 13 = \text{probability that } z \text{ is less than } \frac{13-10}{2}$$
$$= \text{probability that } z \text{ is less than } 1.5$$
$$= 0.9332 \quad \text{(from table)}$$

As another example, suppose we want the probability that x lies between 7 and 13. This equals the probability that z lies between $(7-10)/2$ and $(13-10)/2$, i.e., the probability that z lies between -1.5 and 1.5. Using the properties of the curve, this can be found in several ways and the required probability is 0.8664.

Often we have the reverse problem, i.e., we want to find a value of x which is only exceeded with a given probability (or equivalently for which there is a required less than probability). This amounts to finding percentile points for x. We can do this by using the table the other way round; for instance, it can be seen that the ninetieth percentile point of the standard normal distribution is approximately 1.3—to be more exact it is 1.2816. However, for convenience, some of the more commonly required percentile points are given in Table 10.3.

Table 10.3 Percentile points of the standard normal distribution

Percentile	z
50	0
75	0.6745
80	0.8416
85	1.0364
90	1.2816
95	1.6449
97.5	1.9600
99	2.3263
99.5	2.5758

Suppose we wanted the nineteenth percentile of the variable x considered above; we have:

$$\frac{x-10}{2} = 1.2816 \quad \text{(from table)}$$
$$x = 2 \times 1.2816 + 10$$
$$= 12.5632$$

In other words, there is a probability of 0.9 that x is less than 12.5632.

Another common problem is to find a range of values for a normally distributed variable such that the variable lies within that range with a given probability. Usually we want the range that has the mean as its midpoint, i.e., a range that is symmetric about the mean. We

137

can find these ranges using Table 10.3. For instance, we see that there is a probability of 0.025 that z exceeds 1.96. It must also follow that there is a probability of 0.025 that z is less than -1.96. It is the case, then, that z lies in the range -1.96 to 1.96 with a probability of $1-(0.025+0.025)=0.95$. Similarly, we can deduce that z lies in the range -1.6449 to 1.6449 with probability 0.9, and z lies in the range -2.5758 to 2.5758 with probability 0.99. These are the ranges that are most often required. It is left as an exercise to show that our variable x lies in the range 6.08 to 13.92 with probability 0.95. Other ranges for x can be found in the same way.

As well as giving a good fit to many empirically derived distributions, the normal distribution has many other uses in statistics. We shall be meeting the most important in the next chapter where we see that sample means are approximately normally distributed. Another important use is as an approximation to many other probability distributions; for instance, it can be used under some circumstances to approximate both the Poisson and the binomial distributions. The procedure is quite straightforward and can be found in many elementary statistics texts.

11. Sampling, estimation, and significance testing

11.1 Random samples

A sample is a selection of individuals or items from a *population*, which is defined as the whole group of individuals or items of interest. In the case of, for instance, a sample of families in the United Kingdom it is clear what is meant by the population. In other cases the concept is not so clear, as in a sample of the output from a manufacturing process, where the population would be all items which could have been selected. In theory this might be said to include all future as well as past production. In practice we simply assume that the sample comes from a large number of comparable items and avoid the problem of a population whose members are not all available for selection.

A *random sample* is defined as a selection such that every member of the population has an equal chance of selection. Strictly speaking, this is a *simple random sample* and it is sufficient for every member of the population to have a calculable chance of selection (not necessarily equal). We shall mainly be concerned with the simple case and so will stick to the first definition unless otherwise stated. The statistical analysis of samples assumes that they are random.

There are a number of ways of selecting random samples. We can use a mechanical method such as drawing names from a hat or a drum, but apart from the obvious problem of the size of the population, it is suprisingly difficult to ensure that the names are mixed well enough to make the selection genuinely random. Another approach is to list all the names and simply select, say, every tenth one. This is called *systematic sampling* and depends on being able to list all the population members and on ensuring that the list is in random order, both of which may be difficult to do—it may not be true of an alphabetical list, for instance. In a school with which the author is aquainted an alphabetical division of the pupils resulted in a class in which there were twelve Patels. In practice this method works well in certain applications.

A relatively safe and simple way of obtaining a random sample is to use *random numbers*. Each member of the population is assigned a unique code using the digits 0 to 9. Equivalently, a method is devised for uniquely identifying a member of the population from such a code. A random number table is then used in which these digits occur at random and with equal frequency, or a computer is used to generate the digits according to the same requirements. It is important to distinguish between random and haphazard. If a person is asked to write down some digits 'at random' they will not usually have the properties of random numbers—digits may not occur with equal frequency and there may be some discernible pattern in the selection. At any rate, given random numbers, it is then a simple matter to select the sample. A number with the required number of digits is selected and an individual is then accordingly selected.

The two main purposes of sampling are to estimate something about the population or to check some hypothesis about the population. In both cases, assuming a random sample, statistical analysis is useful in determining the likely accuracy of the result.

11.2 The distribution of the sample mean

Samples can only be approximately representative of the populations they come from; thus, since they are used to estimate or check some characteristic of the population, it is obviously useful to be more precise about what is meant by 'approximately'. To do this we need to know by how much the characteristic we are interested in can vary in a sample from its population value. A characteristic we are very often interested in is the population mean, and we shall concentrate in this section on the statistical theory necessary for the analysis of this case.

We shall from now on be assuming that the population of interest has, effectively, an infinite number of members, i.e., in practice is very large. For small populations, the results we shall be obtaining need some modification.

When we select a sample, we can view it as one of the (infinitely) many that could have been selected. Any characteristic of a sample can therefore be seen as an individual instance from a whole range of possibilities. The first step in statistical sampling theory is to determine how this characteristic varies across all possible samples; in other words, to find its probability distribution. If we are interested in the population mean, the sample characteristic of most interest is the *sample mean*.

The population mean is called μ and is a fixed quantity. The sample mean is the result of a random process which could result in a whole range of different values; it is therefore a *random variable* which we call $\bar{x}$. It is important to be clear of the difference between these two types of mean. We want to find the probability distribution of $\bar{x}$, the sample mean.

The population mean, μ, is the mean *of* something. That 'something' will be an observation or measurement that can be performed for every member of the population and will differ in result from member to member. We could therefore also calculate a standard deviation for these values, let us call it σ, the population standard deviation.

We can prove the following important results for samples of size n:

> The distribution of $\bar{x}$ (possible values of the sample mean)
> (a) has a mean of μ.
> (b) has a standard deviation of $\sigma/\sqrt{n}$. This is called the *standard error*.
> (c) is a normal distribution if the population values are normally distributed.
> (d) approximates to a normal distribution *regardless* of how the population values are distributed. The larger the sample size (n), the better the approximation.

The proof of these results is beyond the scope of this text, but let us examine them more closely, making use of an example.

Suppose we took a sample of employed people and found their personal incomes. Table 13.1 in Chapter 13 shows how personal incomes are distributed across the whole population, Fig. 13.1 gives a frequency polygon for the distribution, and in Sec. 13.4 of the chapter it is shown that for before-tax incomes, the population mean is £3702 with a standard deviation of 2959 (in 1976–77).

Let us suppose that a random sample of five people yielded the following (before-tax) incomes:

$$4464 \quad 2660 \quad 3451 \quad 3792 \quad 5430$$

The sample mean is easily found to be 3959. A second sample of five people might give the following incomes:

$$1406 \quad 5320 \quad 741 \quad 3470 \quad 4680$$

For this sample the mean is 3123. Continuing in this way we could generate any number of

140

sample means for samples of size 5. It is hardly surprising to assert [result (a)] that these means would average out at 3702—the population mean.

Although the sample means will vary from sample to sample, we would not expect them to vary as much as individual values from the population. This is because individual low and high values will to some extent be cancelled out across the sample. Furthermore, it seems reasonable to suppose that the larger the size of the samples, the less will be the variation from sample to sample. From result (b) we see that for samples of size 5, the standard error of the mean is $\sigma/\sqrt{5}$. For the personal income data this gives a value of $2959/\sqrt{5}$, which is 1323 (approximately)—much less than the standard deviation of individual values. If we took samples of size 100, the standard error would be reduced to $2959/\sqrt{100}$, which is nearly 296, so these means would vary much less than those from smaller samples.

Result (c) is hardly surprising, since if the population values have the symmetrical normal distribution, we would expect sample means to be distributed according to the same pattern, although they would tend to be more closely packed around the mean, giving the distribution a more peaked shape.

Result (d) is more difficult to accept intuitively. Personal incomes, for instance, are clearly not normally distributed across the population. As can be seen from Fig. 13.1 in Chapter 13, the distribution is skewed. However, when we take samples from this distribution, high incomes will only occasionally occur, and they will therefore make only a small contribution to the sample mean. This will have the effect of making the distribution of sample means more symmetrical than the parent population. For samples of size 5, the distribution of the sample means will still be skewed, but as the sample size is increased, the distribution will become more nearly symmetrical. In fact, it will get closer to the normal distribution. As a rule of thumb, the means of samples of size 30 from a skewed distribution like this one will give a good approximation to the normal distribution.

This last result is of fundamental importance in the statistical analysis of samples. It is a simple statement of a result known as the central limit theorem, and, as we shall see, lies behind many of the results we shall use in making estimates or checking hypotheses from samples.

11.3 Confidence intervals

In the previous section we saw that sample means (for samples of a reasonable size) are approximately normally distributed. We can now apply some of the properties of the normal distribution that were met in Chapter 10 to the sample mean. For instance, we saw that there is a probability of 0.95 that a standard normal variable lies in the range -1.96 to $+1.96$. In general, this means that a normal variable will be within 1.96 standard deviations of its mean, with a probability of 0.95. We saw above that samples of size 100 of personal incomes have means with a standard error of 296 (remember that we use this term for the standard deviation of means). Now with samples of this size the distribution of the means will be extremely close to the normal distribution; for the population as a whole, the mean personal income is 3702. It follows therefore that there is a probability of 0.95 that the mean of a sample of 100 will lie in the range $3702 \pm 1.96 \times 296$, which is 3122 to 4282.

Suppose that we did not know what the population mean was and were using our sample of 100 to estimate it. It follows from the above that there is a probability of 0.95 that the population mean is included in the range:

$$\text{Sample mean} \pm 1.96 \times 296$$

141

which is

$$\text{Sample mean} \pm 580$$

This is called a *95 per cent confidence interval* for the population mean, since we are 95 per cent confident that the population mean will lie in this interval. In general, we can state that for a sample (of reasonable size) from any population, a 95 per cent confidence interval for the population mean is

$$\text{Sample mean} \pm 1.96 \times \text{standard error}$$

or, in symbols:

$$\bar{x} \pm 1.96 \frac{\sigma}{\sqrt{n}} \tag{11.1}$$

We can find intervals for different levels of confidence by simply varying the multiplier found for the standard normal distribution. We use 1.96 for 95 per cent, and, as we saw in Chapter 10, the multipliers for 90 and 99 per cent confidence are 1.6449 and 2.5758, respectively. These are the most commonly used confidence intervals.

Using this approach we can make quite a precise statement of how approximate we expect a sample mean to be as an estimate of the mean of the population the sample is drawn from. There is, however, one problem with what we have said. If we are using a sample to estimate the population mean, it will usually be the case that we also do not know σ, the population standard deviation. The best we can do is to find the standard deviation of the sample values and use this as a proxy for the population value. With a large sample, this will be accurate enough. It does suggest, though, that using multipliers correct to four places of decimals is rather spurious; they should be rounded to one or two places to be more in keeping with the level of approximation involved. The resulting confidence interval should also be appropriately rounded.

To conclude this section let us consider another example as it might arise in practice. Suppose that a large organization wanted a quick estimate of the turn-round times for the bulk containers it uses for distributing its product, i.e., the times spent by a container from when it leaves the works to its return from a customer, who may use the container for temporary storage. Let us assume that a sample of 50 trip times is selected at random; they are as follows, in days:

21	12	14	15	23
29	9	24	11	29
9	38	25	16	22
14	17	27	47	28
6	12	22	19	55
12	27	3	8	16
17	13	14	18	34
20	15	6	64	32
19	19	15	43	21
15	20	16	23	2

It should be clear that turn-round times are not normally distributed; a histogram for these data will illustrate this. Most of the times are in the 10 to 20 days region, but a few much larger times occur, making the distribution skewed. It is reasonable to suppose that the population

142

reflects this pattern. From the sample data, we find the following (the reader should check these results):

$$\text{Sample mean} = 20.72$$

Sample variance = 151.92   (note that the correction factor of 50/49 has been applied—see Chapter 2)

Estimate of population standard deviation = $\sqrt{151.92}$
$$= 12.33$$

Our best estimate of the mean turn-round time is therefore 20.7 days—perhaps 21 days would be more reasonable—certainly no more than one place of decimals could be justified. A good indication of the likely accuracy of this estimate is given by the 95 per cent confidence interval. Using (11.1) we have

$$20.72 \pm 1.96 \times \frac{12.33}{\sqrt{50}}$$

Performing these calculations and rounding we have:

95 per cent confidence interval is 20.72 ± 3.41
or 17.3 to 24.1

Putting this informally, we can say that we estimate that the mean turn-round is 21 days, and we are fairly sure that at any rate it is between 17 and 24 days.

A 95 per cent confidence interval is commonly used as, effectively, a translation of 'fairly sure', but sometimes the 90 or 99 per cent confidence interval is used—depending on how sure we want to be. Check that, for this example:

90 per cent confidence interval is 17.9 to 23.6 days
99 per cent confidence interval is 16.2 to 25.2 days

It can be seen that the ranges given are not very different.

11.4 Estimation of proportions

A characteristic of a population that is often of interest is the proportion of the members of the population who have some attribute e.g., for human populations, the proportion who buy brand X, the proportion who intend to vote Conservative in the next election, etc. For populations of things, we might be interested in, for instance, the proportion of defectives output from a manufacturing process. We met this idea in Chapter 10 when discussing the binomial distribution.

As we have seen, we can represent this situation by a random variable x where:

$x=1$ means the individual has the attribute
$x=0$ means the individual does *not* have the attribute

Across the population, the proportion of individuals who possess the attribute is simply the mean of x. Let us call it π (note the change of symbol from when we considered the binomial

143

distribution). It is simple in this case to see what the variance of x is across the population. If there are N individuals in the population:

$$\text{Variance} = 1/N(1^2 + 1^2 + 1^2 + \cdots + 0^2 + 0^2 + \cdots) - \pi^2$$
$$= \pi - \pi^2$$
$$= \pi(1 - \pi)$$

Hence, the population standard deviation is

$$\text{Standard deviation} = \sqrt{[\pi(1 - \pi)]} \qquad (11.2)$$

Notice the relationship between these results and those quoted for the binomial distribution.

Estimating a proportion can, then, be considered a special case of the problem of estimating a mean. For this particular case, we have an especially easy way of finding the population standard deviation, using formula (11.2). The probability distribution of x across the population is clearly very far from normal, since it can only take two values. To use the results of the previous sections, we therefore need a large sample. A hundred could be viewed as a minimum size.

If we take a sample of size n, the sample mean of x, which is simply the proportion of the sample who possess the attribute of interest, will be the best single estimate of π, the population proportion. We call the sample proportion p. This was the reason for the previous change of symbols, so that we could distinguish between the population proportion and the sample proportion. Just as before, we can now form confidence intervals for our estimate, since, even in this case, given large samples, the sample mean will be approximately normally distributed. We have

$$\text{Standard error} = \sqrt{\left[\frac{\pi(1 - \pi)}{n}\right]}$$

So, for instance, a 95 per cent confidence interval for π is

$$p \pm 1.96 \sqrt{\left[\frac{\pi(1 - \pi)}{n}\right]}$$

Since we are trying to estimate π, we cannot use this formula as it stands. The usual approach is to use p as a proxy for π in the standard error calculation. For the 95 per cent confidence interval we arrive at

$$p \pm 1.96 \sqrt{\left[\frac{p(1 - p)}{n}\right]} \qquad (11.3)$$

Let us consider a simple example. Suppose a company takes a sample of 500 shoppers to estimate the proportion who buy their brand. It finds that 30 per cent of the sample buy the brand, which is its best estimate of its brand share across the whole population. In this example, $p = 0.3$, so a 95 per cent confidence interval is

$$0.3 \pm 1.96 \sqrt{\left(\frac{0.3 \times 0.7}{500}\right)}$$

which is

$$0.3 \pm 0.04$$

or

$$0.26 \text{ to } 0.34$$

It is often better to express this as a percentage; thus in this case the 95 per cent confidence interval for the brand share is between 26 and 34 per cent. It is simple to modify the formulas given to provide percentage directly, but if they are used in the forms given above, be careful to translate percentages into proportions before using the formula.

We can, of course, find other percentage confidence intervals. For instance, in the above example a 90 per cent confidence interval is between 26.6 and 33.4 per cent. The results of political opinion polls are often quoted with 90 per cent confidence intervals.

A common problem in sampling is to determine what size of sample is necessary for a given accuracy of result. Suppose the company in the above sample wanted their sample survey to give them a 95 per cent confidence interval of ± 0.02, for instance. What size of sample should they take? Let us be more general and suppose that the required interval is $\pm d$. From (11.3), we know that

$$d = 1.96 \sqrt{\left[\frac{p(1-p)}{n} \right]}$$

Rearranging this formula we deduce

$$n = \frac{3.84p(1-p)}{d^2} \tag{11.4}$$

The required sample size can therefore be determined from d, which will be specified, and from p, which we do not know until we have carried out the survey. The simplest way to proceed is to guess p; we may already have some idea of what it is likely to be and we can always try out several values to see what difference it makes to the estimate of n, the sample size. After all, we only need a very approximate answer, since we are in any case likely to round it to some convenient figure. Suppose the company guessed that the proportion was about 0.3; it would then estimate the required sample size as:

$$n = \frac{3.84 \times 0.3 \times 0.7}{0.0004}$$
$$= 2016$$

In practice it would probably then go for a sample of 2000, on the assumption that this would very nearly give the required accuracy. If it wanted to be surer of getting the required accuracy, it could try some other values for p to see what difference it made. We shall next deduce a result which would be helpful here.

Looking back at formula (11.4), we can see that the estimate of n depends on the value of the factor $p(1-p)$. The larger this factor, the larger will be the resulting value of n. But p can only lie between 0 and 1, since it is a proportion, so we can find the value of p which makes $p(1-p)$ as large as possible. Figure 11.1 shows how this factor relates to different values of p.

As can be seen, $p(1-p)$ attains its maximum value (of 0.25) when p is 0.5. It follows that for a given width of confidence interval, the largest possible sample size requirement results when

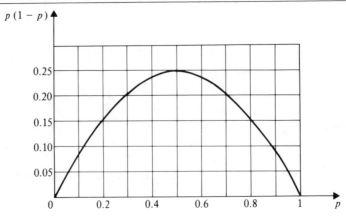

Figure 11.1

p equals 0.5. We can also deduce, more generally, that the nearer p is to 0.5, the larger will be the required sample size.

Returning to the example given above, we can see how this result might be used. Having guessed that the proportion to be estimated was about 0.3, we would err on the side of safety by using a p value nearer to 0.5. Suppose, for instance, we put p equal to 0.4 in formula (11.4):

$$n = \frac{3.84 \times 0.4 \times 0.6}{0.0004}$$
$$= 2304$$

The company might therefore decide to take a sample nearer to 2300 to be sure of getting the required accuracy for their estimate.

Finally, we can always calculate sample size on the worst possible assumption—that p is going to be near to 0.5. For a 95 per cent confidence interval of ± 0.02, this will give a sample size of:

$$n = \frac{3.84 \times 0.5 \times 0.5}{0.0004}$$
$$= 2400$$

One important practical problem to bear in mind when estimating a required sample size, especially when sampling individuals or households, is that we may not be able to contact every member of the sample, or of course people may refuse to cooperate. We shall be saying more on the general subject of non-response in the next section, but the immediate implication is that we may have to start with a larger sample than planned to get the required number of responses.

11.5 Sampling in practice

In this section we shall be looking at some of the practicalities of sampling, with the emphasis on sampling from human populations, although some of the points to be made apply more generally. We shall also see how some of the statistical results that have been discussed lead to certain practical applications.

146

Purpose of sampling

Why sample? The alternative is to consider every member of the population—a census. The main reasons are the obvious ones of speed, expense, and simplicity. Less obvious is the fact that a sample may actually give a more accurate result. Although the use of a sample will inevitably mean that estimates will only be approximate—so-called sampling error—there are many other sources of error which may apply. For instance, with a sample we may be able to use more skilled interviewers, get results over a shorter time span, and use a more detailed questionnaire. It has been shown, for instance, that the census of population is not always entirely accurate. Especially in inner city areas, there are numerous complications arising from multiple occupation of buildings, different cultural ideas of what constitutes a 'family', etc., which may confuse the relatively unskilled census enumerator. A skilfully conducted sample survey might even produce more accurate results in this case, by coping better with these difficulties.

The main advantage of sampling, however, is that for a much lower cost than a census it will often produce results that are 'near enough'.

Planning a sample survey

The importance of careful planning cannot be overstressed. Time spent at this stage can easily outweigh the advantage of a larger but badly planned sample. First of all, objectives should be clearly stated. These should be consistent with the method to be used and the resources available. Next we must decide on the coverage of the sample, e.g., whether individuals or households, the geographical regions to be covered, the kind of time span we are interested in (if we are sampling from records) and so on. Closely related is the question of what *sampling frames* are available. In theory we need, at least in principle, to be able to list every member of the population. In practice, this may not be possible—the lists or sampling frames available will usually only be an approximation to the target population. With human populations we are restricted to such lists as the list of voters, telephone directories, trade directories, etc. It is necessary to devise a means of sampling our target population using an available sampling frame. We must also take their likely inaccuracy into account.

As we have indicated, the above considerations are closely tied to the decision on what method to use and type of *instrument*. With human populations the main choice lies between personal interviews, telephone interviews, and postal surveys. These are in descending order of cost and accuracy and also differ in the nature of the enquiries that can reasonably be made. The usual instrument is some form of questionnaire or check list, and will clearly be influenced by the method to be adopted. The design of questionnaires is beyond the scope of this text and the interested reader is referred to the many books and papers on the subject. Suffice it to say that the wording of unambiguous questions is not at all easy, and traps for the unwary abound in the design of questionnaires.

If possible, a most helpful part of the planning process is the *pilot survey*. The idea is to run through at least part of the investigation with a small sample. This can give an indication of the adequacy of the sampling frame, the variability of response (useful in determining sample size, as we have seen), the non-response rate, the likely duration of the survey, and so on. At the very least, it is a good idea to pre-test the questionnaire if only to see if the questions are being correctly understood.

147

Avoiding bias

Bias occurs if for any reason there is a tendency for the sample to consistently over- or underestimate some characteristic of interest in the population. There are several possible sources of bias. The sampling frame may be biased as it may miss a part of the population that is likely to differ from the part included. For instance, a telephone directory will tend to under-represent the poorer members of society, and if used for a sample aimed at estimating consumption or political opinions will be likely to produce biased results. A non-random selection method, especially if it involves human choice, may lead to bias—this applies to quota sampling, for instance, to be discussed below. The wording of questions can introduce bias. It has been found, for instance, that people are more likely to agree with an interviewer than not, if a question is phrased in this way: 'Do you agree with the following . . .?' As a final example of bias, there is the problem of non-response. It is quite possible that those who cannot be traced or who will not answer differ from those included in the sample. If possible some non-respondents should be followed up to check for this. This is particularly important with postal surveys, where there are likely to be a large percentage of non-respondents.

Increasing precision

The precision of an estimate is simply related to the width of a confidence interval that could be constructed for it. The width of a confidence interval, as can be seen from formula (11.1), depends on the variability of the population (measured by the standard deviation) and the size of the sample. We can therefore increase precision by increasing sample size or reducing variability. The first method is obvious, but how do we reduce variability? One method is called *stratification*.

Instead of sampling at random from the whole population, we can divide the population into *strata* and randomly sample from each stratum. The stratum estimates are then weighted by the size of the stratum to yield a population estimate. Typical stratification would be by sex, age group, geographical region, urban/rural area, etc. If companies are to be sampled we might choose size or type of industry. The idea is to produce strata whose members are less variable with respect to the characteristic of interest than is the case for the whole population. For instance, if we are estimating consumption of beer, men are likely to vary less between them than they do from women. Thus if each stratum is less variable than the whole population, each stratum estimate will be more accurate. Hence the final weighted estimate for the whole population will be more accurate than would be the case for the same total sample size chosen randomly from the whole population. This approach has the additional benefit that the stratum estimates may themselves be of interest. The main limitation is in having an appropriately stratified sampling frame—we may simply not be able to identify the strata we want to use.

Sometimes samples are used to detect changes over time or differences between one population and another. If we take two random samples; as well as the differences we are trying to measure, there will also be the usual variability across a population. We can sometimes reduce variability by using *matched* samples. For differences over time, we could simply use the same sample twice or more times; this is the idea behind the *panel* sample where members of the sample are regularly questioned over a period of time. We may need to replace some members of the sample by others as similar as possible, but essentially we have eliminated across population variability and are left with the differences we are interested in.

In the two-population case, we can apply the same idea by taking two samples that are as similar as we can make them in all other respects than the one we are measuring. For instance, if we were testing the efficacy of a drug, we can compare it with a placebo on two different groups of patients, chosen so as to match in sex and age composition, severity of illness, etc. Again we are eliminating extraneous sources of variation to focus on the difference we are trying to establish. An example of the use of a matched sample is given in Chapter 12, the objective in that case being to estimate changes in earnings over a year.

Reducing cost

When sampling from, say, the U.K. population, a random sample, even with stratification, can be expensive to use if personal interviews are required. The usual approach is to take a small sample of regions and then sample from within those regions only. This is called *cluster sampling*. It reduces cost, because it reduces the geographical spread of the sample. On the other hand, it reduces precision, but this is more cheaply compensated for by increasing the sample size. In the extreme we would only sample from one locality. When this is done the area is not generally chosen at random; it is purposely selected as being in some way representative of the population. Thus certain constituencies are occasionally used in political opinion polling; the same idea is used in the United States with the so-called 'bellwether' states. Since, strictly speaking, this is no longer a randomly selected sample, we must be careful about applying results based on that assumption.

Another widely used non-random sampling method is the use of *quota sampling*, which again is used for economy reasons. In this approach, interviewers are given 'quotas' of subjects with particular characteristics, e.g., sex and age groups. They then stop people in the street and interview them in order to meet this quota. The quotas are chosen so as to give a stratified sample overall, but of course it is not random, since not everybody has an equal chance of walking past the interviewer.

When properly controlled and checked against the occasional random sample, these non-random methods can be very successful and are an economic way of taking a survey. They can give accurate results, but we cannot really use statistical theory to say how accurate, since confidence intervals are not applicable to a non-random sample. In fact, such samples are often treated as if they were random and confidence intervals given. This is only really legitimate where surveys are done regularly and occasionally compared to random sample surveys; this is the case, for instance, with some political opinion polls and television audience research.

11.6 Significance tests

So far we have focused attention on the use of samples for the estimation of some characteristic of the population. Another main use of sampling theory is in testing hypotheses about the population. This is very important in scientific work, for instance in testing new medical treatments or agricultural methods, where we want to test a hypothesis about the effectiveness of a treatment on a population, from the results obtained using a sample. Occasionally, the same type of problem arises in a business context. For instance, we might want to test whether an advertising campaign has increased knowledge about our product by asking a sample of potential consumers.

We shall not be developing a formal approach to significance testing and the interested reader is referred to the many introductory texts on statistical techniques. Instead, some of the main ideas behind significance testing will be demonstrated by example, using the idea of a confidence interval that we have already developed.

A typical problem is that of deciding whether a sample mean is consistent with the sample having come from a population with some specified population mean. The alternative is that the sample has come from some other population, or that the population mean has been changed from some previous value. Suppose, for instance, that a supplier provides sacks of cement to a nominal weight of 25 kg. A sample of sacks is weighed to see if they meet this specification. We test whether the sample comes from a population whose mean is 25 kg (the 'null hypothesis'), with the alternative that the sample comes from a population with some other mean (the 'alternative hypothesis'). We decide to reject the null hypothesis, if the probability that it is true is less than 0.05 (the 'significance level' of the test). We have the following information:

$$Population\ mean = 25$$
$$Population\ standard\ deviation = 0.5$$
$$Sample\ size = 20$$
$$Sample\ mean = 24.6$$

We assume that sample means are normally distributed, and test whether this sample mean could have come from a population with the above characteristics. To do so, we use the sample mean to form a confidence interval for the population mean. We want the confidence interval to be such that there is only a 0.05 probability that it will not include the population mean (resulting from our decision on the significance level of the test); it will therefore be a 95 per cent confidence interval. From formula (11.1), we have:

$$95\ per\ cent\ confidence\ interval\ is\ 24.6 \pm 1.96 \times \frac{0.5}{\sqrt{20}}$$
$$or\ 24.6 \pm 0.22$$
$$which\ is\ 24.38\ to\ 24.82$$

Since the supposed population mean of 25 is outside this interval, we reject the null hypothesis. In other words, it seems that the cement bags are not being produced to specification, and are in fact rather underweight.

There are two things in particular to notice about this example. First, the choice of significance level is arbitrary—we might have chosen 0.1 or 0.01, for example. The choice should depend on the consequences of making a wrong decision as a result of the test. A figure of 0.1 or 0.05 is commonly used, or, if we want to be very sure, 0.01 or even less. Usually the choice is not crucial, since the most likely consequence of rejecting a hypothesis is to embark on some further investigations that would put the matter beyond reasonable doubt. We must, of course, use the appropriate confidence interval to match the chosen significance level. The second point to note is that we need to know the population standard deviation in order to find the standard error of the mean. This will often not be known, in which case we have to estimate it from the sample and use this as a proxy. As long as the sample is reasonably large this is reasonable. We look at the problem of small samples in a later section.

We can apply the same type of procedure when testing a proportion rather than the mean of a variable. Suppose a company knows from previous tests that 30 per cent of the population know its brand name. After an advertising campaign, it takes a sample of 100 and finds that

150

35 per cent know its brand name. Has the advertising campaign had an effect? Applying the same procedure we have:

Null hypothesis: sample from population with proportion 0.30.
Alternative: the population proportion has changed.

We again choose a significant level of 0.05 and assume the sample proportion is normally distributed. Thus:

$$95 \text{ per cent confidence interval is } 0.35 \pm 1.96 \times \sqrt{\left(\frac{0.3 \times 0.7}{100}\right)}$$
$$\text{or } 0.35 \pm 0.090$$
$$\text{which is 0.26 to 0.43}$$

This comfortably includes the supposed population mean, so we cannot reject the null hypothesis. Thus there is no evidence that the advertising campaign has had an effect. We have used a rather small sample for testing a proportion; a large sample would have been better if we were only expecting a small effect. Note that we have used the population standard deviation in calculating the standard error.

It is instructive to apply the above procedure to opinion poll results. Newspapers sometimes claim that some event has caused a significant shift in support for one of the parties, when statistically this is just not the case.

The approach described can be extended in several ways. For instance, it can be used to test for a difference between two samples. The main complication arises in estimating the appropriate standard error, where there are several formulas which can be used depending on the circumstances and the assumptions that are to be made. We shall not pursue the subject any further here.

11.7 Small samples

In the sections on estimation and significance testing, we have noted the problem that arises when we do not know the population standard deviation, and hence cannot calculate the standard error. When the sample size is large we can get round this problem by finding the sample estimate of the standard deviation and using this as a proxy. With a small sample, however, this procedure is not satisfactory, since this estimate may be considerably in error and our confidence interval will therefore be inaccurate. To see how to get round this problem, let us re-state the fundamental result on which the methods so far described are based. It is:

$$\bar{x} \text{ is normally distributed with mean} = \mu$$

$$\text{and standard deviation} = \frac{\sigma}{\sqrt{n}} \quad \text{(the standard error)}$$

As we saw in Chapter 10, this is equivalent to saying:

$$\frac{\bar{x} - \mu}{\sigma/\sqrt{n}} \text{ is a standard normal variate} \quad (\text{mean} = 0, \text{ standard deviation} = 1)$$

Remember that this result is only exactly true if the sample is drawn from a normally distributed population; otherwise it is an approximation which improves as n gets larger. If we

151

have only a small sample, we can only use the methods we have developed if the population is normally distributed. This is the first point to note.

Suppose, furthermore, that we do not know σ, and only have s, the standard deviation estimated from the sample values. To find a confidence interval we need to know the probability distribution of

$$\frac{x - \mu}{s/\sqrt{n}}$$

We have replaced a constant, σ, by a variable, s, since the sample standard deviation will vary from sample to sample. This means that the expression we have arrived at will be more variable than a normally distributed variate. In fact, this probability distribution is known to be what is called the *t distribution*. Its shape depends on the sample size, but it looks very much like a normal distribution, except that it is more spread out for small values of n. As n gets larger, the shape of the t distribution gets closer to the normal distribution. To illustrate this, Table 11.1 shows a selection of the 97.5th percentile points for the t distribution—the multiplier to use for a 95 per cent confidence interval.

Table 11.1

Sample size	97.5th percentile
5	2.776
10	2.262
20	2.093
Large	1.960

As can be seen, the percentile gets closer to the normal distribution value of 1.96 as the sample size gets larger. For small values, the t distribution is clearly more widely spread. The effect of this will be to widen the confidence interval. It can be seen that this will not make much difference unless the sample size is very small—say about 10 or less. For instance, if the example of the cement sacks is re-worked on the assumption that the standard deviation used was derived from the sample (see Sec. 11.6) we would have

$$\text{95 per cent confidence interval is } 24.6 \pm 2.093 \times \frac{0.5}{\sqrt{20}}$$

$$\text{or } 24.6 \pm 0.23$$

Using the multiplier for the t distribution, when the sample size is 20, has made a difference of only 0.01 to each side of the confidence interval. For very small samples, however, the effect could be quite substantial.

To conclude this section, some points about the use of the t distribution should be noted. It only applies when the population values of interest are normally distributed. The sample standard deviation is the square root of the sample variance, which is calculated using a correction factor, as already described, to ensure that it is an unbiased estimate of the population variance. Tables of the t distribution are readily available, usually in the form of percentile points. However, they are not given for different sample sizes, but by a factor known as the 'degrees of freedom'. For the single sample cases we have looked at, this is equal to $n - 1$, one less than the sample size.

11.8 Sampling errors in correlation and regression

Correlation coefficients and regression equations are usually calculated from sample data, and the ideas developed in this chapter for single variable data can also be applied to the case where we are sampling values of two or more variables. We first consider the calculation of the product moment correlation coefficient (see Chapter 7).

If we calculate a correlation coefficient from a sample, we can ask the question: Did it arise by chance, or is there a significant relationship between the variables? In order to answer this we can construct a null hypothesis that the sample value comes from a population with a mean of 0 (no correlation), with the alternative that the population correlation coefficient is non-zero. We can then, as before, use a table of the sampling distribution of the correlation coefficient to determine whether the null hypothesis can be rejected.

There are two main difficulties. First, it is necessary to make some rather restrictive assumptions about how the variables we are correlating vary across the population to determine the probability distribution of the sample correlation coefficient. The tables should therefore be used with caution. Second, unless the sample is very small, a significant value will be rather small—too small for the correlation to be of likely interest if we are looking for a simple two-variable relationship. In practice, especially when the samples are small, we are likely to be comparing several correlation coefficients, in which case the procedure just described is not appropriate. The important point is to be aware of the possibility of sampling error; a formal significance test of the type described will not often be worth while.

We also saw in Chapter 7 how to find a regression equation, which would again usually be calculated using a sample of values. Just as we can ask the question whether a correlation coefficient is significant, so can we with a regression equation. We can in fact use several types of significance test for a regression. First, we can test for overall significance, i.e., we can test whether the sample provides evidence of *any* linear relationship between the variables. If this test is positive we can go on to test for the significance of the *a* and *b* parameters estimated. Are they significantly different from zero? In practice, this procedure is of most importance when we are considering *multiple regression* or the relationship between one variable and *several* other variables, but we do not include details here. If the procedure described in Chapter 7 is followed and a reasonably high value of R (the coefficient of determination) is found, then the relationship will certainly be significant. If R is not close to 1, a single variable relationship would not be of very much use.

What will be of interest, however, is the determination of a confidence interval for the predictions made from the regression equation. There are two possible sources of error for such a prediction.

The variability in y for a given value of x

Unless the relationship between y and x is perfect, the y value related to a particular x value may vary about the value that would be predicted from the regression line. In Sec. 7.3, this was the source of error that we analysed by examining the errors resulting from using the regression equation for the sample of values available. The method described there is reasonably straightforward, but we will now describe an approach which is more efficient computationally, and which leads to a more accurate result. We will use the same example of Chapter 7 so that a comparison can be made between the two approaches. In that example, y (the dependent variable, the one to be predicted) was a delivery cost and x (the independent variable from which the prediction is to be made) was the customer's round-trip distance. The steps in the analysis are as follows:

1. Find R, using formula (7.7); thus:

$$R = (0.9804)^2 = 0.9612$$

Equivalently, formula (7.6) can be squared and R found directly.

2. Find $\sum e^2$, the sum of the squared errors using the following formula:

$$\sum e^2 = (1 - R)\left[\sum y^2 - \frac{1}{n}(\sum y)^2 \right] \tag{11.5}$$

Thus:

$$\sum e^2 = (1 - 0.9612)(177.121) = 6.872$$

This is in fact very close to the value of 6.86 found before, but will in general be more accurate. It is also much quicker to use this procedure, as we do not have to find the predicted y value for every x value in the sample as we did before.

3. As indicated in Chapter 7, we can now estimate the standard error of prediction, when using the regression equation, from the following formula. We call the standard error s_p:

$$s_p = \sqrt{\left(\frac{\sum e^2}{n-2} \right)} \tag{11.6}$$

Thus we have:

$$s_p = \sqrt{\left(\frac{6.872}{8} \right)} = 0.927$$

This result gives us an indication of the variability of the y values about the regression line. As we have seen, if we make the further assumption that the y values are normally distributed, with the regression line prediction as a mean in each case, we can construct a confidence interval for a predicted y value. In Chapter 7 we saw an example of the construction of a 95 per cent confidence interval. This approach is reasonable, providing we have a large sample—greater than about 30, say. With a small sample, such as the one in this example, there are two reasons why the result will be inaccurate. The first reason is that we are using a standard error which has been estimated from the sample. As we saw in the previous section of this chapter, when a small sample is used we should use the t distribution rather than the normal distribution. Thus, for a 95 per cent confidence interval we need the appropriate 97.5th percentile of a t distribution in place of the multiplier used for a normal distribution (1.96, or 2 as approximated in Chapter 7). As we mentioned before, the t distribution depends on a factor called the 'degrees of freedom', which for a regression will equal $n-2$, *two* less than the sample size. From tables, the multiplier for a 95 per cent confidence interval when the sample size is 10 can be found to be 2.306. This will lead to a marked increase in the size of the confidence interval as calculated on the assumption of a normal distribution. However, there is a second reason why our previous calculation of the confidence interval was inaccurate; this is due to the second source of error in using a regression line for prediction purposes.

The error in estimating the regression equation

What we have said so far depends on the assumption that the equation we are using for the regression is correct, i.e., that it has been calculated from the entire population of possible y

and x values. In fact, the equation was found from a sample, and a different sample would have given a different equation. Thus the predicted value of y, about which y varies, is itself a variable point and not fixed as we have assumed. It can be shown that this additional source of error depends on the specific value of x we are using to make the prediction, and that it can simply be added on to the standard error, as already found, in determining a confidence interval. If we are predicting y from some particular value of x, suppose it is $x=k$, then the variance of y can be found from the following formula:

$$s^2 = \left[1 + \frac{1}{n} + \frac{(k-\bar{x})^2}{\sum x^2 - (1/n)(\sum x)^2} \right] s_p^2 \tag{11.7}$$

For our example, suppose we are estimating the delivery cost of a customer for whom the round-trip distance was 50 miles. At the end of Sec. 7.2 we found that this gave an estimated cost of 12.67. To find a 95 per cent confidence interval for this prediction we first find the variance estimate from (11.7). With k specified as 50 we have

$$s^2 = \left[1 + \frac{1}{10} + \frac{(50-48.5)^2}{4404.5} \right] (0.927)^2$$

Performing these calculations and taking the square root of the result will give the estimated standard deviation for y as

$$s = \sqrt{(1+0.1+0.0005)}(0.927) = 0.972$$

It can be seen that this varies only slightly with the value of x chosen, unless it is a considerable distance from the mean of x. Using the appropriate t value, which we stated above is 2.306, we find that the 95 per cent confidence interval is

$$12.67(\pm)2.306 \times 0.972$$

that is,

$$12.67(\pm)2.24$$

It is much larger than the approximate interval we found in Chapter 7.

It should be emphasized that this rather laborious procedure is only really necessary when we use a small sample to estimate a regression equation. For a large sample, the second and third terms in (11.7) will be extremely small, and the difference between the t value and the normal distribution multiplier will be negligible.

Finally, we note that just as we can perform a significance test of the estimated values of a and b, we can also find confidence intervals for these estimates. If a computer package is used for the regression calculations, this information will often be included with the output. Indeed, all the other calculations we have illustrated will often be included, which should indicate the value of using a computer for regression analysis!

11.9 The chi squared (χ^2) test for categorized data

We have concentrated throughout this text on the analysis of data resulting from some type of measurement. The main exception has been in the consideration of attribute data, where we are interested in the proportion of a sample or population who possess some particular attribute. We can extend this idea to the classification of a sample into more than two categories. For instance, we could divide a political opinion sample into categories corresponding to each political party or we could categorize a market research sample into those purchasing each of a range of competitive products. Published economic data are also sometimes split into categories, for instance, the samples taken in the earnings and unemployment surveys are split by region.

The requirement for a statistical test arises in particular when we have a two-way classification. For instance, we might compare voting intentions with the sex of each member of the sample or we might compare brand preferences with the region in which the sample member lives. This will give rise to such questions as: Do men and women differ in their voting behaviour? or Do brand preferences differ from region to region? Where such data arise from a sample, we may well find such differences, but of course the pattern we find will vary from sample to sample and could just occur through chance. We require, therefore, a statistical significance test which will tell us whether the differences we observe could have occurred by chance or not. The χ^2 test can be used for this purpose. We will illustrate its use with some data from the new earnings survey[9] (the relevant data are quoted in assignment 1 at the end of Part Four), shown in Table 11.2.

Table 11.2 Numbers in selected regional and income categories (April 1979 sample)

	South East	South West	Northern	Totals
Lowest income category (below £45 per week)	178	48	28	254
Highest income category (£200 or more per week)	121	6	25	152
Totals	299	54	53	406

Reproduced from *New Earnings Survey*, April 1979, with the permission of the Controller of Her Majesty's Stationery Office.

The question we ask is: Do the regions differ significantly in the numbers of wage earners in the lowest and highest earnings categories? If there was no difference, we would expect the same proportion of low and high incomes in each region. In fact we would expect the sample to split in the same way that the totals do, with the proportion 254/406 in the low income category and the remainder in the high income category. Thus, of the 299 sampled in the South East region we would expect $(254/406) \times 299 = 187$ to fall into the low income category. In general, this is equivalent to saying that the expected number falling in any position of the table (say row i and column j) is E_{ij}, where

$$E_{ij} = \frac{\text{total row } i \times \text{total column } j}{\text{grand total}} \qquad (11.8)$$

Using this formula, the expected numbers for all the other positions in the table can be calculated. They are shown, compared to the observed values, in Table 11.3. Notice that the row and column totals for the expected numbers are the same as for the observed frequencies. Looking at Table 11.3, we see that there are rather fewer low income earners and rather more high income earners in the South East than we would expect. The same is true, perhaps rather surprisingly, in the Northern region, whereas the reverse is the case in the South West. The χ^2 test will determine whether these differences can be reasonably attributed to sampling error.

156

Table 11.3 Observed/expected numbers

	South East	South West	Northern
Low	178/187	48/34	28/33
High	121/112	6/20	25/20

The χ^2 test for this type of data is as follows:

1. For each position in the table, square the difference between the observed and expected frequencies and divide the result by the expected frequency. The χ^2 test statistic is the sum of the resulting figures. Symbolically, if O_{ij} represents the observed frequency in row i, column j and E_{ij} is the related expected frequency, then:

$$\chi^2 = \sum \frac{(O_{ij} - E_{ij})^2}{E_{ij}} \tag{11.9}$$

2. Compare the resulting value with tabulated values of the appropriate χ^2 probability distribution. For instance, for a test at the 0.05 level of significance, we use the 95th percentile point. The χ^2 distribution depends on a 'degrees of freedom' factor, as did the t distribution. If there are r rows and c columns in the table, degrees of freedom $= (r-1) \times (c-1)$. If the value calculated using (11.9) is less than the tabulated value, then we cannot reject the hypothesis that the observed differences arose by chance (the null hypothesis in this case). Otherwise, we have grounds for accepting that the differences are significant and not due to sampling error (the alternative hypothesis).

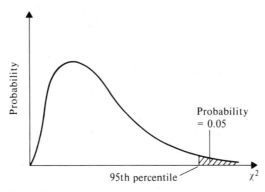

Figure 11.2

Before we apply this procedure to our example, let us look briefly at its rationale. If, in the population as a whole, the two types of categorization we are comparing are independent of each other, we would expect, on average, the observed frequencies from samples of a given size to be close to the expected frequencies we have estimated, using (11.8). The χ^2 value we calculate using (11.9) should therefore, on average, be close to zero. Its actual value for any particular sample will vary from this average, reflecting the fluctuations we would get in the observed frequencies. The probability distribution of χ^2 can be deduced, and its frequency curve will look something like the one illustrated in Fig. 11.2. Notice that χ^2 must always be positive and that the probability tails away sharply as the values of χ^2 increase. The 95th

157

percentile is shown on the diagram, and obtaining a χ^2 value which exceeds this is most unlikely—the probability is of course 0.05. Thus, if, as a result of analysis of the obtained sample, we get a large χ^2, either we have chosen a very unusual sample or, more likely, the hypothesis of independence we have made is incorrect, and the two types of categories we are comparing are related in some way.

The shape of the χ^2 distribution depends on the number of comparisons we are making between observed and expected frequencies, since the more of these we make, the greater will be the probability of a large χ^2 value. Equivalently, this means that, say, the 95th percentile will increase as we increase the number of comparisons. A small selection of 95th percentile points is given in Table 11.4.

Table 11.4

Degrees of freedom	95th percentile
1	3.841
2	5.991
5	11.070
10	18.307

Let us now return to the analysis of our example. The observed and expected frequencies are shown in Table 11.3 and, following the procedure outlined above, we calculate the test statistic using (11.9):

$$\chi^2 = \frac{(178-187)^2}{187} + \frac{(48-34)^2}{34} + \frac{(28-33)^2}{33} + \frac{(121-112)^2}{112} + \frac{(6-20)^2}{20} + \frac{(25-20)^2}{20}$$
$$= 0.433 + 5.765 + 0.758 + 0.723 + 9.800 + 1.250$$
$$= 18.729$$

For this example, degrees of freedom $= (2-1)(3-1) = 2$. We saw above that the 95th percentile of the χ^2 distribution for 2 degrees of freedom is 5.991. The calculated value comfortably exceeds this, so we reject the hypothesis that the region and earnings categories are independent. In other words, there seems to be significant differences in the numbers of wage earners in the lowest and highest income groups between the regions considered.

We conclude with some additional points about the use of this test. A table which compares a two-way categorization is called a *contingency table*, and this will be found to be only one of several applications of the χ^2 distribution if statistical texts are consulted. Another important use is in testing the fit of a theoretical frequency distribution to empirical data; it also arises when considering the probability distribution of sample variances. For about 30 degrees of freedom or more, the shape of the distribution is close to that of the normal distribution, a phenomenon we have noted for several other probability distributions. Again, the interested reader is referred elsewhere for further details.

It is important to note that the χ^2 distribution is only an approximation to the distribution of the statistic calculated using (11.9) for a contingency table. One of the main reasons for this is that the observed freqencies are whole numbers, whereas the χ^2 values are continuously variable. The practical consequence of this is that we should ensure that the expected frequencies are not, on the whole, too small. As a rule of thumb they should be at least 5, with most of them being 10 or more. If necessary, some categories can be combined to ensure this.

The approximation can be improved using what is known as Yate's correction, whereby each observed/expected difference is reduced by 0.5, but this will only make a noticeable difference when the frequencies are small. It is also a good idea to calculate the expected frequencies to at least one place of decimals where the frequencies are small.

Finally, it should be noted that this test is only appropriate where the data derive from a random sample and where the entries in the contingency table are *frequencies*, i.e., record the actual number from the sample falling into some combination of categories. In particular, the test cannot be used where the entries are percentages.

12. Wages and earnings

12.1 The use of published information

Published information on wages and earnings can play an important part in many areas of decision-making. As before three main users can be identified.

Government

First, governments will use the data to help formulate a variety of economic and social policies. Among the most obvious applications would be the establishment of incomes policy. If we accept the economists' definition of incomes policy as being any government intervention in the process of free collective bargaining then it becomes apparent that these policies have been operated more often than not in the post Second World War period in the United Kingdom. Most governments in this period have felt obliged, at some point in their span of office, to introduce some form of incomes policy, whether it be to establish 'norms' for wage settlements, or statutory backed wage increases, or wage 'freezes', or whether it is linked to price and productivity increases, or even where it is referred to as a policy for incomes! The point is that recent past information on wages and earnings would be essential when framing an incomes policy since the major object of the exercise is to slow down the rate of increase of wages and earnings from the previous period in order to slow down the rate of inflation.

Other economic applications of the data would be where regional wages and earnings information is used to influence regional policy. Combined with other indicators wages data can identify those less prosperous areas requiring assistance through the application of regional policy.

The data would be vitally important for such social policies as equal pay for men and women and minimum pay legislation. In both cases the published information would indicate the shortfall that has to be made up if such policies are introduced. We have had, in the United Kingdom, equal pay legislation for a number of years now and the published statistics can be used to establish how effective the legislation has been, while the determination of a legal minimum wage should follow an accurate profile of wages and earnings being earned in the economy.

Employers

For employers, the data will play a part in wage negotiations, manpower policy, and could influence relocation decisions. In practice, however, published data are unlikely to be detailed enough for determining specific wage offers by employers, although it could provide essential background information on average earnings in comparable industries, regions, or occupations, particularly where a restructuring of wages at company level is being introduced. More detailed statistics would be provided by the company itself, or trade association, reflecting, among other things, local market conditions and circumstances.

160

Regional data could influence relocation decisions, particularly where companies are labour intensive (i.e., they use a lot of labour compared with capital and other inputs) and are anxious to move to a relatively cheap labour source. However, it should be realized that for this type of policy problem, as with manpower policy, the business unit will be more concerned with the total cost of labour rather than simply one element of it—wages and earnings. In addition to salaries, the cost of employing labour could include subsidized canteens, transport, training, employers' national insurance contributions, payment in kind, private welfare payments, redundancy payments, and any payroll tax.

Employers are also likely to be interested in information on low pay in order to assess the cost to industries if minimum pay legislation were introduced, and to act as a pressure group in the preceding debate.

Trade unions

The third main group of users, trade unions, will use the data principally for collective bargaining purposes. Increasingly, union negotiators are becoming more sophisticated in wage negotiations, arming themselves with earnings information on an industrial and occupational basis at regional, national, and even international level, in order to support wage claims, together with statistics related to productivity improvements and price changes since the last settlement. Thus it is a well-established practice to justify wage claims on productivity, cost of living, and comparability grounds. The comparability basis does not simply reflect a claim by any union to bring its members' earnings in line with that of similar workers elsewhere since, additionally, unions have a view of their 'rightful' position in the 'league table' of earnings and the earnings differences between groups of workers. If this position is disturbed by some workers obtaining an increase in earnings then other unions will usually make every effort to restore the former 'norm differential'. Wage settlements in one part of the economy will invariably influence other claims and settlements.

Bearing this in mind it is clear that union negotiators will require a substantial array of wide-ranging and detailed data in order to play their part in the collective bargaining process.

Additionally, they act as a pressure group for low paid workers and other deprived groups, and are therefore clearly interested in obtaining the relevant information.

12.2 The published data

Information on average earnings and wages and average hours worked can be found in the *Employment Gazette*,[8] which is the prime source for some data and a secondary source for other data published separately.

There was a major change in the collection and provision of data in 1968 with the introduction of the *New Earnings Survey*.[9] This new approach was an attempt at improving the coverage, quality, and range of data following increasing criticism of available information from employers organizations, trade unions, and even government departments. It would be worth while, briefly, to consider the shortcomings of published data prior to 1968 in order to place the *New Earnings Survey* in its proper context, and to understand more fully the marked improvement arising from the new approach.

Data prior to 1968

Weaknesses of published data before 1968 can be summed up as being the three 'ins'—inconsistent, incomplete, and inadequate.

Inconsistency in the data stemmed from the fact that gaps in the information were filled by the steady proliferation of special surveys relating to specific industries or groups of workers. Inevitably this ad hoc approach resulted in a range of different reporting units being used and differences in frequency and timing of these surveys. Thus, the earliest information available in the post Second World War period was a survey made twice a year (April and October) into the earnings of manual workers and an annual survey (October) into the earnings of white collar workers (administrative, technical, and clerical workers). Later a monthly earnings survey was introduced which did not distinguish between manual and non-manual labour and was concentrated on manufacturing, extractive, and construction industries. The resulting monthly earnings index for these industries was based on a sample survey which included all firms with more than 500 employees but only a proportion of the medium and small sized companies. Also, in this period an occupational analysis of earnings was established which was conducted in January and June each year and covered many occupations in engineering for adult male manual workers. Finally, two total labour cost surveys were carried out by the Department of Employment in 1964 and 1968 which shed more light on the cost of employing labour by including elements mentioned earlier, in addition to salaries. Average total labour cost per employee was calculated for industrial categories within manufacturing, construction, mining, public utilities, banking and insurance, transport, and public administration.

Despite the proliferation of information over time there were still several areas of economic activity and employment for which little, or no, earnings data were available. As we have seen, the manufacturing sector, despite basic inconsistencies, was fairly well covered, but it was in the service sector that gaps in the information were apparent.

Finally, the total range of data provided was inadequate. Even for those areas that were covered there was little, or no, information on the composition of pay (the make-up of pay from basic wage rates to overtime payment and bonuses), on the lower paid workers, nor any information on the earnings of those workers effected by union negotiated agreements as distinct from non-union settlements.

It is interesting to note that criticisms by users and potential users of the data encouraged the Department of Employment to improve the quality of the data provided, and is a clear indication of the importance of this information to decision makers in the economy.

The *New Earnings Survey*[9]

This survey, introduced in 1968, is conducted in early April each year using a relatively small sample (approximately one in every 130 of full-time employees) but results in a comprehensive package of published information. The full results are published each year in six parts under the heading, *New Earnings Survey*. The six parts relate to different aspects of the enquiry, i.e.:

> Part A—summary analysis, giving general results and details of the survey method
> Part B—earnings affected by collective agreements and wages boards and councils
> Part C—industrial analysis of earnings
> Part D—occupational analysis of earnings
> Part E—regional analysis of earnings
> Part F—part-time earnings of women workers

Given these broad classifications the information provided includes:

1. Average gross weekly earnings.
2. Composition of pay (including overtime payment, bonuses, payments by results, commission, payment for unsocial hours—weekend working, night work, etc.).
3. Average gross hourly earnings, including and excluding overtime.
4. Distribution of weekly and hourly earnings around the averages.
5. Average weekly hours and overtime hours.
6. Distribution of hours around the average.
7. Increase in average earnings since the previous survey.

Much of these data is broken down into manual and non-manual workers, men and women, full-time and part-time, and age patterns of earnings.

The survey method

Approximately 170 000 employees are selected each year in a random sample based on national insurance numbers that end in a specified pair of digits. Before 1975, the DHSS provided the name and address of each person's employer to the Department of Employment but given the final phasing out of national insurance cards in that year and its replacement by the PAYE scheme the Inland Revenue now provides the employer information. This administrative change did have some impact on the coverage but will be discussed later in the section dealing with interpretation problems. The forms are then sent to the employer for completion under the authority of the 1947 Statistics of Trade Act.

The questions asked reflect the range of published information listed above; thus questions relate to gross weekly and hourly earnings, and hours worked, during the pay period in early April of the employee in the sample, composition of pay, industry, occupation, age group of the employee, region, type and size of company (in terms of total employees), etc.

It should be clear, then, that the published information assumes that each person in the sample is representative for each of the classifications, i.e., he or she is representative for that industry, occupation, region, age group, manual or non-manual group etc. The obvious problem for users of data based on a sampling approach is the reliability of the sample—the familiar problem of interpreting 'sample statistics'. The question of reliability will be discussed later but one aspect of the survey that has some bearing on this matter is the so-called 'matched sample'.

Matched sample

Although the survey is based on a random sample, it is not a completely different sample each year. A high proportion of people included in one year would have been included in the previous year as well. This is referred to as a 'matched sample', and normally involves about 130 000 of the total sample of approximately 170 000. It is important for two reasons.

First, greater precision can be achieved compared with having a completely different sample each year. With separate samples it would be difficult to judge whether any recorded changes in earnings, etc., from one survey to another reflected a real change or were merely the result of a different sample being used. Improving the precision in this way is of considerable significance for a survey based on a small sample relative to the range and detail of the information published.

Second, the matched sample allowed, for the first time, the possibility of examining occupational and spatial mobility and how earnings capacity was affected. Some commentators felt that this was the most substantial innovation of the *New Earnings Survey* for by including a large number of the same people in consecutive surveys light can be shed on the way people move between jobs, occupations, and areas of employment.

Summary of the *New Earnings Survey*

This new approach was clearly a marked improvement on the information previously available. Being a comprehensive survey the range and depth of data obtained have been increased considerably while consistency has been maintained. For the first time, earnings information is available for the whole range of economic activity and new features introduced, including the matched sample and effects of collective agreements on earnings. By and large, the major weaknesses in published data prior to the introduction of this survey have been overcome.

Although the published information is very comprehensive the Department of Employment can make available (subject to confidentiality) unpublished data which are in even greater detail.

12.3   Interpreting the data

Despite these improvements in quality and range several problems of interpretation remain and certain criticisms have been made. These can be considered under the following headings.

Sampling problems

The most obvious difficulty concerns the fact that the total data published are based on a sample survey with all the usual interpretation problems of sample statistics. However, four factors serve to mitigate this difficulty. First, as we have seen, the matched sample element of the survey improves precision appreciably. Second, for most of the data on average earnings and hours, a measure called the 'standard error' is also published. Its calculation, meaning, and significance has been dealt with thoroughly in the previous chapter and therefore only a brief explanation of the term is required here. Basically, the standard error provides a statistical measure of the potential margin of error between an estimate based on a sample (in this case, average earnings and hours) and the true measure for the population as a whole (which would, of course, be obtained if a complete census was conducted). Clearly a large standard error implies that the true measure could differ substantially from the published estimate, while a small standard error would suggest that the estimate is very close to the true measure. This is more fully understood when it is appreciated that generally the size of the standard error is determined by the size of the sample relative to the total population (in statistical terms) and variability of the data obtained. A relatively small sample together with wide differences in values obtained would generally lead to a large calculated standard error, while a relatively large sample and narrow range of values would invariably result in a small standard error measure.

The inclusion of this measure for most of the detailed figures published is clearly designed to aid users of the data for it does suggest the degree of reliability that can be placed on the published estimates. In addition (and our third factor), where the standard error is greater than 2 per cent of the estimate, the actual value is enclosed in brackets in order to highlight the need for extra caution in using the data. Fourth, some results of the survey are felt to be particularly suspect because of a small sample and are therefore not published at all (the results for an MLH industry in a particular region, for example).

Thus in these four ways—the innovation of the matched sample, the inclusion of standard error measurements, the placing in parentheses of large standard errors, and the decision not to publish what are felt to be particularly unreliable estimates—the Department is attempting to improve the usefulness of the published figures.

Scope and coverage differences

A further, though minor, difficulty concerns changes in the scope of the survey since its inception in 1968. It should be realized that survey questions alter each year, with some questions being dropped or modified and new ones being asked. However, a more substantial change took place in 1975 with the replacement of national insurance cards by the PAYE scheme. The effect of this administrative change on the survey method has been outlined earlier in this chapter, although its real importance is the resulting change in coverage. Since 1975, then, only those employees who pay national insurance through the PAYE scheme are covered by the survey. Those with earnings below the deduction card limit (i.e., low wage earners who consequently do not pay tax or national insurance contributions—mainly young people and women part-time workers) are therefore not covered by the survey. However, given this change, it is now possible for those people with more than one job, and for which the Inland Revenue has records, to be included more than once in the sample—those with a full-time and part-time job, or those with more than one part-time job. The reader should recall that a similar point was made concerning employment data, and for similar reasons.

Delays in publishing

The third consideration relates to the time lag in publishing the results. We have seen elsewhere that one of the drawbacks of comprehensive annual surveys is the time required to collate and publish the material. The full results of the new earnings survey take about a year to be published, which can present some difficulty for users, particularly in the area of collective bargaining where it is vital to have the most up-to-date information but where, in practice, the available data may be as much as eighteen months out of date. This problem has become more acute in recent years, given the higher rates of inflation and the resulting greater frequency of wage negotiations. The Department has responded to this problem, however, by publishing in the *Employment Gazette* certain key results, referred to as 'streamlined analysis', and broader results, under the heading of 'summary analysis', in the autumn following the April survey.

Linked to the problem of time lags is the actual timing of the survey in April each year. Difficulty lies in the fact that for some groups of workers (those in the public sector particularly) April conventionally sees the establishment of new wage awards, but in some cases the pay settlement is delayed several months due to protracted negotiations; however, once settlement is reached the new awards are then back-dated to April. In these circumstances, the increase in earnings will go unrecorded for that year's survey but will be included in the following year.

165

Users of the data must therefore be careful since for those industries and occupations which operate with April settlements the published information may well be invalid for that year.

This problem is clearly a crucial one for the published information dealing with increases in average earnings since the previous survey, and consequently where pay setttlements are delayed in any year, the information on increases in average earnings is omitted from the table but is included as footnotes to the tables.

12.4 Other published data

In addition to the *New Earnings Survey*[9] two further earnings surveys are conducted, one for manual workers and the other for non-manual workers. Both are conducted in October each year, with the results being published in the *Employment Gazette*.[8]

Manual workers survey

This survey into the earnings and hours of manual workers was mentioned in the earlier part of this chapter and has remained in operation despite the introduction of the new earnings survey; indeed, it has been conducted periodically since the late nineteenth century. The information provided, though not as extensive as the new earnings survey since occupational analysis and composition of pay are not included, nevertheless does give a detailed account for manual workers at the MLH level of the SIC.

The survey is based on factory workers, including foremen and supervisors and those working in warehouses, transport, and canteens (but only if employed by the firm), and separate information is published for men, women, youths, and girls, being broken down into full-time and part-time workers. The detail published includes the following:

1. *Industry groups at the SIC order level*
   (a) Average weekly earnings
   (b) Average weekly hours
   (c) Average hourly earnings
2. *Industries at the MLH level*
   (a) Average weekly earnings and numbers employed
   (b) Average hours and hourly earnings
3. *Regional analysis at the SIC order level for full-time men and women*
   (a) Average weekly earnings for men
   (b) Average weekly hours for men
   (c) Average hourly earnings for men
   (d) Average weekly earnings for women
   (e) Average weekly hours for women
   (f) Average hourly earnings for women
4. *Additional data*
   (a) Summary results of the complete survey
   (b) Time series analysis of movements in average earnings and hours
   (c) Average earnings and hours of National Health Service workers

166

The industries covered include:

1. The manufacturing sector (SIC order levels III to XIX)
2. Mining and quarrying, except coal (SIC order level II)
3. Construction (SIC order level XX)
4. Gas, electricity, and water (SIC order level XXI)
5. Transport and communication, except railways (SIC order level XXII)
6. Certain miscellaneous services (SIC order level XXVI)
7. Public administration (SIC order level XXVII)

The range of earnings data is based on total gross earnings and therefore in addition to basic pay would include all overtime, bonuses, unsocial hours payments, etc., in the pay week of the survey in October.

Like the new earnings survey it is based on a sampling approach, although the sample is extensive with returns being obtained on a voluntary basis from about 40 000 establishments, which represents two-thirds of manual workers covered by the survey.

Uses and interpretation The greater industrial detail provided by this survey, compared with the new earnings survey, is particularly useful for collective bargaining purposes where manual workers are concerned. However, since earnings are defined in gross rather than net terms, differences found between industries might not simply reflect basic pay, but differences in composition of the workforce (skilled and unskilled workers) and the opportunity for earning extra income (overtime, bonuses, etc.), which is likely to differ between industries.

Finally, it should be noted that the April earnings survey for manual workers is still conducted, but with the introduction of the new earnings survey in April each year it now concentrates on only a few industries.

Non-manual workers survey

This survey, like the manual workers survey, is conducted each October. It was suspended for a time with the establishment of the new earnings survey but was reestablished in 1973 following a European Economic Community (EEC) request to each member country for information on earnings for this broad category of workers.

Although it can be considered the counterpart to the manual workers survey there are some differences. First, the survey is conducted under the 1947 Statistics of Trade Act and is therefore obligatory. Second, the industries covered are more limited, being confined to the index of production industries (manufacturing, mining and quarrying, construction, and gas, electricity, and water). Third, information is obtained only from full-time workers. Fourth, there is no information on hours worked and therefore no published data on hourly earnings, which may not be particularly meaningful for non-manual workers anyway.

The similarities include the fact, first, that earnings are defined in gross terms and therefore include overtime payments, bonuses, etc., and, second, that a sample approach is used which again is extensive, representing about 80 per cent of non-manual workers in the relevant industries.

The workers covered by the survey include management, professional, scientific, technical, marketing, sales representatives, and office staff, while the information published is on an industrial basis for males, females, and males and females combined.

Finally, although not a criticism, it should be realized that the new earnings survey and the

167

two surveys just described provide detailed information but only on an annual basis. Thus, as we have seen elsewhere, more frequent and up-to-date information may be required by decision makers. Consequently an index of average earnings is compiled each month by the Department of Employment and published in the *Employment Gazette*. It is to this that we now turn.

Monthly index of average earnings

Mention was made of this index earlier in the chapter where it was described as one of the many pieces of information on earnings prior to 1968. It was actually introduced in January 1963, covering the extractive, manufacturing, public utilities, construction, and a few service sector industries. However, from January 1976 the coverage has been extensively increased and information each month, in index form, is available for all the 27 SIC order level categories with the following exceptions:

> SIC order level I, fishing excluded
> SIC order level XXII, sea transport excluded
> SIC order level XXIV, business services excluded
> SIC order level XXV, some services (private sector education, universities, accountancy, and legal services) excluded
> SIC order level XXVII, defence excluded

The information on which the index is calculated each month comes from a sample of private sector firms with more than 25 employees (about 8000 firms are involved); returns from public corporations such as coal-mining, railways, and public utilities; and data provided by the Ministry of Agriculture, Fisheries, and Food for agriculture.

Since it is a monthly index it is clearly essential for the returns to be received and processed promptly. Consequently, the information requested concerns only the total earnings of weekly and monthly paid employees and the number of employees involved. There is no disaggregation into types of workers (by sex, age, occupation, full-time/part-time), regions, or composition of pay.

The data for monthly paid employees are recalculated on a weekly basis and then combined with the weekly paid information. The resulting index, with (currently) January 1976 = 100, is calculated and published for (1) the whole economy, (2) the index of production industries, and (3) the manufacturing industries. Under all three headings seasonally adjusted figures and changes over the previous 12 months are also included in the published information. Finally, the data are broken down into the 27 SIC order level categories with the exceptions mentioned above.

The advantage of this index compared with the annual surveys, previously discussed, is, of course, in providing speedy and up-to-date information on the current trends of earnings in the economy. For businesses this information would be particularly useful since increases in wage costs could lead to the necessity to adjust prices where long-term contracts are concerned. Governments can use the index as an indication of the current performance of the economy and consequently could influence changes in economic policy. More specifically, changes in the index do have some bearing on revisions being made to social security payments.

In summary, then, the major sources of information on wages, earnings, and related topics include annual information provided by the new earnings survey, the manual workers survey,

168

and its non-manual counterpart, together with a monthly index of average earnings. The last three can be found in the *Employment Gazette*, as can the key results of the new earnings survey. It is this latter survey that provides the most comprehensive analysis of earnings for the total economy, although the manual workers survey does give a more detailed industrial analysis, while the monthly index indicates current earning trends. In addition to these regular sources of data the Department of Employment also periodically conducts special enquiries into total labour costs, as we have already seen.

13. Income and wealth distribution

The subject of income and wealth distribution concerns the way in which total incomes and total wealth in an economy are spread across the total population. Although business concerns and producing units in the private and public sector do not generally conduct or use any analysis of income and wealth distribution in their normal decision-making process, nevertheless this does not mean that the subject matter is unimportant. The allocation of income and wealth in the economy does have important economic, social, and political consequences which influences the basic fabric of society within which the business community functions. Indeed, any major redistribution of income is likely to have a direct effect on some companies. For example, the effect of switching a proportion of incomes from the 'wealthy' to the 'poorer' members of the community would almost certainly stimulate the demand for certain types of goods and services since lower income people tend to spend a higher proportion of their income compared with the affluent. This would clearly be of benefit to those firms producing the goods and services facing the expansion in demand, but it would have the effect of reducing the flow of savings, since high income earners tend to save proportionally more of their incomes. Whatever the net effect on the community for good, or ill, the point is that a change in incomes (and wealth) distribution will have important ramifications for the structure of industry and its development.

The present chapter, then, will consider in a little more detail the economic, social, and political aspects of income and wealth distribution before turning to the source, of data and published information. Finally, the major statistical techniques applied to income and wealth distribution data will be explained. An addendum to this section will emphasize that even if income and wealth distribution analysis holds little direct interest for decision-making by companies, nevertheless the techniques used to measure such distribution can be applied to many commercial and industrial problems.

From an economic point of view income and wealth distribution plays a major part in the development process of an economy. One of the common characteristics of present developed economies was a rapid rise in a wealthy middle class in the early stages of industrialization which provided an effective market for goods and services and the financial capital necessary for investment. It was pointed out (but in a different context) in Chapter 3 that many developing nations exhibit wide variation in income and wealth ownership, with the vast majority of people living at subsistence level while a few live in great luxury. Such a situation mitigates against economic development.

The social and political consequences of marked inequality in income and wealth is the friction and tension created in society. In many countries, of course, this has led to the overthrow of existing regimes, while in others it has led to the birth of new political parties and pressure groups aimed at reducing inequality. In Britain, for example, particularly since the Second World War, we can cite health and educational provisions, unemployment and other welfare payments, progressive taxation, national insurance schemes, etc., as government

170

attempts to remove extreme inequalities in the economy in order to establish a more equitable and just society.

13.1 Sources of data

Since the sources of data and range of interpretation problems differ, it would be appropriate to deal with income distribution and wealth distribution separately. However, before using or interpreting data three important definitions should be borne in mind.

The definition of income and wealth

As we have seen elsewhere in this book, incomes can be derived from a number of sources, e.g., employment income (wages and salaries), social security benefits, pensions, returns from investment (interest and dividends), returns from owning and sub-letting capital assets (dwellings). Although employment income is the most significant single element of total income one would have to be careful in interpreting the results of any distributional analysis based on this one component. Incomes at the low end of the scale are likely to be underestimated through excluding the various forms of social security payments, as are incomes at the high end of the scale by excluding returns from investment and capital assets. Clearly, for most analysis, the widest definition of income is desirable.

Although these forms of income are measurable there are several types that are difficult, if not impossible, to evaluate in money terms and yet are important for the recipients in terms of raising living standards. Examples would include income in kind; subsidized travel (company cars, for example), removal allowances, subsidized accommodation, imputed income from home-ownership, etc.

Wealth conventionally includes all forms of assets and therefore personal wealth would be the total value of assets which could be assigned to individuals. Apart from the usual problems of actually valuing these assets and assigning them to individuals, a more conceptual difficulty lies in the realization that in practice the distinction between income and wealth is less clear than might be supposed. To economists the difference between income and wealth is the difference between income and capital. Income can be accumulated and turned into capital through investing in paper securities or fixed assets and likewise capital can be converted into income simply by selling those capital assets. Effectively then the distinction between income and wealth is simply a difference in the degree of liquidity provided, with income at the liquid end of the spectrum and wealth (capital) at the illiquid, but redeemable, end of the spectrum.

These considerations are not simply semantic points; they do have significance for any interpretation of the published data. For example, it will be apparent later that the prime source of data for income distribution excludes capital gains as an element of income despite the fact that it provides an important source of cash flow for those who own and are able to sell capital assets. Moreover, since all wealth distribution tests show marked inequality compared with income distribution, it follows that the ability to realize capital assets and increase incomes is not evenly shared throughout the population.

The recipient

It is important to understand how the receiving unit is defined in order to interpret the data and any analysis in a meaningful way.

171

Most of the information on income distribution is based on household rather than individual income. The reason is that taxation and social security payments are linked to household income and commitments, and not individuals. Thus, if more than employment income is included, it follows that the receiving unit will have to be the household.

The reverse holds for wealth statistics, where, because of the way in which the data are obtained, the recipient is the individual. It can be argued quite convincingly that the notion of individual wealth has little meaning for in reality wealth tends to be a family or household characteristic. Consequently, when analysis shows an increase in equality of wealth-holding, all it may simply reflect are rich individuals spreading their wealth around their families a little more, rather than a more equal dispersion through society as a whole. Furthermore, by basing the information on the individual it may understate the degree of concentration for it ignores the possibility of more than one wealth owner in a family.

It is unfortunate that whereas the individual for income distribution and household for wealth distribution may be more meaningful, in practice, because of the way in which the data are obtained, the reverse applies, i.e., income distribution is based on the household and wealth distribution is based on the individual.

Before and after tax

Published information on the way in which income is distributed is presented in terms of the number of recipients in different income classes. These income classes are determined both before tax is paid and after tax is paid. Once again it is vital to distinguish between the two.

It would be a mistake, for example, to compare the distribution of income before tax in one year with that after tax in another year for any widening or levelling that is found between the two periods may be accounted for by the tax system; in other words, we are not comparing like with like. The problem still remains, of course, whether we choose before-tax or after-tax data for both periods. The answer will depend on the type of analysis being undertaken. For example, an analysis into the distribution of incomes between industries, occupations, etc., would find before-tax information the most appropriate, for otherwise any differences recorded could reflect the differential impact of taxation on the people included rather than real differences between industries, occupations, etc. On the other hand, after-tax data may be more appropriate when conducting an overall test into income dispersion between two time periods since, as we have already seen, the tax regime has been used by governments in the United Kingdom to reduce marked inequality of incomes among the population and it would therefore be appropriate to take this into account. Finally, an obvious test of the effect of taxation on income dispersion would be to compare before-tax and after-tax data in the same year.

13.2   Income distribution

The prime source of data on income distribution comes from the survey of personal incomes (SPI),[12] although some analysis is conducted using the family expenditure survey[10] and the new earnings survey.[9] The last two sources have been covered in Chapters 6 and 12, respectively, and therefore will not be described in detail here.

172

Survey of personal incomes

This survey is conducted by the Board of Inland Revenue. It was established as long ago as the tax year 1937–38, with the results being published in the annual report of the Commissioners of Inland Revenue until 1970, when summary tables have appeared in *Inland Revenue Statistics*[16] with the complete results being published separately on an annual basis.

The survey consists of a random but stratified sample of tax records, with about a million records being examined every five years and a smaller sample of between 100 000 and 150 000 being used in the intervening years. The sample is stratified in order to ensure adequate coverage of the spread of income. Thus all records are analysed for the highest income class; 1 in 30 is taken of those taxpayers liable to higher rates of tax; 1 in 100 is taken of those remaining whose income in the previous year exceeded a certain figure; and a sample of 1 in 1200 is taken for the remainder. In addition, special arrangements are made for employed married women, where a sample of 1 in 400 is used, which is also the sample fraction for those who have left their previous job and have not yet notified the tax office of their new job. The sample is extracted in each local tax office towards the end of the tax year with the tax officer responsible for the record of a selected individual completing the questionnaire.

The purpose of the survey is to provide the Inland Revenue with a tax profile of the economy so that the likely yield of taxes and how this is apportioned between different groups within the community can be assessed. It follows, then, that income covered is that defined for tax purposes. In practice, this definition means that a wide range of income is covered since most are liable to taxation, including employment incomes (above a certain limit), pensions, rent from land and buildings, interest on some British government and public authority securities, securities of foreign governments, and profits. However, some types of income are non-taxable and are therefore not included in the survey or the published results. These would include social security benefits such as unemployment pay, sick pay, student grants, and most forms of income in kind. Finally, it should be appreciated that since 1971 capital gains have been assessed under capital gains tax and are no longer considered as part of income.

The significance of these points regarding coverage will be left to the section dealing with interpretation, but first let us look at the published data.

Published data   Since the survey is based on the financial rather than the calendar year the annual published information represents years ending on 5 April. The complete data, published separately since 1970, include distribution of total and net incomes before and after tax, income and deductions by range of total income, distribution of total income by numbers, earned income by range of total income, investment income by range of total income, deductions by range of total income, numbers of incomes by family size and age, incomes by standard regions by range of total incomes, incomes by metropolitan and non-metropolitan county, and employment incomes by sex and range of employment income. It would be useful to illustrate this with an example of a summary table from the SPI (see Table 13.1).[12]

Interpreting the data   The quality of information provided by the SPI is clearly impressive. Its main advantages are the wide coverage of incomes included since most would be liable for tax, the relatively large sample (particularly every fifth year) which is further cross-checked against known figures of total income to confirm accuracy, and the fact that tax officers complete the information which certainly reduces the risk of reporting errors. However, several interpretation difficulties still remain and have been implied earlier. Basically these

173

Table 13.1 Distribution of total incomes before and after tax, 1976–77

Range of income (lower limit) (£)	Number of incomes ('000s)	Total income before tax (£ million)	Tax (£ million)	Total income after tax (£ million)	Cumulative totals		
					Number of incomes ('000s)	Total income before tax (£ million)	Total income after tax (£ million)
735	944	826	26	800	944	826	800
1 000	2 060	2 590	243	2 350	3 004	3 416	3 150
1 500	2 500	4 370	607	3 770	5 504	7 786	6 920
2 000	2 540	5 710	985	4 730	8 044	13 496	11 650
2 500	2 300	6 310	1 200	5 110	10 344	19 806	16 760
3 000	2 090	6 800	1 330	5 460	12 434	26 606	22 220
3 500	1 980	7 430	1 480	5 950	14 414	34 036	28 170
4 000	1 860	7 880	1 600	6 270	16 274	41 916	34 440
4 500	1 470	6 980	1 450	5 530	17 744	48 896	39 970
5 000	2 070	11 300	2 460	8 810	19 814	60 196	48 780
6 000	1 100	7 100	1 650	5 450	20 914	67 296	54 230
7 000	548	4 080	1 010	3 070	21 462	71 376	57 300
8 000	501	4 420	1 200	3 220	21 963	75 796	60 520
10 000	216	2 350	734	1 620	22 179	78 146	62 140
12 000	135	1 780	632	1 150	22 314	79 926	63 290
15 000	80	1 370	584	786	22 394	81 296	64 076
20 000	56	1 520	832	688	22 450	82 816	64 764
50 000	3	219	155	64	22 453	83 035	64 828
100 000 and over	1	104	78	27	22 454	83 139	64 855
	22 454	83 139	18 256	64 855			

Reproduced from the *Survey of Personal Incomes*, 1975–76 and 1976–77, Table 72, 1978, with the permission of the Controller of Her Majesty's Stationery Office.   *Note*. The published totals are rounded up to the nearest hundred.

difficulties arise from the fact that the survey is aimed at satisfying a need of the Inland Revenue and therefore define incomes in tax terms—the familiar problem of data being provided from the functioning of the administrative system.

First, the data will underestimate the incomes of those people at the lower end of the distribution by excluding those whose earnings are below the deductible limit and/or whose main form of income is non-taxable (social security benefit, etc.)

Second, some underestimate of higher incomes results from the exclusion of capital gains as a part of income and some interest on capital assets being free from tax.

Third, frequent alterations in the tax structure—changes in the threshold of income before tax becomes liable and alterations in allowances—make long-term analysis difficult because the number and distribution of incomes being analysed are continuously changing.

Fourth, since the data are based on tax records, there will certainly be some tax evasion and avoidance. Tax evasion is, of course, illegal and its extent can only be inferred by the successful prosecution of cases brought before the courts by tax investigators. However, its incidence may be spread across the income ranges, which is unlikely to be true for tax avoidance through such things as transferring incomes to tax havens and the formation of private companies. To make such arrangements one would have to have sufficient incomes to make it worth while and to employ skilled accountants and tax experts to advise on how to minimize payments and utilize loopholes in the tax regulations. Clearly, then, tax avoidance is likely to be the preserve of high income earners and as a result the published information may understate incomes at the high end of the range.

Finally, it should be recalled that in most cases a husband and wife are counted as one person, with the wife's earnings (if working) being aggregated with that of her husband. This can present some difficulties for international comparisons where other countries could define the income recipient on a different basis.

In summary, then, the major limitations of the SPI would include the understating of low incomes by excluding incomes below the deductible limit, incomes in the form of social security benefits, and most income in kind; the underestimate of high incomes through the exclusion of capital gains and the effect of tax avoidance; and the frequent changes in taxation regulations. Any interpretation of income distribution from this source must be careful to take these limitations into account.

Other data for income distribution

The new earnings survey[9] and family expenditure survey[10] are additional prime sources of information on incomes and may be useful for income distribution purposes. Both have been described in previous chapters and therefore will not be covered in detail here, confining ourselves instead to their usefulness in terms of income distribution analysis.

For occupational and industrial analysis of income distribution the NES is the most suitable source of information, but the fact that employment income is the only source of income covered makes it less appropriate for more general investigation into income distribution. It is far more limited in this respect than the SPI.

The advantage of the family expenditure survey compared with the SPI and the NES is that its coverage of income is widest of all—including all forms of income, whether taxed or not. Its weakness, however, lies in its reliability. It should be recalled that the response rate is only about 65 per cent and that information on total incomes is provided by the individuals themselves with all the attendant risks of misinformation, either intentionally or not. Although the results may be sufficiently reliable for the purpose it serves, i.e., in establishing the weights for the RPI, it is questionable whether really meaningful income distribution results can be obtained. Certainly any observations on the results should take into account this inherent weakness.

13.3 Wealth distribution

The problems of income distribution pale into insignificance compared with that of wealth distribution. Difficulties rest in defining the coverage of capital assets to be included, the valuation of these assets, and the assignment of them to individuals. The problems involve both conceptual and practical recording difficulties.

Ideally we ought to include both personal assets and public assets, such as roads, educational and health establisments, cultural and recreational facilities, etc., in order to assess total wealth in the economy and examine how it is distributed. However, in practice it is not only difficult to estimate the value of these public assets but to allocate them among the community.

175

Consequently, all data and analysis are based on the concept of personal wealth rather than the sum total of personal and public wealth. It may be that low income and wealth holders utilize these public assets proportionately more than the wealthier members of society; if this is so, then it follows that wealth analysis based only on personal wealth will effectively overstate the degree of concentration.

The valuation of many types of asset also presents serious difficulties since the true valuation will not be known until the asset is sold—at which point it ceases to be an asset for the original owner.

The final problem, assigning wealth holdings to individuals, founders on the difficulty of getting people to provide information on their total and composition of wealth holdings. We will see later that feasibility studies carried out in the 'seventies highlighted the difficulties of wealth surveys in terms of the probable low response and non-response bias.

Because of these factors there is, unfortunately, no regularly conducted wealth survey in the same way as the SPI for instance. Consequently, official estimates of the distribution of wealth are measured in an indirect way, through the use of 'estate duty statistics'.

Published data

The official published information on wealth distribution, such as it is, comes from the Board of Inland Revenue, and is published annually in *Inland Revenue Statistics*. Personal wealth is shown by type of asset, by size of particular types of asset, and by ranges of net wealth and type of asset.

The data are derived from estate duty returns received by the Inland Revenue. This is simply the value of a person's estate at the time of death which may be liable for tax in the form of estate duties prior to 1975 and capital transfer tax since. The assumption is made, therefore, that the value and composition of assets of people who have died during a year represent a random sample of the wealth and its distribution among those living in that year. Consequently, an estimate of the total spread of personal wealth is obtained by simply multiplying by the appropriate mortality ratios obtained from the General Register Office. This approach is referred to as the estate multiplier method.

Interpreting the data

The assumption that people dying are representative, in terms of their wealth characteristics, of those people living is clearly a vital assumption which may, in practice, be incorrect. Certainly substantial sampling errors are likely to be present where the estimates are based on only a small number of cases. Inevitably this would refer to the very wealthy, since there are few of these anyway, and the young age groups because of their low death rate. Apart from these sampling difficulties several other weaknesses are apparent.

First, some underestimation of wealth, particularly at the low end of the scale, is apparent because small amounts of wealth are not liable to estate duty and certain types of assets are excluded (e.g., benefits under some pension schemes and annuities for life).

Second, true wealth may be disguised due to wealthy people establishing gifts and trusts in order to avoid estate duty. However, it has been pointed out that the extent of avoidance may not be as great as one might suppose since it means giving up control of one's assets and is therefore likely to be unattractive for many wealth owners. Nevertheless, in order to fill this

176

loophole in tax arrangements the government introduced, in 1975, the capital transfer tax. If the effect of this tax is to reduce the practice of avoiding estate duty in the way described then clearly the quality of wealth data would have been enhanced. However, where capital transfers continue to be made the original point remains since these capital transfers are not currently included in the estimates of personal wealth.

Third, this method will tend to overestimate wealth since certain assets attain a higher value at death than identical assets in the hands of the living. Thus, life assurance policies include the sum assured plus any bonuses, but if terminated before death the owner will only receive the surrender value which could be less than the sum assured.

Finally, it is worth repeating that wealth distribution estimates are based on the individual, which ignore the likelihood that more than one member of a family or household is individually wealthy. Given that wealth may carry more meaning in respect of families it follows that the degree of concentration shown in the data will understate the true levels of concentration. Thus, any evidence of greater redistribution may simply reflect a sharing out of wealth within families rather than across the total community.

All these problems, of course, are a result of establishing estimates based on the administrative system and, particularly, the basis on which the sample is selected. Given these difficulties of interpretation and gaps in the information, the Royal Commission on the Distribution of Income and Wealth (RCDIW) recommended in 1975 that the CSO undertake a feasibility study into the possibility of establishing a wealth survey. The first study was made the following year by the CSO and the Survey Division of the Office of Population Censuses and Survey (OPCS). The lessons learnt from this first approach were utilized in a second study in 1977. However, despite certain improvements the results were still disappointing and the CSO was forced to conclude that a detailed wealth survey could not be justified for it was unlikely to be successful.

The major problem encountered in both studies was the low response generally, together with a non-response bias which was particularly damaging because the response rate tended to decline as wealth holdings increased. Thus where a high response rate was crucial, i.e., among the major wealth holders in the community, the response rate actually tailed off which, if reflected nationally in a detailed wealth survey, would clearly produce virtually meaningless results.

We are left with wealth distribution estimates being derived from estate duty statistics. Therefore, any interpretation should carefully consider the implications of the weaknesses outlined.

13.4 Statistical techniques

Many of the techniques and graphical representations commonly used in distribution analysis will be familiar to the reader who has studied and mastered the contents of Chapters 1 and 2. They will therefore not be developed in detail but will be used to illustrate their practical application in this field of study. However, one technique, the Lorenz curve, has not been met before and so will be covered more fully. All the analysis will be based on the information in Table 13.1, i.e., income distribution before and after tax for the financial year 1976–77, from the survey of personal incomes. Generally the techniques will be treated in ascending order of usefulness so far as distribution analysis is concerned.

Standard deviation

Since distribution analysis is concerned with the spread or range of data on incomes and wealth it might seem appropriate that the standard deviation would be a useful measure to apply. Although it can certainly give an indication of variability it can tell us nothing about the shape of the distribution or give any indication of the characteristics of the extreme values which are particularly relevant in income distribution analysis. In fact, the standard deviation is more useful as a descriptive measure where variables approximate to a normal distribution which, as we shall see, is certainly not the case with income (or wealth) distribution. Nevertheless, applying the grouped standard deviation formula described in Chapter 2 to the before-tax data in Table 13.1 produces a standard deviation of £2959, which is very nearly the value of the mean and gives a coefficient of variation of 79.2 per cent. (Note that for this calculation an estimated mean was made for each income range except the final open range, where the calculated mean was used.) This indicates, then, that incomes before tax have a very wide distribution around the calculated mean.

Frequency distribution

Figure 13.1 shows the same data but in the form of a frequency polygon. What this can show is the general shape of the distribution—whether it approximates to a 'normal' distribution or is 'skewed'. A long tail at the high end of the values is clearly demonstrated, in other words, a positive skewed distribution. It should be noted that the median value (£3211 p.a.) is less than the mean (£3702), which is further evidence of a positive skewness in the distribution. Although the mode has not been calculated it is clearly within the income range £2000 to £2500, which is less than the median, which, in turn, is less than the mean. This confirms the statement about the characteristics of income distribution made in Sec. 2.3 when dealing with skewness.

Cumulative frequency—the ogive

The ogive, a graphical representation of cumulative frequency, is particularly useful for distribution analysis for it allows the possibility of dividing the distribution into different parts for more detailed investigation. Thus, in Fig. 13.2,[12] by dividing the total number of incomes into four, one can read off the quartile values. The value for Q1 (lower quartile) can be interpreted as showing that the lowest 25 per cent of the income earners had an annual income, before tax, of a little over £2000; Q3 (upper quartile) demonstrates that 75 per cent of earners had incomes below approximately £4700 (or in other words, 25 per cent of the population had incomes in excess of £4700); Q2 is clearly the median, while the difference between Q1 and Q3, the so-called interquartile range, indicates that the middle 50 per cent of income earners had a range of incomes between £2000 and £4700.

Dividing the total data into 10 equal groups produces decile values. These can be more useful than the quartile observations since they allow the extreme sections of the range to be examined in more detail. The highest decile (D9) shows a value in excess of £6300, which means that 10 per cent of the population earn incomes in excess of this figure. The lowest decile (D1) indicates that 10 per cent of the population earn less than £1300 and therefore 80 per cent of the population earn incomes in the range £1300 to £6300.

Even more detail can be obtained by dividing the data into 100 equal groups, i.e.,

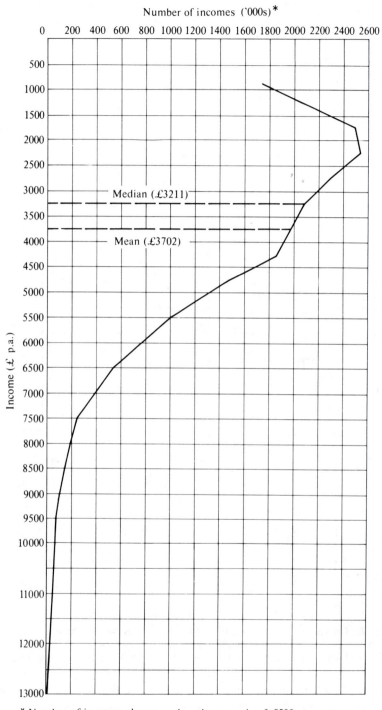

Figure 13.1   Frequency polygon from Table 13.1

179

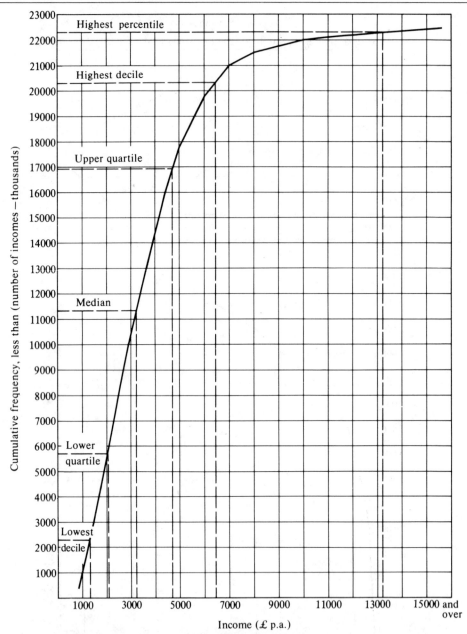

Figure 13.2 Cumulative frequency distribution. Number of incomes before tax by range of incomes before tax (Reproduced from the *Survey of Personal Incomes*, 1975–76 and 1976–77, Table 72, 1978, with the permission of the Controller of Her Majesty's Stationery Office)

percentiles. From the highest percentile (P99) we can see that 1 per cent of the population obtained incomes in excess of £13 100.

Of course, the more detail one goes into, the more difficult it becomes to read off accurate values from the ogive. However, these can be calculated arithmetically as demonstrated in

180

Chapter 2 and give the following approximate values for this distribution:

> *Quartiles*
>> Q1 = £2021
>> Q2 = £3211   (the median)
>> Q3 = £4693
>
> *Deciles*
>> D1 = £1316
>> D9 = £6359
>
> *Percentiles*
>> P1 = £937
>> P99 = £13 121

A comparison of these values with that of an ogive for a different year or a before-tax and after-tax test for the same year would indicate whether incomes (or wealth) have become more, or less, equally distributed. However, a more complete test of this can be obtained with the use of a technique known as the 'Lorenz curve'.

The Lorenz curve

This technique can show graphically the degree of inequality in a distribution. By comparing different distributions, changes in inequality can be demonstrated.

The method is simply to convert the cumulative values for the number of incomes (or wealth holders) and total incomes (or amount of wealth) into percentage terms and transfer these to a graph also calibrated in percentage terms. One important advantage of expressing these values in percentages is that it facilitates comparison over time and between countries where absolute values are likely to be markedly different. Table 13.2[12] and Fig. 13.3 demonstrate this.

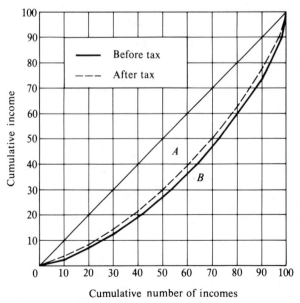

Figure 13.3   Lorenz curve from Table 13.2

Table 13.2   Distribution of total incomes before and after tax 1976–77

Range of income (lower limit) (£)	Number of incomes ('000s)	Cumulative percentage (%)	Total income before tax (£ million)	Cumulative percentage (%)	Total income after tax (£ million)	Cumulative percentage (%)
735	944	4.2	826	0.99	800	1.2
1 000	2 060	13.4	2 590	4.1	2 350	4.9
1 500	2 500	24.5	4 370	9.4	3 770	10.7
2 000	2 540	35.8	5 710	16.2	4 730	18.0
2 500	2 300	46.1	6 310	23.8	5 110	25.8
3 000	2 090	55.4	6 800	32.0	5 460	34.3
3 500	1 980	64.2	7 430	40.9	5 950	43.4
4 000	1 860	72.5	7 880	50.4	6 270	53.1
4 500	1 470	79.0	6 980	58.8	5 530	61.6
5 000	2 070	88.2	11 300	72.4	8 810	75.2
6 000	1 100	93.1	7 100	80.9	5 450	83.6
7 000	548	95.6	4 080	85.8	3 070	88.4
8 000	501	97.8	4 420	91.2	3 220	93.3
10 000	216	98.8	2 350	94.0	1 620	95.8
12 000	135	99.4	1 780	96.1	1 150	97.6
15 000	80	99.7	1 370	97.8	786	98.8
20 000	56	99.98	1 520	99.6	688	99.86
50 000	3	99.99	219	99.9	64	99.9
100 000 and over	1	100.0	104	100.0	27	100.0
Totals	22 454	100.0	83 139	100.0	64 855	100.0

Reproduced from the *Survey of Personal Incomes*, 1975–76 and 1976–77, Table 72, 1978, with the permission of the Controller of her Majesty's Stationery Office.   *Note.* The published totals are rounded up to the nearest hundred.

The 45° diagonal line is the origin for a Lorenz curve since it represents a perfect distribution, that is, 10 per cent of income earners receive 10 per cent of total income, 20 per cent of earners receive 20 per cent of total income, and so on. Thus the difference between the Lorenz curve and the line of perfect distribution (the diagonal) indicates the magnitude of inequality. It follows that the nearer a Lorenz curve is to the origin the greater is the degree of equality. Thus Fig. 13.3 shows quite clearly that incomes after tax are more evenly distributed than before tax, a fact that is not at all surprising given the progressive and redistributive nature of direct taxation.

There is no ambiguity with Fig. 13.3, since the after-tax Lorenz curve is clearly nearer to the origin over the whole range, but occasionally Lorenz curves for different distributions intersect at one or more points, and therefore it is not immediately obvious which distribution is nearer the origin. What analysts do in these circumstances is to calculate the so-called 'Gini coefficient'.

The Gini coefficient is a numerical measure of the degree of inequality and is measured by taking the total area between the Lorenz curve and the origin (shown as A in Fig. 13.3) and dividing by the total area under the origin $(A+B)$. The Gini coefficient is therefore:

$$\frac{A}{A+B}$$

A value of O would result from a perfect distribution since the area, A, would disappear while a value of 1 would show perfect inequality, since the area B would disappear. Thus the

182

range is between O and 1, with low values suggesting a high degree of equality and high values suggesting a low degree of equality. Indeed, many analysts dispense with the graphical representation of the Lorenz curve and concentrate on the numerical value of inequality as given by the Gini coefficient.

This chapter, then, has been concerned with income and wealth distribution; its uses, definitions, and sources; and finally the techniques normally used in distribution analysis. The addendum that follows illustrates that the Lorenz curve can be used in other areas of study.

13.5 Addendum—Other uses of the Lorenz curve and Gini coefficient

Since these two techniques are basically giving some measure of the degree of concentration it is clear that they can be applied in many fields other than income and wealth distribution— in fact, to any problem where a measure of concentration is necessary.

It is a technique used frequently in regional analysis, for the regional imbalance problem is related, to some extent, to the degree of concentration of employment, or output, in slow-growing, stagnant, or declining industries in the less prosperous regions and to the degree of concentration of employment in fast-growing industries in the richer regions. Thus the employment structure of a region can be analysed by arranging the data on employment for each industry on a ranking basis from the largest to the smallest and cumulating the percentage values. The horizontal axis would measure the cumulated percentage of employment and the vertical axis would show the ranks. The subsequent Lorenz curve could then be compared with other regions, with the curve for the nation as a whole and the diagonal which would demonstrate a perfectly even distribution. The further the Lorenz curve of a region is from this origin the greater the degree of concentration (and therefore less diversification) of the employment structure of that region.

Similarly, the Lorenz curve can be used to measure the degree of concentration that exists in different industries. In this case the vertical axis would measure the cumulative percentage, in terms of size (output or assets, or employment, etc.), while the horizontal axis shows cumulative percentage of firms in that industry from the smallest to the largest. The further the resulting Lorenz curve is from the origin the greater the degree of concentration shown, since the origin would indicate a situation where all firms are of equal size.

For businesses this measure of concentration can be widely applicable. It can be used to examine the market share or market concentration of a company. Likewise, it can show the degree of concentration of the production 'mix' of a company and changes in that 'mix' over time, and so on.

Finally, the company producing drums of chemicals and facing a demand pattern shown in Table 1.3 of Chapter 1 may wish to know the degree of concentration of order size. The first step would be to rank the order range in terms of the frequency of orders in that range. Thus the order range 41–50 drums was purchased on 13 out of the 50 orders and therefore would be ranked first, 31–40 would be ranked second, and so on. The rearranged table, together with cumulative percentages, is shown in Table 13.3.

The resulting Lorenz curve, shown in Fig. 13.4, gives a Gini coefficient of approximately 0.4. The diagonal here would, of course, indicate that total orders are evenly distributed over the various ranges. By examining the Lorenz curve of a previous period the company could see

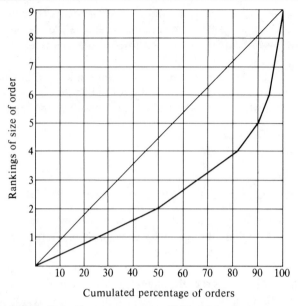

Cumulated percentage of orders

Figure 13.4   Lorenz curve from Table 13.3

whether order size characteristics had changed and, if so, in what way. This in turn could assist in establishing marketing and production strategies.

Table 13.3

Size of order in the range	Ranking	Frequency of orders	Cumulative percentage (%)
41–50	1	13	26
31–40	2	12	50
51–60	3	8	66
61–70	4	8	82
21–30	5	4	90
11–20	6	2	94
1–10	7	1	96
71–80	8	1	98
81–90	9	1	100
		50	100

Self-assessment questions—Part Four

1. Consider the order size distribution first given in Table 1.3 of Chapter 1. Estimate the probabilities of orders in the given ranges and hence deduce the probability of an order in the range 30 to 50 drums. Find also the probability that two orders, selected at random, fall in this range. Why would this *not* be a good estimate of the probability that a particular customer orders twice in this size range?

2. The number of calls arriving in periods of one minute is recorded for a telephone switchboard as follows:

Number of calls	0	1	2	3	4	5
Frequency	17	10	10	8	4	1

Estimate the probability distribution of calls per minute and find its mean and standard deviation. Compare the probabilities of the Poisson distribution with the same mean. Why might you expect this to be a good fit?

3. A firm operates the following quality acceptance scheme for its component suppliers. It takes a sample of 10 items from each batch received and will only accept the batch if none of the items are defective.

(a) Find the probability it will accept a batch which has 10 per cent defectives.
(b) Find the probability it will reject a batch which has 1 per cent defectives.
(c) If the suppliers of the batches mentioned in (a) and (b) send two batches with the same characteristics, find the probability that for (a) both batches are accepted and for (b) both batches are rejected.
(d) Find the size of sample necessary to ensure a probability of 0.95 that a batch with 10 per cent defectives is rejected, according to the above scheme.

4. A company sells coffee in 200-gm jars. The filling machine delivers weights that vary slightly from jar to jar, and in fact the jar weights are approximately normally distributed with a standard deviation of 2 gm.

(a) If the filling machine is set to deliver a mean weight of 200 gm, find the probability that a jar is
  (i) Under 200 gm.
  (ii) Under 198 gm.
(b) Find the weight exceeded by 95 per cent of the jars.
(c) If the mean weight delivered by the filling machine can be adjusted, what should it be changed to if it is required that only 5 per cent of the jars should contain less than 200 gm?

5. In Chapter 2, the mean and variance of the data considered in question 1 above were found. If order sizes are normally distributed, find the probability of orders in each of the size ranges given and compare to the probabilities found above.

6. As part of a time and motion study, a particular task is timed for 50 skilled operators. The times are found to have a mean of 10 minutes with a standard deviation of 1.5 minutes. Find a 90 and a 95 per cent confidence interval for the mean time for the task.

7. A factory has a shop floor workforce of 200 and for a sample month the number of days each person was absent was recorded. The results are given in the following frequency table:

Number of days absent	0	1	2	3	4	5
Number of workers	160	14	10	8	2	6

Find a 95 per cent confidence interval for the mean number of days of absenteeism per worker per month.

8. As credit controller, you check a sample of 500 accounts and find that 15 per cent were unpaid a month after invoicing. Find 95 and 99 per cent confidence intervals for your estimate of this percentage.

9. You are planning two sample surveys:

(a) To estimate the percentage of households in your region that have television.
(b) To estimate the percentage of households with freezers.

You want to be 95 per cent confident that your estimate will be within 2 per cent of the true percentage. What size of sample would you take in each case? In each case make what seems to you a reasonable assumption where necessary.

10. Your company sells its product to schools and you are designing a market research survey of schools to provide more information on this market. Describe briefly how you would design a sampling scheme and the main factors you would take into account. Assume you are working to a budget and that the survey will consist of personal intervals with a senior member of staff in each school selected.

11. It is claimed that a battery has a life of 1000 hours. You check a sample of the batteries and find that their lives (in hours) are as follows:

$$920 \quad 940 \quad 1020 \quad 910 \quad 960$$

Is there any evidence that in fact the battery life is not 1000 hours?

12. Answer question 1(d) from Part Three by giving a 95 per cent confidence interval for the required estimate.

13. You take a sample of users of your firm's product in the Northern region and another in the Southern region. The sample members are classified into three categories according to whether they are light, medium, or heavy users with the following results:

Region	Usage		
	Light	Medium	Heavy
Northern	45	40	15
Southern	35	60	5

Is there any evidence of a different usage pattern between the North and the South?

14. What uses can wages and earnings data be put to?

186

15. List the improvements in published data resulting from the introduction of the New Earnings Survey.

16. Since the NES is based on a relatively small sample (170 000 employees compared with a total workforce of approximately 22½ million), is this likely to reduce its accuracy and usefulness?

17. Given that the NES provides a comprehensive range of data on wages and earnings, what can be the justification for the manual and non-manual surveys and the monthly index of average earnings?

18. What are the major sources of data used for income distribution analysis?

19. Why are the SPI results felt to be particularly reliable?

20. Despite this, what are the coverage problems?

21. Why are there problems in defining wealth?

22. How are wealth statistics derived?

23. Why are income distribution data based on the family while wealth data are based on the individual?

Assignment questions—Part Four

1. The following information is provided by the *New Earnings Survey*[9] for April, 1979:

Distribution of gross weekly earnings for full-time manual men

Earnings range p.w.	Region		
	South East Number in sample	South West Number in sample	Northern Number in sample
Less than £45	178	48	28
£45–£49	142	70	37
£50–£54	273	147	92
£55–£59	404	195	108
£60–£69	1355	586	330
£70–£79	1771	522	422
£80–£89	1949	535	490
£90–£99	1593	416	422
£100–£119	2187	413	595
£120–£149	1343	202	392
£150–£199	571	61	142
£200 and above	121	6	25

Reproduced from the *New Earnings Survey*, April 1979, Table 114, with the permission of the Controller of Her Majesty's Stationery Office.

Analyse the earnings distribution of each region using the Lorenz technique and comment on your results. Discuss the limitation of the data source and the technique used and indicate what impact these might have had on your results.

2. You represent a company that is tendering for the production of the Yellow Pages directory for British Telecom. You need to estimate the potential advertising revenue which can be obtained from the directory. To this end you need to estimate:

(1) The proportion of ordinary entries that are printed in bold type.
(2) The average square inches of display advertising per page.

You decide to procede by using random numbers to select a sample of pages from your local directory, and hence determine the estimates of (1) and (2).

(a) Devise a suitable sampling scheme for selecting pages at random.
(b) Using a copy of a Yellow Pages directory, select enough pages to estimate the proportions of bold type entries in a sample of 1000 ordinary entries. Give a 95 per cent confidence interval for your estimate. How many entries would you have to check to give a 95 per cent confidence interval of ± 1 per cent for this estimate?
(c) Use a sample of 10 pages to estimate (2) above. Find a 95 per cent confidence interval for this estimate, assuming that the square inches of display advertising per page is normally distributed. Can you suggest any reason why this may be a reasonable or an unreasonable assumption?
(d) Strictly speaking, the sample used in (b) is a cluster sample, and in (b) and (c) you are sampling from a finite population. Are either of these factors likely to affect your results? Write up your results in the form of a brief report for management with a technical appendix. Treat the results obtained above as a pilot study and make recommendations for a more accurate study.

Part Five

Part Five consists of two concluding chapters. Chapter 14 covers foreign trade statistics including the balance of payments accounts, which is the foreign trade counterpart of the national income accounts (Chapter 3), with a similar range of recording and interpretation difficulties. The chapter concludes by summarizing a range of national data described in earlier chapters from the viewpoint of international comparisons.

The final chapter draws the threads of the book together by illustrating the way in which data and techniques can be combined and gives detailed suggested answers to four differing assignment topics. The questions involve material covered in the text and are placed within a realistic setting. The chapter is therefore a useful guide to students on how to approach quantitative analysis, and emphasizes and examines a facility for handling data and techniques in an integrated way.

Self-assessment questions complete Part Five, but in this case relate to the material covered in Chapter 14 only.

14. Foreign trade statistics

Foreign trade is of some importance to virtually every nation. For industrial economies a well-known feature is the necessity to import raw materials and foodstuffs. In many cases these commodities could be produced domestically, but only by transferring resources (land, labour, and capital) away from the production of commodities we are 'good' at producing, which would inevitably lower total output and living standards. These gains from international trade therefore come from increased specialization based on comparative cost differences between nations (i.e., different opportunity costs of using resources in one line of production rather than another) rather than absolute cost differences. One interesting aspect of specialization, and a less well-known feature, has been the growth, since 1945, in international trade of semi-manufactured goods. Thus manufactured goods in all countries use sub-parts from abroad in their production and assembly. It is this aspect of international trade that is seen to be crucial in providing the basis for faster economic growth and more rapid improvement in living standards.

Clearly, the necessity to import raw materials and foodstuffs, due either to physical limitations or the comparative cost principal, and the increasing requirement of importing semi-manufactured goods make it essential that we should export goods, capital, and expertise in order to earn sufficient foreign currency to pay for them. Failure to do so would mean a lower growth performance and slower rates of improvement in living standards.

Enough has been said to indicate the importance of foreign trade for a nation and its people, although the degree of importance would clearly differ from country to country depending on the availability of resources and their utilization internally. The United Kingdom, for example, trades a far higher proportion of its GNP than the United States, although in absolute terms the United States is the single most important trading nation. For developing countries foreign trade is likely to be the key to industrialization and growth, and is therefore of paramount importance.

Published information is important since it is recording something that is significant for most countries. A measure of any country's total indebtedness with the rest of the world or total surplus earned from the rest of the world each year would influence government economic policy decisions. How important this influence is will depend on the crucial nature of foreign trade for the economy. In the case of Britain, for example, with a relatively high proportion of economic activity engaged in international trade, a currency that is held throughout the world (sterling being described as a 'key' currency), and, until recently, a low level of reserves of gold and international currencies, our balance with the rest of the world is particularly crucial. The result has been that successive governments since 1945 have found it necessary to deflate the economy in order to solve balance of payments deficits and then reflate when the deficits are replaced by surpluses. The instability created by this constant switching (stop–go policies) of policy may be one of the more important reasons why our growth performance has been less satisfactory compared with other industrial nations. In Britain's case, then, the external balance can have a marked effect on domestic economic activity, both through the economic process and the actions of central government.

At a more detailed level the data could be analysed in order to investigate recurring external problems and suggest appropriate policy measures. At an even more detailed level any company considering entering (or expanding) into foreign markets will almost certainly use the commodity data available in order to assess the market characteristics and potential.

14.1 Available data

Information relating to foreign trade includes (1) the overseas trade statistics (OTS)[17] and (2) the balance of payments accounts.[18] It is important to distinguish between the two since their purpose, and therefore coverage, is quite distinct. The OTS records exports and imports of commodities (sometimes referred to as 'visible goods') while the balance of payments accounts is a comprehensive statement of our total trade with the rest of the world, including commodities, services (known as 'invisibles'), and capital flows. The OTS, therefore, has a far narrower coverage although it does present data in much more detail than is found in the balance of payments.

The object of the OTS, by recording the flow of goods (exports and imports), is to indicate the availability of commodities in the domestic economy. The balance of payments, on the other hand, is concerned with the financial flows of all our external transactions. Thus the OTS measures the commodity impact of foreign trade and the balance of payments measures the financial impact of total trading. It follows that an item will only be included in the balance of payments if a change in ownership occurs, for only then will compensating payment flows take place, whereas the OTS will record all commodity transactions irrespective of whether a change in ownership takes place.

Although the foregoing emphasizes their distinct nature, nevertheless there is a link between the two since the OTS provides much of the data for the visible trade element of the balance of payments. For this reason, it would be logical to start our investigation with the OTS and then proceed to the balance of payments accounts.

14.2 Overseas trade statistics[17]

As already mentioned, the data relate to the flow into and out of the country of commodities, and is published annually by the Department of Trade under the heading *Overseas Trade Statistics*. The published data record exports and imports for each month of the year, initially in summary form but then broken down into detailed commodity groups according to an international trading classification, and also trade with important trading partners (the EEC, for example) and individual countries. In addition, exports and imports of unwrought refined gold bullion are included and in the last few years the importance of trade in oil has led to its inclusion in the statistics. Apart from the OTS, a separate publication by HM Customs and Excise, *Statistics of Trade through U.K. Ports*,[19] provides information on the flow of trade through U.K. ports and U.K. economic planning regions.

Information on imports

The data for imports are based on an analysis of import documents required to obtain customs clearance and pay the appropriate customs duties before entry. These documents from the various points of entry in the United Kingdom are then passed to the Customs and Excise Statistical Offices at Southend-on-Sea, where compilation takes place.

The customs declaration is therefore the key to the published data and requires information on: the value of the consignment in £ sterling terms, the weight and detailed commodity description including the international trading classification, the country from which the goods were consigned to the United Kingdom, the port of entry, and the country with whom the carrying vessel is registered.

The consignment value of the goods is measured as the market valuation (what the seller would receive from a buyer) at the port of entry into the United Kingdom and would therefore include the cost of insurance and freight from the consigning country to its entry into United Kingdom territory. Imports are therefore recorded on a CIF basis, i.e., including the costs of insurance and freight. Where a foreign currency valuation is given, it is converted into sterling terms at the rate of exchange operating at the time of the customs document.

The international trading classification, known as the standard international trade classification (SITC), was established in 1958 through the United Nations, in an attempt to obtain consistency of trade records among nations and facilitate more meaningful international comparisons. As with all classifications, changes have taken place. The system was revised in 1968, when it was referred to as SITC (R), and was more recently revised in 1978, now being described as SITC (Revision 2). Since 1978 the following 10 major sections are used, each one having many sub-divisions:

Section 0 Food and live animals, chiefly for food
Section 1 Beverages and tobacco
Section 2 Crude materials, inedible, except fuels
Section 3 Mineral fuels, lubricants, and related materials
Section 4 Animal and vegetable oils, fats, and waxes
Section 5 Chemicals and related products not specified elsewhere
Section 6 Manufactured goods classified chiefly by material
Section 7 Machinery and transport equipment
Section 8 Miscellaneous manufactured articles
Section 9 Commodities and transactions not classified elsewhere

It should be noted that in the United Kingdom information on the exporting country is on a country of consignment basis, i.e., the country from which the goods were originally despatched to the United Kingdom. This convention presents a major international comparison difficulty since the country of consignment may not be the country of origin, or manufacture, or shipment of the goods, and any one of these could be (and is) adopted by other nations as the basis for recording trade. We will consider this in more detail later.

Information on exports

Although, normally, approval is not required and customs duty is obviously not applicable on exports, nevertheless customs declarations are still required and it is these documents that provide the information on exports in the OTS. However, since customs clearance is not normally required for exports a certain laxity in the forwarding of documents became particularly noticeable in the late 'sixties, with delays and even failure to submit information. The subsequent under-recording of exports led the government to take new powers in the 1971 Finance Act and exporters or their agents are now required to submit documents within 14

193

days of the shipment of goods. Generally the information required is the same as for imports, but some differences occur.

First, the export value includes the price of the commodity plus all other costs involved in depositing the goods on board the exporting vessel at the U.K. frontier (internal transport costs, dock dues, loading charges, insurance, commission, etc.). This is referred to as 'free on board' (FOB). Although this is a different basis compared with imports (which is CIF), nevertheless there is a certain consistency since both imports and exports are being valued at the same place—i.e., at the U.K. frontier.

Second, since 1974, exports are listed in terms of the country of destination—defined as the final country to which the goods are being despatched from the United Kingdom. Prior to 1974 exports were listed on the same basis as imports, i.e., by country of consignment. In most cases there is little difference between the two approaches.

Recording conventions

As with all recorded data certain definitions and conventions have to be adopted. A summary of these is given below.

Coverage   As we now already know, the OTS records the flow of commodities irrespective of any change in ownership. However, not all goods that cross the U.K. frontier enter the statistics. Generally there can be three reasons for this. First, bearing in mind the fact that the main purpose of the data is to record the availability of commodities for the domestic economy, all those goods that enter or leave the country but will not have a permanent influence on availability are excluded. Second, there are some goods which are excluded quite simply because of practical recording difficulties. Third, some commodities have strategic importance and are therefore excluded from the published data on security grounds.

Examples of the first category would be all those goods entering or leaving the country on a temporary basis and would include such diverse items as the transporting vehicle of the goods, works of art intended for exhibitions, the necessary props for touring companies (i.e., musical instruments, theatrical effects, etc.), and commercial samples. Also excluded are goods purchased and imported by foreign governments for consumption in their embassies in the United Kingdom. Similarly, goods leaving the United Kingdom for our embassies overseas would not be included as an export. The reason of course is that foreign embassies in London are considered as part of their territory and not part of the United Kingdom, while our embassies abroad are considered part of the U.K. territory. For a similar reason equipment entering the country but destined for foreign government forces in the United Kingdom would be excluded, as would equipment leaving this country for our forces overseas (though stores for the NAAFI are included in the statistics).

Additionally, used clothing and household goods exported by charitable organizations and emergency aid for disaster areas, personal and household effects and legacies, and stores and fuel on board transporting vehicles for consumption en route are all excluded.

The sale or purchase of sea-going vessels and aircraft while abroad will not be recorded in the statistics since customs documentation would not have been completed and is an example of the second category of exclusions. For similar, practical reasons, U.K.-registered merchant ships plying the world for trade will go unrecorded where this trade does not cross the U.K. frontier, since customs would not have been notified.

194

The type of goods excluded from the data on security grounds include atomic energy materials, uranium ore, and concentrates.

The basis of recording   Apart from these exclusions all goods that enter the United Kingdom are recorded in the statistics, even those commodities that technically do not cross the customs boundary and pay duty by going into customs bonded warehouses. Many of these goods that enter bonded warehouses are worked on in some way, by being refined, or processed, repacked, or combined and assembled with other goods, and then re-exported. These re-exports are then included with and not separately distinguished from conventional exports. Thus, in the United Kingdom, goods entering bonded warehouses would be included as imports and those leaving for overseas as exports. This procedure is referred to as the 'general system' and differs from the so-called 'special system' adopted by many other countries, particularly the remainder of the EEC. The special system excludes goods entering bonded warehouses (or subsequently being re-exported to other countries) except where major work like processing is carried out in bond.

The fact that countries differ in their approach does present difficulties for international comparisons, since like is not being compared with like. It might seem a simple matter to get countries to adopt a common system and avoid this inconsistency but the point is that each country uses the system which appears most appropriate to them. In Britain's case the reason for adopting the general system is the importance attached to processing and refining, etc., the goods in bond, which has a substantial impact on employment and economic activity domestically. However, for those countries with large international ports and insubstantial processing while in bond, the special system would clearly be more appropriate since most of the goods entering bonded warehouses would be destined for other countries. In these circumstances the general system would distort, through exaggeration, the level of international trade of that country and therefore the special system would produce more meaningful data.

However, pressure for consistency in data presentation among the Community member countries has led Britain to publish some data on the comparable 'special system' and these are included as part of the range of data provided in the OTS.

Definition of the United Kingdom   For trade statistics the United Kingdom is defined as mainland Britain, Northern Ireland, the Isle of Man, the Channel Islands, and the U.K. part of the continental shelf. The latter is clearly important, given the discovery and exploitation of oil around these shores in the last decade and consequent international flows of oil recently.

Apart from the exceptions mentioned earlier all goods that enter or leave this area will be included as imports and exports in the trade statistics. For the United Kingdom and other countries that adopt the general system, the statistical boundary is therefore the geographical territory while the special system is based on the customs boundary.

Application of the data

The range of data provided are both detailed and broadly based, with information on some 1800 commodity headings, country-based information, and area information, including trade with the EEC, North America, etc.

While the commodity and country-based information would be of direct interest for international marketing decisions by companies the broader based information is suitable for analysing the changing characteristics of U.K. trade. In terms of the latter it shows, for example, that since 1945 the United Kingdom has increased its trade in semi-manufactured goods (as with most other developed nations) and is also trading more with Europe (particularly the EEC) and less with the Commonwealth over time.

Figures 14.1 and 14.2 illustrate these points with the use of pie charts (introduced in Chapter 1) showing commodity and area trading for two selected years, 1959 and 1979.

Figure 14.1 clearly shows the growth in trade with the EEC, although part of the expansion shown for 1979 would have been due to the enlargement of the Community in 1972. Two-thirds of the value of trade with the rest of the world in 1959 was with the overseas sterling area, composed mainly, but not entirely, of Commonwealth trade. Indeed, the overseas sterling area accounted for 38 per cent of total trade in 1959. Given the end of the sterling area in the early 'seventies this category is no longer shown but would be included in the rest of the world segment. This, as we can see, fell dramatically from over 54 per cent of total trade in

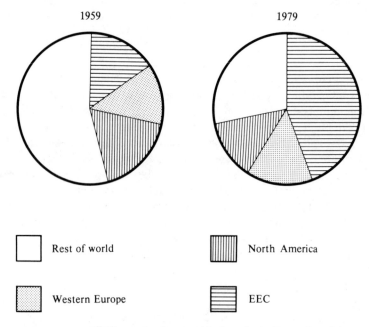

Figure 14.1   Visible trade. Geographical analysis (Reproduced from *U.K. Balance of Payments*, 1969 and 1980, with the permission of the Controller of Her Majesty's Stationery Office)

1959 to 29 per cent by 1979. Just to emphasize the change in direction of trade, the EEC and Western Europe categories combined only accounted for 28 per cent of total trade in 1959 but 58 per cent by 1979.

Turning to Fig. 14.2 it should be appreciated that before the 'sixties semi-manufactured goods and finished manufactured goods were not separately identified. The proportion of trade shown for manufactured goods in 1959 therefore includes both types of commodities and although it cannot demonstrate the growth in trade of semi-manufactured goods the fact that it is now separately shown is an indication of its growing importance. Indeed, for several years within this period imports of semi-manufactured goods was the largest single category. Other noticeable features are the dramatic fall in imports of food, beverages, and tobacco, and the

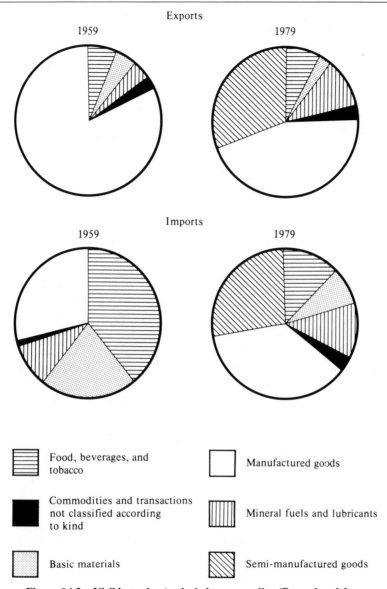

Exports

1959   1979

Imports

1959   1979

Food, beverages, and tobacco

Manufactured goods

Commodities and transactions not classified according to kind

Mineral fuels and lubricants

Basic materials

Semi-manufactured goods

Figure 14.2 Visible trade. Analysis by commodity (Reproduced from *U.K. Balance of Payments*, 1969 and 1980, with the permission of the Controller of Her Majesty's Stationery Office)

substantial increase in imports of both semi- and finished manufactured products. Additionally, the manufacturing base for most of our exports is clearly shown for both years.

Interpretation difficulties

As we might have expected there are certain difficulties with the OTS data, particularly when used for international comparisons. Many of these problems have been mentioned earlier and largely result from differences in conventions and definitions adopted by countries.

197

Differences in country recording   Before 1974 the United Kingdom recorded both exports and imports on the basis of country of consignment, but exports are now determined by country of final destination. The problem is not that exports and imports are being recorded differently, since in practice consignment and final destination are likely to be the same; the real difficulty is that countries can adopt a wide variety of alternative recording conventions. In addition to these two some countries use country of origin, or manufacture, or shipment.

The result of this inconsistency is that, for many goods, exports and imports will not match in national trading statistics. The United Kingdom, for example, will record imports as coming from the country that consigned them; however, in the event that this was not the country of manufacture then an anomaly is possible, since the country of manufacture could record a flow of goods to the United Kingdom, but the United Kingdom would record imports as coming from a different country—the country of consignment. In addition, the consigning country would show an import from the manufacturing country which is not matched in the records of the latter country, since they would show an export to the United Kingdom. Finally, the records of the consigning country of an export to the United Kingdom would be matched by a similar import in the United Kingdom, but now double counting would have occurred since the country of manufacture would also show an export of the same item to the United Kingdom.

These possibilities clearly show the difficulties that can arise in using international data given differences in the recording basis.

The 'general' and 'special' systems   Since either system can be used once again inconsistency results, with some countries using their geographical boundary as the frontier for recording trade (the general system) and others using their customs boundary (the special system). Thus some trade flows would be recorded in certain countries but ignored in others.

Different exclusions   Although nations adopt similar criteria for determining goods that are to be excluded from their statistics, i.e., goods in transit or entering and leaving on a temporary basis, goods that have strategic characteristics, or simply those goods that are difficult to record, nevertheless there is sufficient scope for differences to occur in these exclusion lists. Indeed, it would be unique if the lists were identical between nations for each would have their own customs, conventions, and practice. The treatment of fish and produce from the sea illustrates the point, with some countries excluding all trading in fish from their statistics while others include such trading. Yet other countries compromise between the two extremes by including imports of fish landed by foreign registered vessels but, because of recording difficulties, excluding as an export fish landed in foreign ports by their own registered ships.

Different commodity classifications   Despite the common use of the SITC, some countries still use their own classification system which clearly increases difficulties for international comparisons. Even where countries adopt the international classification system there is still the possibility of mis-recording by the exporting and importing agents, although it has been suggested that commodity descriptions are likely to be more accurate on import documents than on exports since they determine the duty payable.

Timing differences   It is obvious that some time elapses before goods reach their destination and therefore at any point in time a country would have recorded exports which would not be matched by the receiving country's record of imports. In practice this difficulty is likely to be

THE BALANCE OF PAYMENTS ACCOUNTS

unimportant except towards the end of a calendar year where some goods would be recorded as an export in one year but included as an import by the receiving country in the following year. This does have more serious implications for the balance of payments accounts recorded on an annual basis, as we will see later.

The U.K. monthly published data on exports and imports also reflect timing differences because of processing arrangements of the documents. Generally monthly data on imports actually refer to goods imported during that calendar month because of the necessity to obtain customs clearance before the goods can be moved. With exports, however, because of the 14 days' grace allowed from the time of shipment before documents are required and the fact that processing of the export documents begins before the end of the calendar month, it follows that the monthly figures for exports do not necessarily refer to goods actually shipped during that month.

Different valuations   Finally, it is worth while noting again that the value of a commodity exported from one country will be different from the value of that commodity received as an import since it would have carried the extra cost of insurance and freight charges, i.e., exports are valued on an FOB basis while imports are valued at CIF.

The different valuations should not present major difficulties for the users of the data once they are aware of this convention. However, as with timing difficulties, it does present more of a problem for the balance of payments accounts for it is essential here that exports and imports are valued on the same basis. Otherwise we would have the absurd situation of all countries tending to have balance of payments deficits since exports would be valued lower than imports. Clearly adjustments are required for balance of payments purposes and will be described in the following section.

14.3   The balance of payments accounts

To grasp the concept and nature of this set of data two key words should be appreciated— 'balance' and 'accounts'. Strictly speaking, the balance of payments is not a set of statistics but a set of accounts which, like all good accounts, should balance. This is, in fact, the foreign trade counterpart to the national income accounts (described in Chapter 3), which, the reader should recall, also balanced. Indeed, many of the recording and conceptual problems of the national income accounts are similar to that found in the balance of payments accounts.

It might seem strange to talk about our external transactions being balanced each year when, as a nation, we seem to have been beset by almost continuous balance of payments problems since the end of the Second World War, with long periods of deficits being interspersed by shorter periods of surpluses. The answer, of course, is that an excess of imports over exports (i.e., a deficit) has to be financed in some way—either by using our reserves of foreign exchange and gold or by borrowing from international agencies or other countries. Clearly, nations cannot run deficits indefinitely because of the finite nature of their reserves and the problems of building up loans from overseas—even if this were possible. Thus the use of reserves and borrowing facilities is seen only as a temporary measure to finance the deficit while more fundamental adjustments are made to remedy the basic weakness in the economy. When successful the deficits will be turned into a surplus and are accommodated in the accounts either by paying back previous borrowings or adding to our reserves of foreign exchange and gold. Both deficits and surpluses are compensated in order that the balance of payments is balanced each year, but this does not mean that balance of payments problems do not arise for, as mentioned, the United Kingdom has struggled with these difficulties over several decades now.

The structure of the accounts

The complete balance of payments data, presented annually, are set out in three accounts:

1. Current account.
2. Investment and other capital transactions.
3. Official financing.

The current account is sub-divided between so-called visible trade (exports and imports of commodities) and invisibles—services (shipping, civil aviation, insurance, banking, tourism, construction work, etc.), interest, profits and dividends, and transfers. The last item, transfers, is distinguished from the other elements in the accounts since it refers to what might be called 'free gifts', in the sense that compensating payment or repayment is not expected. It includes government grants and technical cooperation to overseas countries, subscriptions to international organizations, and private transfers by individuals and organizations, including missionary societies and charitable institutions.

Investment and other capital transactions includes the outward and inward flow of investment capital for fixed investment (i.e., investment in plant and equipment) and also investment in paper assets—so-called portfolio investment. It shows separately private sector and government sector flows of long-term capital. The latter includes long-term intergovernment loans and subscriptions to international lending bodies. Other items include lending by U.K. banks, import and export trade credit, and some official and private short-term transactions not covered elsewhere in the accounts.

Ignoring for the moment some additional items, the net balance of these two accounts produces the crucial and familiar balance of payments deficit or surplus. It is described in the data as the balance for official financing, but it is also referred to as the basic balance. This balance is then compensated by an opposite, but equal, movement of items in the third account, official financing. It includes changes in reserves of gold and convertible currencies, drawings, and repurchases (borrowing and repayment) with the International Monetary Fund (IMF), and similarly with other monetary authorities, and foreign currency borrowing by the government and U.K. public bodies.

In order for the accounts to balance the following sign convention is adopted. Exports of goods and services, found in the current account, would appear as positive items while imports would be shown with negative values. In the second account an outflow of capital investment (investment overseas by U.K. private or public sectors) would be recorded as a negative item, since this represents money leaving the country, while foreign capital investment in the United Kingdom appears as a positive item since it represents an inflow of capital. Consequently, if exports of goods and services are exceeded by imports and there is a net outflow of long-term capital then the balance of payments will be in deficit. It would appear in the accounts as a negative balance. This deficit would be offset by official financing either through an outward flow of gold and convertible currencies and/or an increase in borrowing from the IMF or other monetary authorities. Thus an outward flow of currencies would appear as a positive value, as would an increase in borrowing. A balance of payments surplus would lead to an increase in reserves of gold and convertible currencies and/or repayment of previous loans, and in either case would be represented by negative values.

Table 14.1   Summary balance of payments, 1979

		£ million
Current account		
Visible balance		− 3404
Invisibles		
Services balance	+ 3579	
Interest, profits, and dividends balance	+ 289	
Transfers balance	− 2327	
Invisibles balance	+ 1541	+ 1541
Current balance		− 1863
Capital transfers		−
Investment and other capital transactions		+ 1170
Balancing item		+ 2403
Balance for official financing		+ 1710
Allocation of SDRs (+)		+ 195
Gold subscriptions to IMF (−)		−
Official financing		
Net transactions with overseas monetary authorities		− 596
Foreign currency borrowing (net):		
by HM Government		−
by public sector under exchange cover scheme		− 250
Official reserves		− 1059

Reproduced from *Balance of Payments Accounts*, 1980, Table 1.1, with the permission of the Controller of Her Majesty's Stationery Office.

It might seem odd that a fall in our reserves and an increase in our foreign liabilities through borrowing is represented as positive values in the accounts and an increase in reserves and reduction in overseas liabilities are recorded as negative values. This is simply an accounting convention and reflects the necessity to demonstrate how a deficit or surplus is accommodated so that a balance is obtained.

Table 14.1 from a recent 'Pink Book' illustrates these points.[18] Several items appear in the summary table that have not so far been mentioned.

Allocation of SDRs   SDRs refer to a new type of IMF borrowing facility introduced in 1970, called the special drawing rights. It is distinct from conventional IMF borrowing arrangements partly because no additional subscriptions are required when borrowing facilities are increased. It always appears in the accounts as a positive item since it represents, as stated, an increase in borrowing facilities.

Gold subscription to IMF   This item represents the payments to IMF which are required when conventional IMF borrowing facilities are increased. It would effect all nations belonging to the IMF who would have to pay 20 per cent of the increase in borrowing potential in the form of gold or convertible currencies. In practice, these so-called 'quotas' are increased only infrequently—e.g., since 1958 gold subscriptions have been required on only four occasions. Since it is an outflow of capital it is always given a negative sign despite the fact that it implies that our borrowing potential with the IMF has been increased.

Foreign currency borrowing by public sector under exchange cover scheme   This refers to U.K. local authorities and public corporations borrowing from ovserseas. It is included in official financing since the foreign currency obtained is added to the official reserves.

Balancing item   The balancing item is analogous to the residual error in the national income accounts. It is the net total of errors and omissions in the current and investment accounts, and its value and sign is determined by the difference between the known changes in reserves and overseas borrowing or repayments of loans and the records of exports and imports of goods, services, and capital flows. In other words, it is the difference between official financing and the net balance of the current and investment account.

Errors and omissions in the accounts are partly due, like the residual error in the national accounts, to the wide variety of sources used in its compilation, as we shall see later. In addition timing errors may be partly responsible since the balance of payments data are based on records of transactions but the corresponding payment flows may take place in a different time period. Moreover, given more flexible exchange rates in the last decade the sterling rate may differ between the transaction records and subsequent payment flows.

How then can we interpret the balancing item? The value shown in Table 14.1 for 1979 is + £2403 million. Several possibilities arise. The positive value means that exports of goods and services could have been undervalued, or imports overvalued. Alternatively, the errors may occur in the investment account with either an under-recording of foreign investment capital in the U.K. (imports of long-term investment) or an over-recording of our investment overseas. Of course, in practice it is unlikely that one element in the accounts is responsible for the total error and therefore a combination of all these possibilities is more likely. In years when the balancing item is negative the reasoning would be the reverse of the above.

Sources of data

As we have just seen, the wide variety of sources used in the compilation of the accounts is one explanation for the existence of a balancing item. It presents problems of inconsistency, as well as incompleteness and the necessity to process the basic data—problems similar, in fact, to those encountered in the national income accounts.

Visible trade   The overseas trade statistics[17] provide the basic data on exports and imports of goods. However, since the OTS and the balance of payments fulfil different functions it is necessary to adjust the OTS figures before they can be included in the balance of payments accounts. Two types of adjustment are made: valuation and coverage.

A valuation adjustment on the import figures is necessary since these are recorded on a CIF basis in the OTS; and therefore deduction of freight and insurance is made so that both exports and imports are being valued on an FOB basis.

Coverage adjustment to the export and import figures are necessary since certain items are excluded from the OTS, but since payment flows occur it is essential that they be included in the accounts. Examples would be secondhand ships and ships delivered abroad. The reverse applies to secondhand aircraft imported or exported for repair. These are included in the OTS, but must be excluded from the balance of payments since there is no change in ownership.

Invisible trade   The invisible part of the current account represents a wide variety of items based on different sources and therefore with a marked range of reliability. Records of

202

government transactions stem from government departments and must be assumed to be accurate. Information on sea transport are based on inquiries made by the General Council of British Shipping. Again it is felt to be reasonably accurate although provisional estimates may be subject to substantial error. Estimates of travel expenditure and civil aviation are based principally on the international passenger survey, which would be subject to sampling errors. Much of the data for financial and other services is provided by the Bank of England, who in turn obtain information from Lloyds Register of Shipping, the British Insurance Association, and their own surveys into net earnings of U.K. banks for services. Other data stem from inquiries conducted by the Department of Trade—particularly that relating to royalties. Several individual categories are subject to substantial margins of error where estimates are based on information from companies; examples include construction work overseas, consultancy earnings, and services associated with oil and natural gas exploration.

The source of information for interest, profits, and dividends differs according to the type of investment on which earnings are obtained. Direct investment earnings of companies are obtained from a voluntary inquiry conducted by the Department of Trade which is supplemented by estimates for non-response for the published figures. Similar investment earnings by banks and insurance companies come from inquiries conducted by the Bank of England and the British Insurance Association, respectively. For earnings from portfolio investment most of the data originate from Inland Revenue records. The latter is felt to provide less reliable estimates than direct investment earnings.

Investment and other capital transactions   Once again we see a variety of sources used, given the heterogeneous nature of the components of this account. For official long-term capital transactions the data come from official records while much of the data for private sector capital flows came from the operations of exchange control before its abolition in October 1979. Other sources have already been mentioned, i.e., the Bank of England inquiry into overseas portfolio investment, Department of Trade inquiries, the British Insurance Association, etc. In addition, oil companies' outward and inward investments are notified by the oil industry to the Bank of England. With the passing of exchange controls more reliance has to be placed on these inquiries and some previously published data are no longer available.

Official financing   Changes in reserves and increase or decrease in our liabilities overseas are precisely known from official records. It is for this reason that we can be certain about the net value of errors and omissions; it is the difference between official financing and the estimates for visible and invisible trade and capital flow.

Uses and interpretation difficulties

It is unlikely that private sector companies would make much use of the information provided in the 'Pink Book'. If they are engaged in overseas trade or considering entering foreign markets then the overseas trade statistics would be more appropriate. However, for central government the balance of payments figures are of some concern, particularly for major trading countries like Britain. A bad series of trading figures with the rest of the world could lead to major internal policy changes.

The data are also used by analysts concerned with establishing changes in our trading characteristics and, in Britain's case, with suggesting where fundamental problems exist. For such tests, caution should be used when analysing component values or even totals for the main accounts. The existence of a balancing item is a warning that errors and omissions occur due to mis-reporting, missing items requiring estimates, values obtained from inquiries which involve sampling errors, processing errors, and timing differences.

14.4 Conclusions

The problems of comparing internationally foreign trade statistics have been outlined in the present chapter. These difficulties are not, however, confined to foreign trade data, as we have seen elsewhere in the book. The increasing tendency to make international comparisons of a wide range of internal data makes it more important than ever to appreciate the problems involved in making such comparisons. Since this is the final sources chapter it is appropriate to emphasize these points with illustrations from earlier chapters.

One major difficulty springs from differences in concepts and recording conventions which reflect varied circumstances and customs; each country would be producing data suitable for its own purposes. We have seen in the present chapter how the United Kingdom adopts the 'general' system for recording trade while many other countries use the 'special' system. Earlier chapters pointed out the problems involved in comparing internationally such measures as unemployment, productivity, the distribution of income and wealth, per capita income, and activity rates. Recorded differences in unemployment figures could be ambiguous if adjustments for different definitions of unemployment and recording conventions have not been made. Similarly, productivity measures would depend on what has been included in the output and input series and how these data have been obtained. Once again, substantial differences in the approach taken by countries is likely. For income and wealth distribution comparisons the crucial factors would be the definition of the recipient and what is included as income and what is included as wealth. The conceptual problem of distinguishing between income and wealth has been discussed in Chapter 13 and clearly raises the likelihood that some assets would be considered as part of income by some countries and wealth by others. The problem involved in making international comparisons of per capita income measures has been covered in Chapter 3. There it was pointed out that the scope for differences in the way in which nations estimate their national income is substantial, given the complex nature of such statistics. Additionally, for this measure an estimate of the total population is required, and for some countries even this basic information is open to considerable doubt. For activity rates (dealt with in Chapter 9) like productivity calculations, international comparisons will be made difficult because of different definitions and recording practices for the numerator and denominator measurements. It was also pointed out that differences in activity rates may be explained (if only partly) by social custom and institutional differences, which clearly must be considered in any interpretation.

Apart from the realization that different concepts and recording procedures are likely to occur, it must also be borne in mind that the degree of sophistication shown in the collection and provision of data can differ greatly from country to country. As all the sources chapters in this book testify, even a country with a well-established statistical service such as Britain produces data which in some cases are doubtful and invariably present interpretation problems. These difficulties, however, may be minimal compared with some countries for whom even a basic indicator such as a total population estimate will have a large margin of error. Clearly, we cannot expect the degree of accuracy to be identical for all countries.

A major theme of this book has been to emphasize the need for caution when handling published data. If this is necessary for internal data then it becomes even more necessary when dealing with statistical information from a number of countries.

15. Integrative assignments

The major theme of this book has been the emphasis placed on combining knowledge of sources with statistical techniques in an approach which we feel is more meaningful for quantitative analysis. The aim of this final chapter is to illustrate this approach with a series of integrative assignments which draws on material covered in the preceding chapters and helps to establish the importance of extracting, applying, and interpreting statistical information.

Assignment 1

A hypothetical wage claim using specified data

Assignment question

The National Union of Mineworkers have failed to agree their pay award for 1980 with the NCB. Their claim has now gone to arbitration. The NUM claim for a 20 per cent increase is based on the following grounds:

1. Changes in the cost of living.
2. Improvements in the productivity of their members.
3. Comparability over recent years with workers in the gas, electricity, and water industries.

The NCB has employed you to examine the mineworkers claim and to present a written report to the arbitration panel. The report should be prepared under the following headings and should contain suitable graphs and/or diagrams:

1. Introduction and aims of the report; method of approach. $(12\frac{1}{2}\%$ of marks)
2. Miners wages and the cost of living. $(25\%$ of marks)
3. Miners wages and productivity. $(37\frac{1}{2}\%$ of marks)
4. Miners wages compared with the gas, electricity, and
   water workers. $(12\frac{1}{2}\%$ of marks)
5. Conclusion and recommendation. $(12\frac{1}{2}\%$ of marks)

For section 2 you are required to comment on whether you feel the statistics used have validity for collective bargaining purposes.

For section 3 you are required to calculate an index of productivity and discuss whether the NUM should use productivity as an argument in seeking a pay increase.

Statistics available

A. *General index of retail price*
    1976: 89.5
    1977: 93.2
    1978:100.0
    1979:113.1
    1980:134.7

B. *Tax and price index*
    1976: 84.5
    1977: 98.5
    1978:100.0
    1979:113.8
    1980:133.6

C. *Employment in coal production at NCB
collieries ('000s)*
1976:241.0
1977:238.7
1978:231.7
1979:229.1
1980:220.0

D. *Average shifts worked per week in coal mining*
1976:4.7
1977:4.2
1978:4.1
1979:3.7
1980:3.6

E. *Coal production ('000 tonnes)*
1976:2381
1977:2346
1978:2376
1979:2353
1980:2290

F. *Average weekly earnings of miners (£ per week)*
1976: 76.75
1977: 82.36
1978: 95.65
1979:116.51

G. *Average weekly earnings of workers in the gas,
electricity, and water industry (£ per week)*
1976: 68.42
1977: 72.72
1978: 87.78
1979:104.30

Suggested answers

1. *Introduction and aims of the report; method of approach*   The aim of this report is to represent the views of the NCB on the mineworkers claim for a 20 per cent increase in pay, which they justify on cost of living, productivity, and comparability grounds. In using the specified data we intend conducting a critical but, we feel, fair analysis of this claim.

Since the basic unit of measurement provided varies (tonnes, thousands, days, pound sterling, etc.) it would be appropriate to convert all the values into index numbers before analysis takes place. In addition it would be more useful to make the earliest year, 1976, the base year of 100 in order to draw out more easily percentage changes that have taken place. This, of course, would necessitate re-basing the two price indices (data A and B).

2. *Miners wages and the cost of living*   Reconstructing tables A and B gives the following:

A. *General index of retail price*
1976:100.0
1977:104.1
1978:111.7
1979:126.4
1980:150.5

B. *Tax and price index*
1976:100.0
1977:116.6
1978:118.3
1979:134.7
1980:158.1

From the mineworkers viewpoint the TPI presents the most favourable picture since this shows an increase of 58.1 per cent over this time period compared with a rise of 50.5 per cent for the RPI. However, these data should be compared with those shown as data F. Reconstructing this table in index form gives:

F. *Average weekly earnings of miners; index form*
1976:100.0
1977:107.3
1978:124.6
1979:151.8

Up to and including 1979, average weekly earnings increased by 51.8 per cent, which is appreciably higher than the RPI (an increase of 26.4 per cent) or even the TPI (an increase of 34.7 per cent).

It would appear from the data, illustrated in Fig. 15.1, that the cost of living justification is unsubstantiated—earnings have risen much faster than either of the official price indices. The only proviso is that the TPI value for 1980 is in excess of the index of average earnings in 1979, but at best would only justify a claim of 6 or 7 per cent to bring earnings in line with prices as measured by the TPI.

However, doubts must be expressed over the use of the RPI or even the TPI as a measure of the 'cost of living'. First, the RPI embraces a far wider range of goods and services than one would normally expect in a cost of living index, and it should be noted that the RPI is never described in the official publications as a cost of living index. Second, the ability to buy goods and services would be determined not only by their prices but by the amount of disposable incomes that consumers have. Clearly, the RPI is unable to cast any light on the latter since it is simply measuring changes in prices. From this point of view the TPI would appear to be more meaningful for it includes not only price changes but also changes in disposable income.

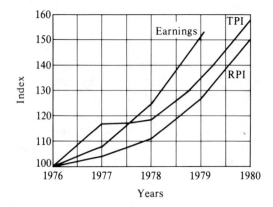

Figure 15.1   Earnings, RPI, and TPI in index form

Nevertheless, there are still substantial problems in interpreting this index since by combining the RPI with tax changes all the conceptual and practical difficulties associated with the RPI are included.

Pertinent to this wage claim is the realization that the RPI is based on the concept of a nationally representative basket of goods and services, and we should therefore expect a range of experience around this average. Mineworkers may suffer more, or less, from inflation than is indicated by the RPI by having a basket of goods and services different from that assumed in its construction and by living in areas that exhibit greater, or lesser, price changes than is shown by the official index.

The use of both indices as measures of the cost of living and basing wage claims on them is therefore questionable. At best they can only serve as approximate measures of the effect of inflation on mineworkers.

3. *Miners wages and productivity*   For the productivity basis of the claim we need to consider the data marked C, D, and E. Reconstructing in index form the data for employment (C) and coal production (E) gives:

C. *Employment in coal production at NCB*
     collieries; index form
      1976: 100.0
      1977: 99.0
      1978: 96.1
      1979: 95.1
      1980: 91.3

E. *Coal production; index form*
      1976: 100.0
      1977: 98.5
      1978: 99.8
      1979: 98.8
      1980: 96.2

Coal production has clearly declined—by 3.8 per cent in the period covered by the data. However, it is noticeable that employment in coal mining has also fallen, and by a larger amount than output (an 8.7 per cent fall in employment), which therefore implies an increase in productivity. A simple productivity index (output divided by input) based on the above data is illustrated in Table 15.1.

Table 15.1

Productivity index (a)
1976: 100
1977: 99.5
1978: 103.8
1979: 103.9
1980: 105.4

This productivity measure clearly represents output per employee year and shows an improvement, albeit a very small one, over the time period examined. But a more useful measure would be output per employee hour for it is quite likely that the number of hours worked each year has changed—particularly over a period of five years. Unfortunately no data are available here on hours worked, but we do have information on the average shifts worked per week over these years, shown as data D. Using these data and the information from data E we can calculate production (in thousand tonnes) per shift which can then be indexed for consistency (see Table 15.2).

Table 15.2

	Average shifts worked per week	Indexed	Production per shift ('000 tonnes)	Indexed
1976	4.7	100.0	506.6	100.0
1977	4.2	89.4	558.6	110.3
1978	4.1	87.2	579.5	114.4
1979	3.7	78.7	635.9	125.5
1980	3.6	76.6	636.1	125.6

With this information we can now either divide the index for production per shift by the index for employment (data C) or divide the productivity index from Table 15.1 by the index for average shifts worked (column 2 in Table 15.2). Either way, allowing for rounding-up errors, would result in the productivity index illustrated in Table 15.3.

Table 15.3

Productivity index (b)
1976:100.0
1977:111.4
1978:119.0
1979:132.0
1980:137.6

This would be a more meaningful index than that shown in Table 15.1 since it takes account of both the reduced workforce and the reduction in average shifts worked. It is therefore a measure of the output per employee shift, but is based on the assumption that the hours worked per shift are identical over these years. The increase in productivity is now shown to be fairly substantial—an improvement of 37.6 per cent over the period as a whole. To see whether this justifies the current wage claim we would have to compare the index of average weekly earnings with the productivity index. This is done in Fig. 15.2 which clearly

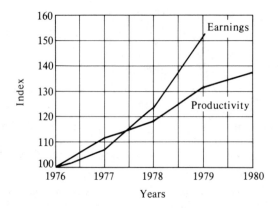

Figure 15.2   Earnings and productivity in index form

demonstrates that by 1979 average weekly earnings was oustripping productivity, more noticeably in 1979 itself. In index terms, wages, in 1979, are already substantially above productivity shown for 1980. The productivity basis of the wage claim is therefore doubtful.

However, all these considerations are based on the assumption that the workforce alone is responsible for the productivity improvements. In practice this may not be so. It is possible that part of the gain stems from capital investment in more modern machinery and in addition is likely to reflect geological factors such as more easily accessible coal seams. It can be argued that these factors may have increased the difficulty of mining and therefore productivity is greater than the figures suggest. However, no data are presented on this, or capital investment, and therefore positive conclusions are not possible. The major point is that the efficiency of the labour force is just one factor among many that can influence productivity. Once again we must conclude that the productivity basis of the wage claim is doubtful.

4. *The comparability basis of the claim* The information presented in data F and G show that the average weekly earnings of miners have been approximately £10 higher than those earned in the gas, electricity, and water industry for each of the four years shown. However, converting these values into index numbers with 1976 as the base year indicates that the gap has been marginally reduced with earnings in the public utility sector increasing by 52.4 per cent compared with 51.8 per cent for the miners:

F. *Index of average weekly earnings of miners*

1976:100.0
1977:107.3
1978:124.6
1979:151.8

G. *Index of average weekly earnings in gas, electricity and water industry*

1976:100.0
1977:106.3
1978:128.6
1979:152.4

Even if we accept the aim of the miners to maintain their differential vis-à-vis public utility workers, this would warrant a claim of less than 1 per cent. The crucial factor, of course, is the wage claim of public utility workers, but there is no information on this.

5. *Conclusion and recommendation* Given the data available it would seem that the 20 per cent claim by the NUM is difficult to justify. Even if we accept the TPI as a measure of the effect of inflation on members this would only warrant a maximum increase of 7 per cent. The productivity basis of the claim is even more doubtful. Though productivity clearly has occurred, and has been substantial, nevertheless wages have been increasing at an even faster rate, and therefore there can be no claim for 'catching up' with past productivity. Turning to the third basis of the claim it is clear that mineworkers have almost managed to maintain their wages differential over the public utility workers. At best a wage increase of less than 1 per cent could be justified on this criterion.

On the evidence, then, a wage increase substantially less than that claimed by the NUM appears more realistic, with a figure of 7 or 8 per cent perhaps being justified.

It is accepted, however, that more detailed information on the basis of past productivity improvements, proposed future productivity, and the wage settlement in public utility industries could influence the final settlement.

Notes on the assignment
This suggested answer illustrates how an integrated assignment can be tackled. It demonstrates the four elements of any quantitative analysis described in the Preface, namely, knowledge of sources reorganizing the data, knowledge of techniques, and the final report and conclusion.

Although the techniques used are elementary, the assignment did not call for anything more sophisticated. Indeed, the quality and range of data provided would hardly justify more complex techniques. Nevertheless, the assignment does serve to show the integrative aspect of the subject and would test the ability of students to handle a range of disparate data in a realistic setting.

It should be emphasized that the exercise here is a hypothetical one although the data are genuine. In reality the range and extent of data used in collective bargaining would be far more extensive and detailed than that presented here, and certainly the NUM would have used data that were far more favourable to its case than that shown. For instance deflating the earnings data to give 'real' as opposed to 'money' incomes.

Assignment 2

Unemployment and vacancy analysis

Assignment question

1. From the information given in Tables 2.2 and 3.1 of the *Employment Gazette*[8] (see Tables 15.4 and 15.5) select the appropriate data and regress unfilled vacancies on unemployment using figures for March, June, September, and December for the years 1978 to 1980 inclusive.
2. Use the regression equation to estimate the number of vacancies you would have expected for December 1977 and comment on any differences between the predicted and observed value shown.
3. Plot the data, including the linear regression on a graph and comment on the relationship you have established.
4. What qualifications would you make to your conclusions as a result of deficiencies in the data source?

Suggested marking scheme

1. 40% of marks.
2. 10% of marks.
3. 10% of marks.
4. 40% of marks.

Initial comments

The assignment requires that students extract from published data the most relevant material, reorganize this material into more manageable form, and determine which is the independent variable (x) and the dependent variable (y). These three decisions are seen to be crucial since they will influence the remainder of the assignment answer. A bad initial choice of data and confusion between the dependent and independent variables will undermine the resulting analysis.

Suggested answers

1. *Selecting the data and determining the function* The unemployment data (Table 15.4) covers Great Britain and therefore the column marked Great Britain in Table 15.5 would be the relevant data to use for vacancies. Since this information is seasonally adjusted it would be appropriate to use the seasonally adjusted figures for unemployment in Table 15.4. Under this heading the column marked 'number' should be used since it is consistent with the vacancy data which are also measured in terms of thousands. Thus column 5 in Table 15.4 should be compared with column 12 in Table 15.5. The fact that the unemployment figures exclude school leavers should not present too much of a problem since it should be noted that the vacancies derive from employment offices and not youth employment offices and therefore the notified vacancies as well as unemployment relate to adults, i.e., we have reasonable (though not perfect) consistency between the two variables.

A practical issue is that many small calculators could not handle the values shown in most published data and therefore require simplification. For this assignment the decision is made to divide the unemployment and vacancy data by 10 and to round up to the nearest whole

212

Table 15.4

2·2 UNEMPLOYMENT
GB summary

THOUSAND

GREAT BRITAIN	MALE AND FEMALE										
	UNEMPLOYED			UNEMPLOYED EXCLUDING SCHOOL LEAVERS					UNEMPLOYED BY DURATION		
	Number	Per cent	School leavers included in unemployed	Actual	Seasonally adjusted		Change		Up to 4 weeks	Over 4 weeks aged under 60*	Over 4 weeks aged 60 and over*
					Number	Per cent	Since previous month	Average over 3 months ended			
1975	935·6	4 1	45 3	890 3		3 9					
1976	1,304·6	5 6	81·6	1,223·0		5 2					
1977 Annual	1,422·7	6 0	99·8	1,322·9		5 6					
1978 averages	1,409·7	6 0	93 7	1,315·9		5 6					
1979	1,325·5	5 6	78 0	1,247·5		5 3					
1980	1,715·9	7 3	120 1	1,595·8		6 7					
1975 Dec 11	1,152·5	5 0	32 1	1,120·4	1,120·8	4 9	37·0	44·2	209	826	118
1976 Jan 8	1,251·8	5 4	38·0	1,213·8	1,149·5	4 9	28·7	35·3	207	923	122
Feb 12	1,253·4	5 4	28·0	1,225·4	1,180·0	5 1	30·5	32·1	213	918	122
Mar 11	1,234·6	5 3	21·7	1,212·9	1,194·9	5 1	14·9	24·7	192	921	122
April 8	1,231·2	5 3	21·3	1,209·9	1,209·5	5 2	14·6	20·0	210	899	122
May 13	1,220·4	5 2	35·1	1,185·3	1,220·8	5 2	11·3	13·6	187	911	122
June 10	1,277·9	5 5	118·2	1,159·7	1,227·6	5 3	6·8	10·9	269	886	123
July 8	1,402·5	6 0	199·4	1,203·1	1,230·1	5 3	2·5	6·9	356	923	123
Aug 12	1,440·0	6 2	194·5	1,245·4	1,240·7	5 3	10·6	6·6	258	1,056	126
Sep 9	1,395·1	6 0	142·3	1,252·8	1,245·5	5 3	4·8	6·0	237	1,032	126
Oct 14	1,320·9	5 7	78·0	1,243·0	1,244·5	5 3	−1·0	4·8	250	946	125
Nov 11e	1,311·0	5 6	54·3	1,256·7	1,255·2	5 4	10·7	4·8	..	..	..
Dec 9 e	1,316·0	5 6	48·0	1,268·0	1,264·9	5 4	9·7	6·5	..	..	..
1977 Jan 13	1,390·2	5 9	48·2	1,342·0	1,275·6	5 4	10·7	10·4	207	1,053	130
Feb 10	1,365·2	5 8	39·4	1,325·8	1,278·3	5 4	2·7	7·7	211	1,028	126
Mar 10	1,328·1	5 6	31·3	1,296·8	1,280·0	5 4	1·7	5·0	193	1,010	125
April 14	1,335·6	5 7	50·4	1,285·3	1,287·6	5 5	7·6	4·0	223	989	123
May 12	1,285·7	5 5	42·0	1,243·7	1,283·2	5 5	−4·4	1·6	197	969	120
June 9	1,390·4	5 9	142·7	1,247·7	1,323·3	5 6	40·1	14·4	288	982	120
July 14	1,553·5	6 6	241·6	1,311·9	1,337·0	5 7	13·7	16·5	389	1,046	118
Aug 11	1,567·0	6 7	220·4	1,346·6	1,337·1	5 7	0·1	18·0	269	1,178	120
Sep 8	1,541·8	6 6	166·2	1,375·7	1,357·6	5 8	20·5	11·4	242	1,175	125
Oct 13	1,456·6	6 2	92·6	1,364·0	1,363·1	5 8	5·5	8·7	253	1,079	125
Nov 10	1,438·0	6 1	68·6	1,369·4	1,367·7	5 8	4·6	10·2	230	1,083	125
Dec 8	1,419·7	6 0	54·3	1,365·4	1,366·7	5 8	−1·0	3·0	201	1,092	126
1978 Jan 12	1,484·7	6 3	57·4	1,427·3	1,362·9	5 8	−3·8	−0·1	199	1,156	130
Feb 9	1,445·9	6 1	46·6	1,399·2	1,354·4	5 8	−8·5	−4·4	203	1,114	129
Mar 9	1,399·0	5 9	37·6	1,361·3	1,351·2	5 7	−3·2	−5·2	189	1,082	128
April 13	1,387·5	5 9	56·7	1,330·8	1,342·4	5 7	−8·8	−6·8	220	1,041	127
May 11	1,324·9	5 6	44·7	1,280·2	1,326·4	5 6	−16·0	−9·3	185	1,015	125
June 8	1,381·4	5 9	139·2	1,242·2	1,319·4	5 6	−7·0	−10·6	276	983	123
July 6	1,512·5	6 4	231·7	1,280·8	1,307·6	5 6	−11·8	−11·6	366	1,024	122
Aug 10	1,534·4	6 5	210·9	1,323·6	1,309·9	5 6	2·3	−5·5	250	1,160	124
Sep 14	1,446·7	6 1	130·7	1,316·0	1,296·5	5 5	−13·4	−7·6	220	1,102	125
Oct 12	1,364·9	5 8	76·4	1,288·5	1,287·5	5 5	−9·0	−6·7	235	1,006	124
Nov 9	1,330·8	5 7	52·9	1,277·9	1,275·1	5 4	−12·4	−11·6	203	1,004	124
Dec 7	1,303·2	5 5	39·8	1,263·4	1,264·8	5 4	−10·3	−10·6	191	988	124
1979 Jan 11	1,391·2	5 9	44·4	1,346·9	1,281·5	5 4	16·7	−2·0	201	1,063	127
Feb 8	1,387·6	5 9	36·7	1,350·9	1,305·2	5 5	23·7	10·0	200	1,061	127
Mar 8	1,339·8	5 7	23·9	1,310·9	1,299·8	5 5	−5·4	11·7	176	1,038	126
April 5	1,279·8	5 4	23·9	1,255·9	1,265·9	5 4	−33·9	−5·2	166	989	125
May 10	1,238·5	5 2	36·2	1,202·3	1,246·9	5 3	−19·0	−19·4	160	957	121
June 14	1,281·1	5 4	137·1	1,144·0	1,223·6	5 2	−23·3	−25·4	266	898	117
July 12	1,392·0	5 9	204·2	1,187·8	1,217·1	5 2	−6·5	−16·3	335	941	117
Aug 9	1,383·9	5 9	173·1	1,210·8	1,202·8	5 1	−14·3	−14·7	232	1,035	117
Sep 13	1,325·0	5 6	106·0	1,219·0	1,202·4	5 1	−0·4	−7·1	212	995	118
Oct 11†	1,302·8	5 5	64·0	1,238·8	1,218·3	5 2	15·9	0·4	231	953	118
Nov 8	1,292·3	5 5	45·5	1,246·8	1,223·6	5 2	5·3	6·9	203	969	120
Dec 6	1,292·0	5 5	35·7	1,256·3	1,236·8	5 2	13·2	11·5	197	974	121
1980 Jan 10	1,404·4	6 0	42·6	1,361·7	1,275·4	5 4	38·6	19·0	202	1,079	125
Feb 14	1,422·0	6 0	35·2	1,386·8	1,319·9	5 6	44·5	32·1	212	1,085	125
Mar 13 e	1,411·7	6 0	29·3	1,382·4	1,349·5	5 7	29·6	37·6	199	1,087	125
April 10	1,454·7	6 2	50·0	1,404·6	1,393·0	5 9	43·5	39·2	231	1,097	127
May 8	1,441·4	6 1	45·8	1,395·6	1,418·0	6 0	25·0	32·7	199	1,116	126
June 12	1,586·6	6 7	178·3	1,408·3	1,468·0	6 2	50·0	39·5	338	1,123	126
July 10	1,811·9	7 7	282·1	1,529·9	1,535·9	6 5	67·9	47·6	433	1,249	129
Aug 14	1,913·1	8 1	252·0	1,661·1	1,622·2	6 9	86·3	68·1	300	1,476	137
Sep 11	1,950·2	8 3	196·3	1,753·8	1,707·9	7 2	85·7	80·0	292	1,520	138
Oct 9	1,973·0	8 4	137·2	1,835·8	1,810·3	7 7	102·4	91·5	329	1,500	144
Nov 13	2,071·2	8 8	103·4	1,967·8	1,942·5	8 2	132·2	106·8	309	1,616	147
Dec 11	2,150·5	9 1	88·6	2,061·8	2,045·3	8 7	102·8	112·5	283	1,718	149

* † See footnotes to table 2 1

number. This may appear a dangerous oversimplification but in practice the rounding up is likely to cancel out and should not alter the measured relationship by very much. Furthermore, many students (and researchers!) who use the precise values shown only finish up with a spurious kind of accuracy since they ignore, or are unaware of, the fact that most published data present estimated values.

Table 15.5

3·1 VACANCIES
Regions: notified to employment offices: seasonally adjusted *

THOUSAND

	South East	Greater London †	East Anglia	South West	West Midlands	East Midlands	York-shire and Humber-side	North West	North	Wales	Scotland	Great Britain	Northern Ireland	United Kingdom
1975 Dec 5	43·0	20·7	3·5	7·9	5·3	6·3	8·0	10·3	7·9	4·5	14·7	110·8	2·3	113·1
1976 Jan 2	42·3	20·5	3·4	8·4	5·1	6·6	7·4	9·9	7·1	4·6	14·2	108·9	2·3	111·2
Feb 6	44·0	21·4	3·4	8·5	5·5	6·5	8·2	10·2	7·2	4·6	14·3	111·2	2·2	113·4
Mar 5	45·8	22·9	3·6	8·0	5·9	6·8	8·3	10·5	7·1	4·7	14·4	115·2	2·1	117·3
April 2	45·7	22·8	3·6	7·9	6·2	6·8	8·8	10·2	7·4	4·9	13·9	115·5	2·2	117·7
May 7	44·0	21·6	3·5	8·1	6·2	6·6	9·2	10·0	7·0	5·0	14·3	113·7	2·3	116·0
June 4	43·7	22·2	3·3	7·0	6·1	6·6	8·7	9·6	7·3	4·6	14·4	111·3	2·1	113·4
July 2	45·6	23·4	3·4	7·7	6·4	7·0	9·8	10·3	8·2	5·1	14·5	118·2	2·1	120·3
Aug 6	49·6	25·0	3·5	8·2	6·9	7·8	10·4	10·7	8·0	5·5	14·8	125·8	1·9	127·7
Sep 3	50·6	26·2	3·4	8·4	7·4	8·1	10·6	11·3	8·0	5·8	14·6	128·3	2·2	130·5
Oct 8	50·7	26·0	3·7	7·9	7·4	7·8	10·7	11·2	8·2	5·5	13·7	127·2	1·9	129·1
Nov 5 e	52·0	27·2	3·8	8·2	7·7	8·3	11·0	11·6	8·4	5·7	13·9	130·7	1·9	132·6
Dec 3 e	54·0	28·7	3·9	8·6	8·1	8·8	11·3	12·0	8·7	5·9	14·2	135·4	1·9	137·3
1977 Jan 7 e	56·0	30·3	4·0	8·8	8·6	9·3	11·5	12·3	9·0	6·1	14·5	139·7	2·1	141·8
Feb 4	60·0	32·1	4·1	9·1	9·1	9·8	11·9	12·7	9·2	6·2	14·8	146·0	1·8	147·8
Mar 4	61·7	33·2	4·3	9·3	9·5	10·1	12·1	12·7	9·0	6·0	15·1	149·3	1·8	151·1
April 6	62·3	33·7	4·1	8·8	9·2	10·6	11·8	12·4	8·8	6·0	15·8	149·6	1·8	151·4
May 6	64·6	36·3	4·0	8·8	9·4	10·5	12·7	12·5	9·2	5·9	15·4	152·9	1·7	154·6
June 1	63·2	35·8	4·3	8·2	9·2	10·3	12·5	12·4	8·6	6·0	16·3	151·1	1·9	153·0
July 8	62·9	35·2	4·8	8·3	9·4	10·7	12·5	13·2	8·7	6·1	16·6	153·4	2·0	155·4
Aug 5	64·2	34·8	4·9	8·7	9·9	10·5	12·6	12·6	8·8	6·1	16·7	154·9	2·1	157·0
Sep 2	60·6	33·2	4·9	8·3	9·9	10·1	12·1	12·0	9·0	5·9	16·9	149·7	2·0	151·7
Oct 7	64·7	35·1	4·6	9·0	10·4	10·5	12·6	12·8	9·2	6·4	17·7	157·6	2·1	159·7
Nov 4	68·2	37·1	4·9	9·5	10·1	10·2	12·7	12·8	9·3	6·6	15·9	160·8	2·0	162·8
Dec 2	70·9	38·2	5·4	10·1	10·9	10·7	12·8	13·6	9·2	7·0	17·7	168·3	2·0	170·3
1978 Jan 6	74·9	40·5	5·6	11·3	11·9	11·1	13·6	14·9	10·0	7·1	18·6	178·8	1·9	180·7
Feb 3	78·7	42·4	5·6	11·5	11·7	12·1	13·5	15·2	9·6	7·2	19·0	183·6	1·9	185·5
Mar 3	81·6	44·4	5·9	11·2	11·9	12·2	13·5	15·2	9·9	8·5	20·1	189·6	1·9	191·5
April 7	84·6	46·0	6·1	11·8	12·3	12·4	15·2	15·6	10·1	8·0	20·8	196·5	1·8	198·3
May 5	88·7	48·0	6·3	12·3	12·4	12·9	13·9	15·7	10·1	7·9	21·2	201·6	1·8	203·4
June 2	92·3	50·3	6·3	13·3	13·0	13·4	14·6	16·0	10·5	8·1	21·0	208·7	1·8	210·5
July 30	93·1	50·2	6·2	13·6	13·0	13·4	15·1	15·5	9·7	8·4	21·4	209·6	1·7	211·3
Aug 4	94·5	49·0	6·2	14·0	12·9	13·6	15·1	16·8	10·4	8·2	20·8	212·5	1·6	214·1
Sep 8	101·7	55·2	6·8	13·8	13·5	14·4	15·8	17·3	10·5	8·7	20·6	222·3	1·5	224·8
Oct 6	104·8	56·8	7·1	15·0	14·1	15·7	15·6	18·1	10·8	8·9	21·4	231·5	1·4	232·9
Nov 3	105·0	56·2	7·2	15·6	14·4	16·0	15·9	18·4	11·0	8·8	20·7	233·7	1·4	235·1
Dec 1	107·2	57·0	7·2	15·5	14·2	16·2	16·5	18·4	11·3	9·0	21·2	236·7	1·4	238·1
1979 Jan 5	107·1	55·9	7·1	15·6	14·0	16·2	16·4	18·6	10·8	8·2	21·1	234·9	1·3	236·2
Feb 2	106·0	56·0	6·8	15·1	13·2	15·0	15·3	17·7	10·0	8·5	20·5	227·8	1·2	229·0
Mar 2	108·1	56·7	6·7	14·8	13·6	14·9	15·6	18·5	10·1	8·9	19·7	230·7	1·3	232·0
Mar 30	110·9	58·3	7·8	16·4	15·4	16·0	16·2	20·4	10·5	9·0	20·0	242·1	1·5	243·6
May 4	113·4	58·5	8·2	17·6	15·9	16·2	17·0	20·8	11·0	10·7	22·1	253·1	1·5	254·6
June 8	114·9	58·2	9·1	18·4	16·0	16·1	17·3	21·1	11·4	10·7	22·3	257·4	1·4	258·8
July 6	113·2	57·3	8·6	17·5	15·6	15·7	16·6	20·6	11·2	10·3	22·0	251·5	1·4	252·9
Aug 3	109·8	54·3	8·6	16·9	15·6	15·6	16·8	20·6	10·7	10·2	22·3	247·3	1·3	248·6
Sep 7	109·2	54·2	8·3	17·5	14·8	15·4	16·1	20·7	10·3	9·8	22·5	244·6	1·3	245·9
Oct 5	106·4	52·8	8·3	17·2	14·0	14·5	15·8	19·4	10·0	9·6	21·8	237·1	1·3	238·4
Nov 2	104·4	52·2	8·3	16·5	14·0	14·4	15·0	18·6	9·8	9·5	22·1	233·3	1·3	234·6
Nov 30	100·3	51·1	7·8	15·8	13·1	13·0	13·5	17·0	9·7	9·1	21·6	221·0	1·3	222·3
1980 Jan 4	94·2	48·3	7·1	14·5	12·0	12·0	12·5	16·2	9·1	8·2	19·8	205·7	1·2	206·9
Feb 8	85·9	44·4	6·6	14·1	11·4	11·6	11·6	14·9	7·6	7·6	19·3	190·2	1·2	191·4
Mar 7	80·4	40·5	6·1	14·7	10·8	10·6	10·5	14·0	7·2	7·2	18·3	179·5	1·3	180·8
April 2	76·0	38·8	5·5	12·8	9·8	9·0	9·7	14·0	6·7	7·1	17·1	167·3	1·2	168·5
May 2	72·1	36·1	5·9	12·2	9·2	8·9	8·3	13·6	6·8	7·1	17·6	161·8	1·2	163·0
June 6	64·7	32·6	5·2	10·6	8·1	8·7	7·7	11·5	6·1	6·1	16·6	145·5	1·2	146·7
July 4	55·1	27·9	4·1	9·1	6·8	7·0	7·1	9·6	5·0	5·4	15·6	125·0	1·0	126·0
Aug 8	51·9	25·6	4·0	8·2	6·4	7·1	6·2	9·6	5·3	5·2	15·7	119·4	1·0	120·4
Sep 5	49·3	24·9	3·8	7·6	5·7	5·7	5·7	8·8	5·1	5·2	15·2	112·1	0·7	112·8
Oct 3	43·1	20·9	3·3	6·7	5·5	4·7	5·8	7·9	4·8	4·5	13·4	99·7	0·7	100·4
Nov 6	38·2	18·2	3·2	7·0	5·2	5·0	5·7	8·1	4·8	4·6	14·1	96·5	0·7	97·2
Dec 5	39·8	19·3	3·4	7·7	5·2	5·3	6·5	8·1	5·0	5·1	15·0	101·2	0·8	102·0

Note: The figures relate only to the number of vacancies notified to employment offices and remaining unfilled and include some that are suitable for young persons.
* The series from January 1977 onwards have been calculated as described on page 281 of the March 1980 issue of *Employment Gazette*.
† Included in South East.

Finally, we have to determine the dependent/independent variables. The question states, '... regress unfilled vacancies on unemployment ...'. Since it is convention to regress y on x it follows that unfilled vacancies must be our dependent variable (y) and unemployment our independent variable (x). To confirm this we note that question 2 requires a prediction, based on the regression function established, for unfilled vacancies; therefore this must be the dependent variable.

214

The data tested will therefore be:

		Vacancies y ('000s/10)	Unemployment x ('000s/10)
1978	March	19	135
	June	21	132
	September	22	130
	December	24	126
1979	March	23	130
	June	26	122
	September	24	120
	December	22	124
1980	March	18	135
	June	15	147
	September	11	171
	December	10	205

The following formula was used to calculate the values for a and b:

$$b = \frac{\sum xy - (1/n)(\sum x)(\sum y)}{\sum x^2 - (1/n)(\sum x)^2} \qquad (7.3)$$

$$a = \left(\frac{1}{n}\right)\sum y - b\left(\frac{1}{n}\right)\sum x \qquad (7.4)$$

Where

$$\sum x = 1677, \qquad \sum y = 235, \qquad \sum x^2 = 241\ 085, \qquad \sum xy = 31\ 557$$

the following regression function was obtained:

$$y = 46.274 - 0.191x$$

2. *The estimate and comparison with observed value* Using this function the estimated value for vacancies in December 1977 would be:

$$y = 46.274 - 0.191 \times 137$$

Therefore,

$$y = 20.107$$

Converting this value back on the same basis as the published data we would expect vacancies for December 1977 to be 201.1 thousand. This compares with the observed data of 168.3 thousand. On the face of it, the difference of 19.5 per cent would seem to be substantial. Several points can be made.

First, we should not expect the predicted value to be identical with the observed since the forecast has been based on a relationship established in linear form; the function specifies the line of 'best fit', not a 'perfect fit'. Second, if we look at the array of paired observations in Fig. 15.3 it is noticeable that only one of the 12 actually lies on the regression line with several being some distance from it. Moreover, if we place the observed value for December 1977 on to the diagram it becomes apparent that the difference between observed and predicted values is approximately the same as for four other values. The conclusion must therefore be that, though large, the difference between observed and predicted values is one we could have expected.

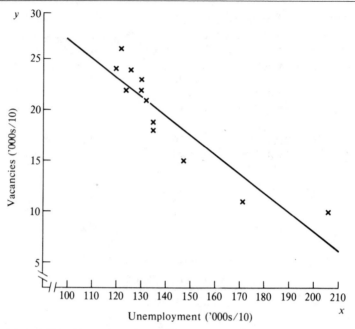

Figure 15.3 Unemployment and vacancy analysis

There are significance tests which can be applied here which would determine whether any difference is statistically significant. One technique in particular consists of establishing 'limits of prediction' at specified confidence levels, but this detail is not required in the current assignment.

3. *The graph and relationship established* Figure 15.3 shows the paired data and linear regression. What it demonstrates quite clearly is the negative relationship between unemployment and unfilled vacancies. When vacancies are high unemployment is low and when vacancies are low unemployment tends to be high.

This relationship is one we would have expected, since at its basic level both unemployment and vacancies reflect the level of spending in the economy. Thus a recession implies a low level of spending and therefore a low level of demand for labour which, in turn, would be reflected in higher unemployment and fewer job opportunities (smaller number of vacancies). The reverse would hold in the recovery period. It follows that the relationship established is not one in which unemployment levels *cause* vacancy levels, or indeed the reverse; both would be influenced by aggregate demand, one in a positive direction (vacancies) and one in a negative direction (unemployment).

4. *The data source* Without questions being raised on the quality and reliability of the data used the preceding statistical analysis would be assuming either: (a) that both sets of data are accurate or (b) that both sets of data are inaccurate but by the same proportional amount and in the same direction, i.e., both are overestimates (or underestimates) by the same percentage. In the latter case any inaccuracies would cancel out. In terms of the calculated functional relationship established, the slope of the line would remain the same (the regression coefficient

216

of -0.191) but the position of the line and each set of observed data would be either higher or lower in the diagram, depending on whether we conclude that both unemployment and vacancies are underestimates or overestimates. Effectively the regression constant would then be a higher value (if data are underestimated) or a lower value (if the data are overestimated). Even assumption (b) therefore would have an effect on the value of the regression function. The major question, however, is whether either assumption is realistic. We must consider the unemployment and vacancy data in some detail.

The information on unemployment that we have used here comes from employment offices in the so-called 'monthly count' of those registered as unemployed and available for work. Immediately, then, the possibility is raised that there may be many more people in the economy who are willing and available for work but do not register as unemployed. If we wish to analyse the labour market and establish the level of spare labour capacity in the economy then it is clear that the unemployment data present only a partial aspect of this. In addition to concealed unemployment we must accept that there will be an element of 'labour hoarding' in which people in employment are not being fully employed. Both factors would lead us to conclude that the effective level of spare labour capacity is substantially higher than that shown in the official figures for unemployment.

These arguments would therefore suggest that the unemployment figures indicate the minimum level of spare labour capacity. However, a contrary view holds that a proportion of those registered as unemployed are virtually unemployable, for a variety of reasons, and to include these in the category of spare labour capacity is erroneous; spare labour capacity is less than the figures suggest.

A synthesis of these arguments is possible by adjusting the official data downwards to allow for the 'unemployables' and then adding to this an estimate covering concealed unemployment and labour hoarding. In practice, the task would be difficult since it would have to rely on substantial labour market surveys, given the paucity of published information. Without these results it is impossible to estimate with any precision a measure of spare labour capacity which takes into account adjusted unemployment, labour hoarding, and concealed unemployment.

Data on vacancies are based on those notified to employment offices and remaining unfilled at the time of the monthly count. Once again there are conflicting claims that they underestimate and overestimate the true situation. Since there is no obligation on employers to notify vacancies with the employment offices and there are many alternative outlets for job advertising then the published figures represent a minimum level of vacancies in the economy. Department of Employment surveys suggest that the published figures account for only one-third of total vacancies which is, of course, a serious underestimation. The overestimate case is based on the argument that, for a variety of reasons, some vacancies are virtually 'unfillable', and in addition some vacancies may not be genuine, being based on forecasts of labour turnover.

On balance, it would seem that the published data for unemployment and vacancies are both underestimates. Although it would be circumstantial if the level of underestimation were the same, the degree of error may be similar enough for us to conclude tentatively that the relationship established above would not be substantially altered except in the case of the regression constant, which would have a higher value.

This tentative conclusion should not be taken as suggesting that unfilled vacancies can measure unsatisfied demand for labour and unemployment can measure unsatisfied supply of labour and that simply deducting one from the other would establish the net excess demand or supply. There are at least two difficulties with using the data in this way. First, some people

217

will be represented on the vacancy data but not included in the unemployment category, given the increasing tendency to forecast labour turnover mentioned above and the necessity in many occupations to work out notice before leaving. Second, vacancy and unemployment characteristics may not match; the skills demanded could differ from the skills offered or, where these are compatible, geographical differences could result in vacancies remaining unfilled and the unemployed not being absorbed into the workforce. Clearly in this case the degree of labour and capital mobility would be crucial.

Notes on the assignment

It should be appreciated that this assignment is not a labour market analysis in the sense of establishing net surplus or demand for labour. The problems of using published data for this purpose are pointed out in the suggested answer to question (4). What it does set out to establish is a relationship between vacancies and unemployment. The resulting negative relationship is one we should have expected and although not called for in the assignment it is interesting to note that the correlation coefficient for this data is -0.912. The negative correlation is therefore confirmed and would give a coefficient of determination of 0.83.

The student should understand that the result is based only on the 12 pairs of observations taken and it would be quite legitimate for him or her to raise doubts in the assignment on the data required for analysis and specified in the assignment question. For example, it could be suggested that if quarterly data are required it would have been more appropriate to calculate quarterly averages—by adding the three months in each quarter and then dividing by three. This would reduce the risk of an extreme value in any month distorting the relationship. Such comments would clearly identify the brighter student.

For those more advanced, in which standard error and limits of prediction are required, the following results were obtained:

> Standard error is approximately 2.24.
> Limits of prediction at the 95% level of confidence $= 5.13$.
> Limits of prediction at the 99% level of confidence $= 7.39$.

This gives a range at the 95 per cent level of:

$$20.107 \pm 5.13$$

and at the 99 per cent level of

$$20.107 \pm 7.39$$

Since the observed value is 16.83 and this falls within the range established at the 95 per cent level it is clear that the difference between the observed and predicted is *not* statistically significant.

Assignment 3

Forecasting passenger car statistics

Assignment question

A car manufacturer is planning his operations for the U.K. market. He is interested in the total market and the supply of cars produced in the United Kingdom. The data in Table 15.6 are available from published sources.[15, 20]

218

Table 15.6

Year	Total registrations of new cars in United Kingdom ('000s)	U.K. car production for home market ('000s)
1970	1097	918
1971	1302	1027
1972	1663	1308
1973	1645	1142
1974	1234	938
1975	1166	736
1976	1256	768
1977	1285	753
1978	1561	728
1979	1676	678
1980	1460	574

Reproduced from *Economic Trends* and from *British Business*, with the permission of the Controller of Her Majesty's Stationery Office.

1. Plot the above two time series on a graph. Use the data to estimate the U.K. production as a percentage of total car sales, and plot this percentage as a time series also.

(10% of marks)

2. In order to estimate the trend of all three time series, it is only necessary to select two of them—the third series can then be deduced. Select two of the series that you feel would be most appropriate for trend estimation. Use the regression method or moving averages (three- or five-year) to estimate the trend in each of your selected series. Give reasons for your choice of method in each case. Plot the resulting trends on the graphs produced for 1 above.

(50% of marks)

3. From an examination of your graphs and the trend estimates give a forecast for 1981 of all three time series. Give some indication of a likely range for the forecast values.

(10% of marks)

4. Comment on your results and the validity of your analysis. Suggest any way that your forecasts might be improved and any other factors that could be taken into account.

(20% of marks)

Suggested answers

1. U.K. percentages of the total market are (in order from 1970 onwards):

83.7, 78.9, 78.7, 69.4, 76.0, 63.1,
61.1, 58.6, 46.6, 40.5, 39.3

Strictly speaking, we are not comparing like with like here, since we have found U.K. *production* as a percentage of total *sales* for the same periods, whereas there will in practice be a time lag between the production of the car and its sale. However, since we are dealing with annual figures, this is not likely to make a very significant difference, assuming the time lag is not too large on average. The data are plotted in Figs 15.4 and 15.5.

2. Examination of the graphs shows that the percentage time series is clearly the most suitable for trend estimation, since it is much more consistent than the other two series. It shows quite

219

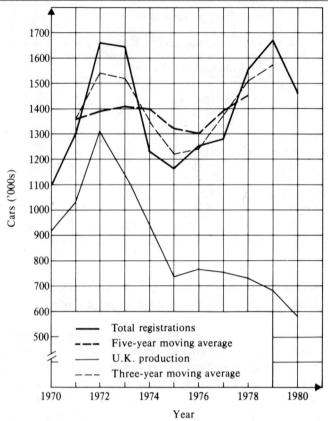

Figure 15.4

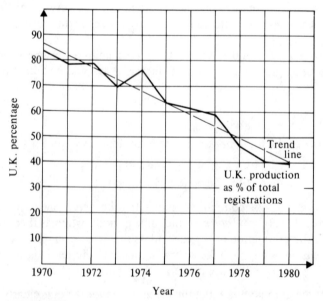

Figure 15.5

220

a steady decline over the 10-year period, and it looks as if a linear trend will show a good fit. The regression method would be a reasonable way of estimating this trend. The calculations are as follows, putting $y =$ U.K. percentage of market and $x =$ year, counting 1970 as year 1. Let the equation of the trend line be:

$$y = a + bx$$

Calculations for b:

$$
\begin{aligned}
n &= 11 \\
\Sigma x &= 66 & \Sigma y &= 695.9 \\
\Sigma x^2 &= 506 & \Sigma yx &= 3667 \\
(1/11)(\Sigma x)^2 &= 396 & (1/11)(\Sigma y)(\Sigma x) &= 4175.4 \\
\text{Denominator} &= \underline{110} & \text{Numerator} &= \underline{-508.4}
\end{aligned}
$$

$$b = -508.4/110 = -4.62$$

Calculations for a:

$$a = 63.26 - (-4.62) \times 6 = 90.98$$

Equation of trend line for U.K. percentage of total market:

$$y = 91.0 - 4.62x$$

The equation is shown plotted in Fig. 15.5 and fits the data quite well. As a numerical measure, the coefficient of determination can be found (in this case it is 0.94, confirming the visual impression).

Examination of the other two time series, shown plotted in Fig. 15.4, does not show a very clear trend pattern emerging. The total registrations data show some evidence of cycling about a slight upward trend, but is clearly very variable. The U.K. production series shows no clear overall pattern. It seems to behave quite differently from 1975 onwards than for the period before. After 1975 there seems to be a consistent downwards trend—possibly curved. Before 1975 the pattern is more like the cycling behaviour of the total registrations series. During the early part of the period, U.K. production accounted for a large percentage of the total market, so it is not surprising that the two series show the same sort of pattern.

There seems to be little point in attempting to fit a trend to the whole of the U.K. production data because of the change in pattern that appears. We could split the data into two and fit a trend to the data from 1975 onwards, but with so few data points available we have no way of telling whether the trend will continue its downwards path or whether it will show a new cyclical pattern—in which case it could very well start to go up again after 1980. On the whole, the best bet would seem to be to attempt to fit a trend to the total registrations data, by smoothing out as much as possible of the variability. With highly variable data like these it is probably best to use a moving average approach to estimate the trend. Three-year and five-year moving averages for the data are as shown in Table 15.7.

The three- and five-year moving averages are shown plotted on Fig. 15.4. As can be seen, the three-year moving average has not smoothed the data very effectively. The five-year average is better, but is still showing some variability. A six- or seven-year moving average would probably be better still, but would not give many points for a time series of this length, so would not be of much use in indicating the trend. Although it is not entirely satisfactory, the five-year moving average is perhaps as good an indication of trend as we can get without

Table 15.7

Year	Total registrations	Three-year moving average	Five-year moving average
1970	1097		
1971	1302	1354	
1972	1663	1537	1388
1973	1645	1514	1402
1974	1234	1348	1393
1975	1166	1219	1317
1976	1256	1236	1300
1977	1285	1367	1389
1978	1561	1507	1448
1979	1676	1566	
1980	1460		

having more data available. It would seem to indicate that in fact there is very little trend in the data, with perhaps a slight upwards movement. With highly variable data like these, another approach is to partly smooth it with a moving average and then fit a regression line to the moving averages if a straight line trend seems a reasonable approximation. With these data, if a regression line is fitted to the five-year moving averages it will be very nearly a horizontal line, with a very slight positive slope, which tells us no more than we would surmise from looking at the moving averages.

In conclusion, then, we have found a marked and quite consistent downwards linear trend in the U.K. percentage of the market data. A regression line gave a good fit, and indicated that the percentage is reducing by about 4.6 each year. This is illustrated in Fig. 15.5. We might suppose that this linear trend is unlikely to continue unchanged, and indeed the last few data points seem to indicate some flattening out. The total registrations data show very little consistent trend, although if anything there may be a very slight upwards movement. The most pronounced feature of these data is a very marked cycling behaviour, with a big swing between peak and trough.

3. *U.K. percentage of market forecast, 1981* Putting $x = 12$ in the regression equation we obtain:

$$y = 91.0 - 4.62 \times 12 = 35.6$$

This would be our best estimate. We could go on to find a confidence interval for this estimate, but there does seem to be clear signs from the last few data points that the trend is flattening out. A reasonable guess would be that, if anything, this is likely to be an underestimate. From the graph, it appears that if the pattern of the last few years continues the percentage might be nearer to 38. A reasonable estimate would be:

1981 U.K. percentage estimate: 35–38%

Total registrations forecast, 1981 Looking at the overall trend in the data, there seems to be only a slight upwards movement, and from the graph of the five-year moving average we might estimate the 1981 trend to be about 1450. If we just look at the last two or three moving average points we would estimate the 1981 trend to be nearer 1500, if that trend were to persist. With such a marked cycling pattern, however, this would be a rather hazardous assumption so an estimate of 1450 is perhaps about the best we can do. Since we have not attempted to determine whether the cyclic behaviour of these data is at all consistent, we can only treat it as random variation about the trend. A simple measure of the variation is given by the mean absolute deviation. Differencing the five-year moving averages from the actuals we find a MAD of 156. If we assumed the variations from the trend to be normally distributed, this is equivalent to a standard deviation of approximately 1.25×156, which is 195 [see result (2.9) in Chapter 2], and a 90 per cent confidence interval would thus be $\pm 1.645 \times 195$, or ± 320, while an 80 per cent confidence interval would be about ± 250. This would be a more reasonable range to give for a forecast, although it is still very large. About the best we can do, then, is to give as an estimate:

1981 total registrations estimate: 1450 ± 250

U.K. production forecast, 1981   We obtain this by multiplying the total registrations forecast by the U.K. percentage forecast. We have given a fairly narrow range for our U.K. percentage forecast, but it would be unlikely that the actual outcome would coincide with an extreme of this range and at the same time that the actual total registrations for 1981 would coincide with the extreme of our estimated range for that series. A fairly cautious estimate would be:

Lowest estimate of U.K. production $= 0.35 \times 1250 = 437$
Highest estimate of U.K. production $= 0.38 \times 1650 = 627$

Rounding these results gives:

1981 U.K. production estimate: 440–630

4. A number of comments on the validity of the analysis are included above. In this section they will be summarized and some additional points mentioned. Let us first consider the U.K. percentage trend analysis. Although the regression method gave a straight line which showed a good fit to the data, it is always hazardous to extrapolate a straight line into the future— things do not usually continue going down (or up) indefinitely. In the long run, trends tend to tail off and even reverse. As was noted above, there are signs that this is already happening with these data.

The total registrations data present different problems because of their variability. There are clearly very wide swings around the trend, which means that any forecast based on the trend alone must be open to a very large error. With these data, there appears to be a cyclical pattern which shows some regularity. We might speculate that the period of the cycle is about six or seven years from peak to peak. There is clearly not a long enough series to establish whether or not this is so. If it were the case, we would use this as the period of the moving average and estimate cyclical factors in just the same way as seasonal factors are established. A forecast trend would then be adjusted by the appropriate factor.

Many indicators of general trends in the economy as a whole show cyclical variations, which suggests a way in which the forecast could be improved. Unfortunately, in recent years these cyclical patterns have tended to vary in period from cycle to cycle, so even if we had more data for the car registrations series, a regular pattern would be unlikely to emerge, since this series is likely to behave in a similar way. However, it is possible that the movements in the car registrations data would correlate with some general economic series such as disposable income or some measure of output. A regression model could possibly be developed which linked car registrations to one or more economic indicators. Forecasts of those indicators (regularly produced) could then be used to forecast car registrations.

Of course there are many factors that are likely to influence car registrations. Some possibilities are: car prices, car tax rates, company profitability (since many new cars are bought by companies), depreciation and tax allowances, availability of credit for financing private purchases, the rules affecting car hire purchase agreements, etc. In the case of the U.K. percentage figures there are additional factors such as import agreements, tariffs and trade agreements, import taxes, the level of the pound compared to foreign currencies, and the relative prices of U.K. and foreign cars. Further investigation of any data available on these factors would be necessary before their importance could be established.

Assignment 4

Analysis of sample data

Assignment question

An insurance company is investigating the market for life assurance. A pilot study is conducted by telephoning a random sample drawn from the London telephone directory. They are asked to give their total annual life insurance premiums. The survey results in 50 replies, giving the following values in pounds (simulated data):

54	0	25	48	14	21	53	92	2	242
20	198	99	290	38	79	71	350	80	0
226	26	77	240	46	85	84	122	15	50
348	55	22	99	93	28	63	80	55	206
54	114	96	26	93	30	304	3	364	6

1. Draw an appropriate diagram to show the pattern of variability in these data.

   (25% of marks)
2. Find the mean, median, and standard deviation of the data, and discuss their appropriateness as descriptive measures of average and variation in this case.

   (25% of marks)
3. Find a 95 per cent confidence interval for the mean annual premium in the whole population. (10% of marks)
4. Find a 95 per cent confidence interval for the proportion of the population who are 'underinsured' if this is interpreted as anything under an annual premium of £60. How big a sample would be necessary to make this interval ± 5 per cent? (20% of marks)
5. Comment on the sampling method and make suggestions for a full survey. (20% of marks)

Suggested answers

1. The best type of diagram to show the pattern of variability in a set of data is probably a histogram or a frequency polygon—a cumulative frequency diagram could also possibly be used. In order to produce such a diagram, the first step is to group the data into a frequency table. Examination of the numbers shows that they vary from 0 to 364, with most of them in the lower end of this range. This suggests that the distribution is positively skewed and that the groupings used for the frequency table should be of unequal width, with the class width increasing as the numbers get bigger. If we used equal class widths, we would have widely

224

differing frequencies from class to class, and with only 50 data points this would produce a confused picture. A good first step is to list the data in order of magnitude; it is then a question of experimenting with various possible groupings. The object is to produce a histogram where the bars tend to either smoothly increase or decrease in height. Of course, this may not be possible and too much 'massaging' of the data should be avoided, since we may be imposing a pattern that is not really there.

Table 15.8   Frequency table

Annual premium in the range	Frequency	Height of histogram bar (base unit = 20)
0– 19	7	7
20– 39	9	9
40– 79	12	6
80–119	11	5.5
120–199	2	0.5
200–299	5	1
300–399	4	0.8

In this case, with only 50 numbers, about six to eight classes would be indicated. A possible frequency table is shown in Table 15.8. Because it is the *area* of the bars of a histogram which must be proportional to the frequency, the height of each bar must be proportional to the frequency divided by the class width. In the table the right-hand column gives the height based on units which equal the frequency for a range of width 20, so in each case the frequency is divided by the number of 20's in the class range.

Figure 15.6 shows the resulting histogram. As can be seen, the pattern is of a large proportion of premiums falling into the lower ranges, tailing off slightly to the £120 per year point, and then dropping sharply with only a small proportion of premiums in the higher ranges, which nevertheless extend a long way—probably up to at least £400 and in practice possibly much further. The distribution is therefore very skewed, and not surprisingly a bit like the distribution of personal income.

2. The measures of average and variation required could all be estimated from the frequency table. However, since the original data have been obtained and are not too extensive, it does not take long using a calculator to work them out directly. The calculations are as follows:

$$n = 50$$
$$\sum x = 4886$$
$$\bar{x} = 4886/50 = 97.72$$

Mean annual premium = £97.72

In order of increasing magnitude:

$$\text{25th premium} = 63$$
$$\text{26th premium} = 71$$
$$\text{Median} = \tfrac{1}{2}(63 + 71) = 67$$

Median annual premium = £67

In purely descriptive terms, the median gives a better idea of an average premium than the mean. Only 14 of the 50 premiums in the sample are above the mean and it would therefore

225

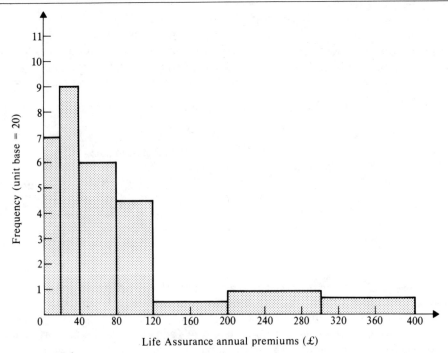

Figure 15.6

give a distorted picture of what the average person pays. This is typical for a skewed distribution and was found to be the same, for instance, when looking at the distribution of personal incomes, which shows a similar pattern.

Calculations for the standard deviation are as follows:

$$\sum x^2 = 957\ 728$$
$$\text{Variance} = (1/50)(957\ 728) - (97.72)^2 = 9605.4$$
$$\text{Sample variance} = (50/49)9605.4 = 9801$$
$$\text{Standard deviation} = \sqrt{(9801)} = 99.0$$
$$\text{Standard deviation of annual premiums} = £99$$

The variance has been corrected to allow for the fact that this is sample data, but clearly this makes little difference for a sample of this size. As a descriptive measure, the standard deviation for a single set of data tells us very little unless the distribution is approximately normal, which is clearly not the case here. When compared with the mean it is clear that the data are very variable (in fact, the coefficient of variation is just over 100 per cent), but otherwise the standard deviation is not very informative. A better indication of the variation in the data would be given by measures such as the quartiles; better still, reference to the histograms gives a clearer picture.

It should be noted that all the measures calculated have been based on a sample. In view of the variability in the data, they are therefore liable to sampling error. They are likely to be, to some extent, different to the true population measures and thus may be giving a slightly distorted picture.

226

3. The calculations for the confidence interval are:

$$\text{Standard error} = 99/\sqrt{50} = 14.0$$
$$95\% \text{ confidence interval} = 97.72 \pm 1.96 \times 14.0 = 97.72 \pm 27.44$$

Rounding these results, we have:

$$95\% \text{ confidence interval for mean annual premium} = £70 \text{ to } £125$$

This confirms the point made above that estimates from a sample are liable to sampling error, and, as can be seen, it is possible that the estimated mean is considerably in error.

Note that technically the confidence interval should have been calculated using the multiplier for the t distribution in place of 1.96, the normal distribution multiplier. This is because we have used the sample standard deviation, and sample means are approximately normally distributed. However, with a sample of 50, the difference is slight as the appropriate t value is very nearly the same as the normal distribution multiplier; it is, in fact, approximately 2.01.

4. From the sample of premiums it can be seen that 24 of them are less than £60. Thus:

$$\text{Proportion underinsured} = 48\%$$

In order to find a confidence interval for this estimate, we need to estimate the standard error.

$$\text{Standard error} = \sqrt{[(0.48 \times 0.52)/50]} = \sqrt{(0.004\ 992)} = 0.071$$

Thus:

$$95\% \text{ confidence interval} = 0.48 \pm 1.96 \times 0.071 = 0.48 \pm 0.14$$

It is usually best to express results in percentage terms. Thus:

$$95\% \text{ confidence interval for proportion underinsured} = 34 \text{ to } 62\%$$

It should be noted that with a sample of 50, the assumption that the proportion is normally distributed is very approximate.

The sample proportion is very close to 50 per cent, which is the value that maximizes the standard error. In estimating a required sample size it is best to err on the side of caution, so we will use a value of 0.5 instead of the sample proportion, although in this case it will clearly make little difference. We require a 95 per cent confidence interval of ± 5 per cent or ± 0.05. Putting this value in the appropriate formula, we have

$$n = \frac{3.84 \times 0.5 \times 0.5}{(0.05)^2} = 384$$

Required sample size for 95% confidence interval of $\pm 5\% = 384$

Note that this is the *maximum* size of sample required for this width of confidence interval.

5. The first thing to determine is the *coverage* of the sample. From the information given it is not clear whether individuals or households are covered. In this case it would seem best to consider households as the sampling unit, and this should be made clear.

Next comes the question of an appropriate *sampling frame*. The sample was found from a telephone directory which means that part of the population are excluded. It is likely that low income earners are under-represented in a telephone directory, which is related to the

227

representation of premium payments, as we have noted above. If the company is interested in the underinsured this possible bias could be important. On the other hand, the company may only be interested in sampling those who would be likely to afford higher premiums and may not be concerned about this possible bias. At any rate, any estimate made for the whole population would have to be corrected to allow for this possible bias, either by contacting a sample of people who are not on the telephone or perhaps collecting income data from the sample and comparing these to the published national figures.

The present sample data were obtained by telephone interviews. We are not given the non-response rate, but might guess that it was substantial. This may have been aggravated by the fact that some people could view this type of information as 'sensitive' and would be reluctant to divulge it over the telephone. A further problem with the choice of *instrument* in this case is the accuracy of the figures given, which is clearly open to question. The company could possibly check this by using its own records and/or carrying out some personal interviews. This latter course would also put them in a better position to decide on the best instrument to use for the full survey. With only the information given, it is impossible to make any firm recommendation on the best method to use in the full survey. The company would need to weigh the points made above in the light of its objectives for the survey.

A final criticism of the sample used is that it is only based on London. It is, in other words, a *cluster sample*. It is impossible to say whether this may have biased the results, but it will certainly reduce the precision of the full survey if it is restricted to the London region. The company will have to decide whether the extra cost of obtaining a wider geographical spread is justified.

Finally, an important consideration in the design of the full survey is whether or not it should include *stratification*. In this case, the strata that can be based on the sampling frame used (whether the telephone directory or the electoral roll, for instance, is used) may not be of much benefit. If the telephone directory is used a stratification on sex would be the only obvious one. If it were possible, desirable stratification factors would be such things as age and income. The only way to achieve this would be to take a two-stage sample. The first large sample would obtain information on, for instance, income and age—it might be possible to do this using the telephone. A second example is then drawn from the first, using the information obtained to divide it into strata. This will add considerably to the cost of a survey, a factor which must be weighed against the extra precision obtained. This two-stage approach has particular advantages if a small part of the population (e.g., high income earners) needs to be intensively sampled; this may be a factor in this case.

Note on the assignment
Although the data are not real, this is a realistic example. A population distribution was established from published data on tax relief given for life assurance premiums. The sample values were simulated by randomly sampling this distribution.

Self-assessment questions—Part Five

1. What are the coverage and conceptual differences between the overseas trade statistics and balance of payments accounts?

2. Where do the OTS data come from?

3. Why are imports valued more highly than comparable exports in the OTS?

4. What would be the likely effect on available data of (a) the United Kingdom adopting the 'special' system of recording and (b) the EEC countries adopting the 'general' system?

5. What are the major inconsistencies that create difficulties for international comparisons of overseas trade statistics.

6. How can balance of payments problems arise when the accounts are balanced each year?

37. How and where would the following trade flows be recorded in the balance of payments accounts?

(a) Relief to earthquake victims in Italy, totalling £100,000.
(b) A U.K. family spending £200 on a foreign holiday.
(c) Payment of previous IMF borrowings, equalling £100 000.
(d) Outward flow of machine tools valued at £15 000.
(e) Suppply of U.K. goods to British embassies overseas, valued at £50 000.
(f) Inflow of official reserves of gold and convertible currencies, totalling £500 000.
(g) American investment in plant and equipment in the Northern region of the United Kingdom of £500 000.
(h) Payment of dividend from overseas investment, valued at £1000.

8. What does the balancing item show and how is it calculated?

9. Assuming the total foreign transactions of the United Kingdom were those represented in question 7, draw up a summary balance of payments accounts and:

(a) Show whether the balance of payments was in deficit or surplus.
(b) Establish the value and sign for the balancing item.

10. Suggest the range of possible explanations for the balancing item derived in the previous question.

11. What is the prime source of data used in constructing the visible trade part of the balance of payments accounts and why are adjustments necessary before inclusion?

12. Summarize the major interpretation difficulties of the balance of payments accounts.

Answers to self-assessment questions

Where questions are unanswered it is because there is no unique solution. Diagrams are not included and for predominantly numerical questions only the numerical solution is given.

Part One

2. (b) 12.08
   (c) 7.5
   (d) 16.46
   (e) Quartiles $= 3.75, 7.5, 11.25$; 80th percentile $= 15$; percentage $= 64\%$
3. Income, output, and expenditure.
4. Basically for two reasons: firstly, many errors are likely to be compensated, and secondly, the income and expenditure approaches do not use entirely independent sources.
5. Tax assessment statistics; central government accounts; and census of production.
6. Market price would include expenditure subsidies and taxes which, when removed, results in factor loss measurements.
7. If capital consumption were not included then we would be continously exaggerating our stock of fixed assets from which goods and services are produced, since we would not be allowing for the depreciation of fixed assets during the year. By allowing for this we can derive a value for national income, i.e., GNP minus capital consumption equals national income. The major estimating difficulties include, (a) necessity to estimate the life-time of fixed assets, (b) the 'straight-line' assumption for their pattern of use, (c) ignoring technical change, (d) allowing for price movements in the calculation of assets.
8. National income divided by total population, which therefore gives a figure of average income per head of the population
9. Since it only measures the value of goods and services produced during a year it clearly excludes environmental features which many people may feel are an important influence on living standards.

Part Two

1. The annual census of production, the quarterly sales inquiry, and the monthly index of industrial production.
2. Gross output would be sales within a year adjusted for changes in stocks, and net output would be gross output less the cost of all inputs purchased from other industries.
3. The national income accounts equate value added and net output by summing incomes and profits at each stage of the production process, whereas net output in the census of production is obtained by estimating and deducting the cost of all inputs used at each stage. Consequently, since it is not possible to account for all inputs, it follows that net output in the census of production will be greater than the value added.

230

4. The problems relate to geographical and commodity classifications since multi-unit enterprises typically have a number of establishments (factories) throughout the United Kingdom and produce a wide range of different products.

5. The reason is that many factors that influence productivity either do not lend themselves to quantitative measurement or have a low level of reliability. Estimates of employment, however, are more readily available and relatively more reliable.

6. The most obvious role is in the wages negotiation process, particularly that part of any claim associated with changes in the cost of living. The information will also be of major importance where governments are formulating and operating an incomes and prices policy. In addition, where the major objective of this policy is to slow down the rate of inflation, then, clearly, commentators will use the published information to test how successful such policies have been. Changes in state pensions are likely to be influenced by the experience of price movements for these groups, and with the growing introduction of private pension schemes and financial securities that are 'index-linked' (thus affording some protection for investors against inflation) it is obvious that official measures of price changes are required.

   For businesses the information would be vital where the prices of long-term contracts are concerned. The wholesale prices index is likely to be most useful here since it is a measure of changes in the prices of materials and inputs used in the production process.

7. New weights are established for each calendar year and are based mainly, but not entirely, on a year's family expenditure survey results ending in the previous June.

8. 0.164.

9. First, the RPI is attempting to measure not inflation as such but the effect of inflation on the 'average household'. The resulting average figure may be reasonably accurate for many households, but there are likely to be other households whose inflation experience is considerably different from that shown in the published figures, resulting from different spending patterns, shopping habits, income groups, geographical locations, etc. Second, the index is not representing inflation for the total economy but only one aspect of this, i.e., consumer spending. Third, since it is a base-weighted index it will overstate inflation to the extent that consumers are adjusting their spending patterns during the period when weights are held constant. Fourth, although it purports to indicate the effect of inflation for consumers it gives only a partial view since it does not take into account changes in a person's disposable income.

10. The RPI measures price changes while the TPI measures a combination of price changes and changes in direct taxes and national insurance contributions. The TPI is more meaningful therefore in terms of measuring the ability of consumers to purchase goods and services, since it takes into account both price movements and movements in disposable income.

11. It provides an early warning of changes in the inflation rate (since it is at the wholesale stage), and may give a better measure of inflation than the RPI, since it excludes most forms of indirect taxation.

12. 91.7, 94.6, 101.1, 100.0; percentage increase = 4.2%

13. 93.0, 91.9, 247.6; weighted mean index (1971 weights) = 106.5

14. Laspeyres index = 106.7, Paasche index = 106.8

15. (a) 104.2
    (b) 107.8

    (c) Chain base index = 112.3, direct index = 112.5

    (d) 122.5

16. (a) 104.1

    (b) 107.7

    (c) Chain base index = 112.1, direct index = 112.2

17. Taking WPI (1975 = 100) as 146.2, 165.8, 197.4, deflated indices are 100, 91.9, 83.3.

Part Three

1. (b) $y = -1.50 + 1.048x$

    (c) 0.955

    (d) 208.1 (see also solution to question 12, Part Four)

2. (a) 0.894

    (b) 0.907

    (c) Number of staff

    (d) $y = 76.1 + 4.00x$

4. $y = 67.0 - 2.80x$ ($x = 1$ for 1969); forecast = 33.4

5. Moving averages: $-$, $-$, 118.9, 123.7, 128.6, 133.0, 136.6, 139.4, 142.0, 144.8, 147.8, 151.5, 156.4, 162.6, $-$, $-$

6. (a) Forecasts: 2.260, 2.260, 2.251, 2.231, 2.196, 2.171, 2.182, 2.216, 2.245, 2.230, 2.224, 2.256, 2.288, 2.322, 2.342, 2.366, 2.386, 2.390

    (b) Forecast = 2.372, standard error is 0.060 (excluding January 1979), so approximate 95% confidence interval is ± 0.117

7. (a) -0.9, -0.4, 0.7, 0.6

    (b) 0.95, 0.97, 1.05, 1.03

8. $\log y = 3.557 + 0.141x$ ($x = 1$ for 1969, logs to base e); forecast = 190.4

9. (a) 'Temporarily' stopped, (b) registered for part-time work, (c) severely disabled people, (d) adult students, (e) school leavers, (f) those registered but temporarily ill.

10. On the grounds that the recorded unemployment figures are more economically meaningful since they would refer to those wholly unemployed, who are seeking full-time employment, and are not severely handicapped.

11. It would be necessary to use the unemployment rate when comparisons are being made over time, between countries, or between localities and regions. This is because the size of communities, countries, regions, etc., differ, which makes it difficult to interpret and compare absolute values.

12. Seasonally adjusting the unemployment data will highlight the underlying unemployment trends by eliminating, as far as possible, that part of unemployment associated with seasonal characteristics.

13. First, there are likely to be many people who do not register as unemployed but who nevertheless might wish to obtain employment, i.e., concealed unemployment. Second, those employees not being fully utilized, i.e., labour hoarding.

14. The major point here is that a number on the unemployment register may be virtually unemployable, or at least for whom it is very difficult to find suitable employment. An additional argument is that the social and economic distress associated with unemployment is less significant these days compared with the inter-war years. This claim is clearly based on using the data to indicate the social and economic impact of unemployment rather than its use in indicating excess labour capacity.

15. Flow statistics can shed additional light on the functioning of the labour market by emphasizing its dynamic nature compared with the static approach of the monthly 'stock' counts.
16. (a) The published data under-records unfilled vacancies.
    (b) A conceptual problem, since some recorded vacancies may refer to people currently in employment.
    (c) Some vacancies may be 'unfillable' or very difficult to fill.
17. The problems here would be those outlined in question 16 above as well as the following: (a) the increasing tendency of employers to base vacancy notifications on forecasts which might prove inaccurate and (b) the dangers of a 'mis-match' in occupational and/or spatial terms between the unemployment and vacancy data.
18. Since 1971 a census of employment has been conducted in June each year by means of a postal inquiry. This replaced the previous 'card count' system.
19. The result of this change is significant because it effectively altered the definition of employees in employment and is dangerous for potential users since the description (employees in employment) remains the same. The differences involve conceptual and coverage aspects.
20. (a) How the numerator and denominator is defined and measured.
    (b) The realization that economic, social, and demographic differences may explain the results.

Part Four

1. 0.02, 0.04, 0.08, 0.24, 0.26, 0.16, 0.16, 0.02, 0.02; probability in range 30–50 = 0.50; probability two in range = 0.25; the same customer's order sizes are not likely to be independent.
2. 0.34, 0.20, 0.20, 0.16, 0.08, 0.02; mean = 1.50, standard deviation = 1.40; Poisson probabilities are: 0.22, 0.33, 0.25, 0.13, 0.05, 0.02.
3. (a) 0.349
   (b) 0.096
   (c) 0.122, 0.009
   (d) 29
4. (a) (i) 0.5, (ii) 0.159
   (b) 196.7
   (c) 203.3
5. 0.01, 0.04, 0.11, 0.20, 0.25, 0.21, 0.12, 0.05, 0.01
6. 10 ± 2.50, 10 ± 2.94
7. 0.48 ± 0.16
8. $15\% \pm 3.1\%$, $15\% \pm 4.1\%$
11. 95% confidence interval for mean life is 950 ± 54, so 1000 is only just acceptable at the 0.05 level of significance.
12. Using approximate method: 208.1 ± 19.6
    More exact method gives: 208.1 ± 30.2
13. $\chi^2 = 10.25$, which is significant at the 0.05 level.
14. *For governments*: (a) formation of incomes policy, (b) as an influence in regional policy, (c) more 'social' types of policies as equal pay and minimum pay legislation.

For employers: (a) in the collective bargaining process, (b) in manpower policy, (c) may play a part in relocation decisions.

For trade unions: (a) in the collective bargaining process, particularly the comparability basis of many wage claims, (b) acting as a pressure group for low paid workers, etc.

15. (a) More consistency since the range of data stems from one survey with common definitions and reporting unit.
    (b) More complete with all industries and regions being covered.
    (c) More detailed treatment, i.e., information on the make-up of earnings, separate data on wages and earnings effected by collective bargaining, etc.
    (d) The introduction of a 'matched' sample.

16. The problem of accuracy and interpretation difficulties are eased in four ways. First, the 'matched' sample increases precision substantially; second, inclusion of standard error measurements indicates the potential margin of error of the published data; third, if the standard error is relatively large (2 per cent of the estimated value), then it is enclosed in brackets to warn users that less reliability can be attached to that estimate; and fourth, where the standard error is particularly large (usually due to a very small sample), the detailed data are not published.

17. Since both surveys are aimed at narrowly defined groups of workers compared with the more general NES, then some greater detail is possible, particularly in the industrial data provided. However, the non-manual workers survey was actually reintroduced as a response to an EEC request. The advantage of the monthly index of average earnings is clearly in providing more frequent information compared with the annual survey approach.

18. The survey of personal incomes, the income section of the family expenditure survey, and the new earnings survey.

19. (a) Because it is based on a relatively large sample.
    (b) Because the information is provided by tax officials.

20. (a) Not all forms of incomes are taxable and despite its wide coverage the SPI is therefore not complete.
    (b) The existence of tax evasion and avoidance will lead to some under-representation of incomes.

21. Because the difference between income and wealth is only in the degree of liquidity afforded by the asset; incomes will be a liquid asset while most forms of wealth tend to be less liquid assets. However, income can be turned into wealth, and vice versa. The problem then is drawing the line between different types of assets.

22. From the Inland Revenue estate duty statistics, based on the so-called estate multiplier method.

23. Because, assuming income distribution is based on the SPI, both income and wealth analysis stem from administrative sources. The SPI is based on the tax unit (normally husband and wife combined) and wealth data are based on the value of assets of the deceased.

Part Five

1. The OTS is concerned with the physical flow of commodities while the balance of payments records the monetary valuations of all types of foreign transactions.

2. From the customs and excise import and export documentation.

3. Because they would have carried a higher transport and insurance charge compared with exports (i.e., CIF compared with FOB).

4. (a) Some reduction in recorded trade, since not all goods going into bonded warehouses are worked on in some way.
   (b) Serious over-recording of trade for many EEC countries with major international ports.

5. (a) Differences in defining the trading partner, (b) different systems (special or general), (c) different exclusion lists, (d) commodity classification differences, (e) differences in timing, (f) different valuation of exports and imports.

6. The accounts are balanced each year by changes in our reserve holdings of convertible currencies and through IMF and other borrowing. Clearly, we cannot continuously run down our reserves or borrow and therefore measures to solve external payments problems eventually have to be tackled.

7. (a) Part of transfers balance in invisibles .... $-£100\,000$
   (b) Part of services, in invisibles .... $-£200$
   (c) In official financing .... $-£100\,000$
   (d) Part of visible balance in current account .... $+£15\,000$
   (e) Would not be recorded since British embassies would be considered part of U.K. territory.
   (f) In official financing .... $-£500\,000$
   (g) Investment and other capital transactions .... $+£500\,000$
   (h) Part of invisibles .... $+£1000$

8. It shows the net errors and omissions in the current and investment accounts. Its value and sign is given by the difference between these two accounts and official financing.

9. Current account   £

		£
Visible balance		$+15\,000$
Invisibles		
Services	-200	
Interest, profits, and dividends	$+1\,000$	
Transfers balance	$-100\,000$	
Invisible balance	$-99\,200$	$-99\,200$
Current balance		$-84\,200$
Investment and other capital transactions		$+500\,000$
Balancing item		$+184\,200$
Balance for official financing		$+600\,000$
Official financing		
Net transactions with overseas monetary authorities		$-100\,000$
Official reserves		$-500\,000$

   (a) The balance of payments was in surplus ($£600\,000$).
   (b) $+£184\,200$

10. An under-recording of exports; an over-recording of imports; an under-recording of foreign investment in the United Kingdom; an over-recording of U.K. investment overseas.

11. The overseas trade statistics. Coverage and valuation adjustments are necessary before the OTS data can be included in the balance of payments, given that both sets of data have different objectives and therefore different conventions and definitions.
12. The existence of errors and omissions is acknowledged with the inclusion of a balancing item. Mis-reporting, the use of estimates and values based on sample surveys, processing errors, and timing problems are likely to be responsible for this.

References

1. Central Statistical Office, *The National Income and Expenditure Survey*, HMSO (annual).
2. Central Statistical Office, *Studies in Official Statistics*, No. 13, Maurice, R. (Ed.), *National Accounts Statistics: Sources and Methods*, HMSO, 1968.
3. Central Statistical Office, Hall, G. S., and C. R. Cook, 'Introducing personalised forms for the quarterly inquiry into manufacturers' sales', *Statistical News*, HMSO, February 1978.
4. Department of Industry, Business Statistics Office, *Business Monitor, Annual Census of Production Reports*, HMSO (annual).
5. Department of Industry, Business Statistics Office, *Business Monitor, Quarterly Statistics of Manufacturers' Sales*, HMSO (quarterly).
6. Central Statistical Office, Mitchell, B., 'Measuring value added from the census of production', *Statistical News*, HMSO, May 1978.
7. Utton, M. A., *Industrial Concentration*, Penguin Modern Economics, 1970.
8. Department of Employment, *Employment Gazette*, HMSO (monthly).
9. Department of Employment, *New Earnings Survey*, HMSO (annual).
10. Department of Employment, *Family Expenditure Survey*, HMSO (annual).
11. Barry, D., and B. Corry, 'Should we scrap the R.P.I.?' *Accountancy*, May 1980.
12. Board of Inland Revenue, *Survey of Personal Incomes*, HMSO (annual).
13. Department of Employment, 'Duration of unemployment for males and females, April 1980', *Employment Gazette*, HMSO, June 1980.
14. Office of Population Censuses and Surveys, *Population Trends*, HMSO (quarterly).
15. Central Statistical Office, *Economic Trends*, HMSO (monthly).
16. Board of Inland Revenue, *Inland Revenue Statistics*, HMSO (annual).
17. Department of Trade, *Overseas Trade Statistics*, HMSO (monthly and annual). (Formerly *Overseas Trade Accounts of the UK*.)
18. Central Statistical Office, *Balance of Payments Accounts*, HMSO (annual). (Now *UK Balance of Payments*.)
19. HM Customs and Excise, *Statistics of Trade through U.K. Ports*, HMSO (quarterly and annual).
20. Department of Industry, *British Business*, HMSO (weekly).

A guide to further reading

Sources of statistics

Central Statistical Office, *Annual Abstract of Statistics*, HMSO (annual).
Central Statistical Office, *Financial Statistics*, HMSO (monthly).
Central Statistical Office, *Monthly Digest of Statistics*, HMSO (monthly).
Central Statistical Office, *Regional Trends*, HMSO (annual). (Formerly *Regional Statistics*.)
Central Statistical Office, *Social Trends*, HMSO (annual).
Department of Employment, *British Labour Statistics*, HMSO (annual).
HM Treasury, *Economic Progress Report*, HMSO (monthly).

Discussion on sources

Central Statistical Office, *Facts from Your Figures*, HMSO, 1977. A free publication aimed at showing how several key statistics are obtained and how they could serve a useful purpose for business decision-making.
Central Statistical Office, *Government Statistics, A Brief Guide to Sources*, HMSO (annual). A useful guide to a wide range of published statistics with information on departmental responsibilities and contact points for enquiries.
Central Statistical Office, *Statistical News*, HMSO (quarterly). Discusses developments in the provision of published statistics.
Central Statistical Office, *Profit From Facts*, HMSO, 1979. A free publication showing, with a series of case studies, how businesses have used published data to improve the quality of their decision-making.
Edwards, Bernard, *Sources of Economic and Business Statistics*, Heinemann, 1972. A comprehensive coverage of official statistics related to economic and business indicators. Definitions, collection procedure, and the source of published data are discussed.
Open University, *Statistical Sources*, D 291, Open University Press, 1975. Several packages of material designed for Open University students taking the statistical sources course. Collection and provision of data are discussed with examples of application.
Pickett, Kathleen G., *Sources of Official Data*, Longmans, 1974. This is one of a series of social research publications. It covers the population census, labour force data, education, and sampling frames.

Statistical techniques

Conner, L. R., and A. J. H. Morrell, *Statistics in Theory and Practice*, Pitman, 1972. Written at a similar level to this text and covering most of the techniques. Also includes some discussion of sources.

238

Lapin, L. L., *Statistics for Modern Business Decisions*, Harcourt, Brace, Jovanovich, 1978. A good example of the many U.S. texts for introductory business statistics. Well-presented and comprehensive coverage of techniques to a little beyond the basic level.

Miller, R. B., and D. W. Wichern, *Intermediate Business Statistics*, Holt, Rinehart and Winston, 1977. A text for the student who wants to go beyond the basic level, especially for further treatment of regression methods and time series analysis.

Owen, F., and R. Jones, *Statistics*, Polytech Publishers, 1977. Another parallel text so far as techniques are concerned, with a slightly wider coverage.

The normal distribution

z	Probability of less than z	z	Probability of less than z
0.0	0.5000	1.5	0.9332
0.1	0.5398	1.6	0.9452
0.2	0.5793	1.7	0.9554
0.3	0.6179	1.8	0.9641
0.4	0.6554	1.9	0.9713
0.5	0.6915	2.0	0.9772
0.6	0.7257	2.1	0.9821
0.7	0.7580	2.2	0.9861
0.8	0.7881	2.3	0.9893
0.9	0.8159	2.4	0.9918
1.0	0.8413	2.5	0.9938
1.1	0.8643	2.6	0.9953
1.2	0.8849	2.7	0.9965
1.3	0.9032	2.8	0.9974
1.4	0.9192	2.9	0.9981
		3.0	0.9986

z is the standard Normal variable with mean 0 and standard deviation 1

239

Index

Typeset by CCC, printed and bound in Great Britain by
William Clowes (Beccles) Limited, Beccles and London